General

HANDBOOK OF
THERMOPHYSICAL PROPERTIES
OF SOLID MATERIALS

THE MACMILLAN COMPANY
NEW YORK · CHICAGO
DALLAS · ATLANTA · SAN FRANCISCO
LONDON · MANILA

IN CANADA
BRETT-MACMILLAN LTD.
GALT, ONTARIO

HANDBOOK OF THERMOPHYSICAL PROPERTIES OF SOLID MATERIALS

Revised Edition
VOLUME V: APPENDIX

Alexander Goldsmith
Thomas E. Waterman
Harry J. Hirschhorn
Armour Research Foundation

THE MACMILLAN COMPANY   NEW YORK, 1961

First printing

Library of Congress Catalog Card Number: 61-11362

The Macmillan Company, New York
Brett-Macmillan Ltd., Galt, Ontario

Printed in the United States of America

FOREWORD

A ready source of reliable thermophysical property data on high temperature materials has been needed increasingly in recent years to support feasibility studies and design of advanced military and civilian aerospace systems. Thermophysical properties are regarded in the *Handbook* as those physical properties which influence the conductive and radiant behavior of materials. Previously, mechanical properties and chemical stability were thought the only criteria necessary to consider in making a satisfactory selection of materials for the construction of aerospace systems. However, many parametric design studies employing high-speed computers have fallen short of expectations because of serious lack of dependable thermophysical data on additional properties. This lack of data is understandable, of course, in light of the serious experimental measurement difficulties at high temperatures, the oftentimes limited availability of sample materials, and the great expense involved.

The materials covered in the *Handbook* include those elements, alloys, ceramics, cermets, and intermetallics having melting points above 1000°F. Polymeric and composite materials also are included because of their importance in modern technology. The point-value properties—that is, density, melting point, heat of fusion, heat of vaporization, and heat of sublimation—along with the temperature-variable properties—that is, specific heat, thermal conductivity, thermal diffusivity, thermal expansion, emissivity, reflectivity, vapor pressure, and electrical resistivity— are reported in terms of the Rankine and Kelvin absolute temperature scales. This somewhat arbitrary decision on temperature scales was made in an attempt to hasten the trend toward the use of absolute temperatures and the centimeter-gram-second system by engineers and technologists. Each reported value is shown and annotated and, where possible, "most probable" curves are recommended. A materials index which catalogs the contents and aids in the location of data is provided, along with appropriate conversion tables to make the data digestible to a wide variety of users. In order that the data can be substantiated properly, material composition and investigator are carefully referenced. This will be especially helpful to those who wish to carry out further studies.

* * *

Since 1954, it has been the constant objective of the Thermophysics Branch of Materials Central, Wright Air Development Division, to sponsor programs (1) to measure the thermophysical properties of established and experimental high-temperature materials; (2) to promote applied research on new measurement techniques providing greater precision, greater speed, and higher temperature limits; (3) to provide a better theoretical understanding of the thermophysical behavior of materials at high temperatures, thereby permitting property prediction with greater certainty; and (4) to compile, evaluate, and consolidate all primary thermophysical data in the literature into a convenient form useful to scientists and design engineers. It was toward fulfillment of the last objective that the program leading to the publication of the *Handbook* was initiated. Based on technical goals and requirements set forth by the Thermophysics Branch, Materials Central, Wright Air Development Division, the Heat Transfer Section of the Armour Research Foundation was contracted to carry out this task. A. Goldsmith directed the over-all Armour effort. From July 1, 1957 to August 31, 1960, the Armour group worked to compile, evaluate, and consolidate the thermophysical-property data available in the open literature in the period 1940–1957 into four volumes. A fifth volume serving as an appendix contains a list of references and the author index.

I should like to acknowledge, on behalf of the U. S. Air Force, the thoughtful and dedicated efforts of A. Goldsmith, T. E. Waterman, and H. J. Hirschhorn, the principal contributors. Our thanks go also to I. B. Fieldhouse, supervisor of the Heat Transfer Section, for his guidance and encouragement of the Armour Research Foundation effort, and to S. W. Bradstreet, W. H. Colner, J. S. Griffith, W. A. Gans, J. I. Lang, D. Brast, G. Buzyna, M. Deahl, S. Chmel, A. Karazija, J. Schmugge, and Mary A. Scroll for their valuable contributions. I should also like to acknowledge the technical contributions of George Sonnenschein, Hyman Marcus, and Paul Dimiduk of the Thermophysics Branch, Wright Air Development Division, who aided in setting up the objectives and format and in providing important coordination inputs during the course of this program. And, finally, without the encouragement and support of E. M. Glass, H. C. Sullivan, and L. F. Salzberg, this compilation may well have been impossible.

Jules I. Wittebort
Chief, Thermophysics Branch
Physics Laboratory, Materials Central
Wright Air Development Division
United States Air Force

PREFACE

This appendix is the fifth volume of the report on thermophysical properties of solid materials, and contains all the indexes and lists of references for the preceding four volumes of data. Thermophysical property data, and their variation with temperature, are presented for a great number of solid materials, based on literature published during the period 1940–1957. Each reported value is shown and annotated, and recommended "most probable value" curves are given in the first four volumes. Materials covered include elements, alloys, ceramics, cermets, intermetallics, polymerics, and composite materials. Except for materials in the last two categories, only those melting above 1000° F are included. Properties covered include the following: melting point, density, latent heats, specific heat, thermal conductivity, thermal diffusivity, emissivity, reflectivity, thermal expansion, vapor pressure, and electric resistivity.

Jules I. Wittebort
Chief, Thermophysics Branch
Physics Laboratory, Materials Central
Wright Air Development Division
United States Air Force

TABLE OF CONTENTS

INTRODUCTORY REMARKS AND EXPLANATORY TEXT

I. INTRODUCTION

At the initiative of the Materials Laboratory, Wright Air Development Center, and under its sponsorship, a program was undertaken to compile, evaluate, and consolidate all original test data on thermophysical properties of solid materials published during the period 1940–1957 inclusive. This publication contains the accumulated information and represents three years of effort.* The data are presented in four volumes, divided as follows:

1. Elements
2. Alloys
3. Ceramics
4. Cermets, Intermetallics, Polymerics, and Composites

Each volume is designed to be expansible so that it will lend itself to the inclusion of new data as well as to the substitution of others. Additional data sheets for inclusion in these volumes will be published when available.

The collected data were obtained from a search of the following sources: (a) Chemical Abstracts, (b) Ceramic Abstracts, (c) Metallurgical Abstracts, (d) Nuclear Science Abstracts, and (e) Armed Services Technical Information Agency (ASTIA).

A detailed description of contents and of the method of presentation of data is given in the following several pages.

II. MATERIALS

Materials included in this survey are those which may find application in the design of aircraft, missiles, space vehicles, conventional or nuclear power plants, or allied equipment. Generally, only materials melting above $1000°F$ are included; exceptions are limited to the categories of plastics or composite materials. A listing of materials covered in the literature search is given in the Materials Index, which is described in Section IV-A below. This index also serves as a guide to the arrangement of data, and as a page numbering system. Due to the lack of published data, some of the materials listed in the index may not be represented by data sheets.

---

*Manuscripts released by authors 30 June 1960 for publication as a WADC Technical Report.

III. PROPERTIES

Physical properties included in this survey are the following:

Property	Symbol	Property	Symbol
1. Density	ρ	7. Thermal Conductivity	k
2. Melting Point	MP	8. Thermal Diffusivity	α
3. Latent Heat of Fusion	Δh_f	9. Emissivity, Reflectivity	ϵ, R
4. Latent Heat of Vaporization	Δh_v	10. Linear Thermal Expansion	$\Delta L/L$
5. Latent Heat of Sublimation	Δh_s	11. Vapor Pressure	p
6. Specific Heat		12. Electric Resistivity	r
(constant pressure)	c_p		

The first five properties in the above list are given as single point values, in individual tables grouped on a single sheet. The others are presented graphically as functions of temperature. All data on linear thermal expansion have been reduced to a datum of 20°C; i.e. $\Delta L/L = 0$ at 528°R (293°K).

IV. CONTENTS

Each of the four volumes of data consists of four sections arranged in the following order:

1. Introductory remarks and explanatory text
2. Materials Index
3. Tables of Conversion Factors
4. Body of Data

The fifth volume, or Appendix, consists of the following sections:

1. Introductory remarks and explanatory text
2. Materials Index
3. List of References
4. Author Index (alphabetic)
5. Expanded Listing of Materials Index (numerical)
6. Alphabetic List of Materials

A. *Materials Index*

The Materials Index, located in the front portion of each volume following these introductory pages, gives the order in which the body of data is arranged. It is based, with few exceptions, on the chemical composition of materials, and is arranged in outline fashion. It can have four orders of subdivision designated by Roman numerals, capital letters, common numerals and lower case letters such as:

I.
  A.
    1.
      a.

Each category, even in the lowest order, represents a family of materials, rather than a specific one, so that the number of individual materials that can be accommodated is virtually unlimited. The index lends itself to future expansion.

B. *Body of Data*

The body of data is arranged by materials in the order of the Materials Index. Properties for a given small family of materials are given in the order listed in Section III above. Each plotted point or numerical value in the body of data is identified as to source by reference to the List of References.

C. *List of References*

The List of References gives complete bibliographic notations for all the references from which usable data have been extracted. These are arranged chronologically by year of publication, and in an arbitrary sequence within any given year.

D. *Author Index*

The Author Index is arranged in alphabetic order by author's surname. Co-authors are also included. Each entry is cross-referred to the List of References where a complete bibliographic notation is given.

E. *Expanded Listing of Materials Index*

This is an expanded list of ALL materials by their material index number for which at least one property is reported herein. It also lists some of the more common trade names to show their location in the material index, even if no data are reported for them.

F. *Alphabetic List of Materials*

This index lists the names of ALL materials for which some property is reported in the handbook, and shows their location in the volumes which are arranged by materials. The names are those given by the authors of the original articles. The index also lists some of the more common trade names, even if NO DATA are reported for them in the handbook. To assist the reader most of the optional variations of material names have been listed, but it is obviously impossible to list each and every possible permutation and abbreviation of material names.

V. METHOD OF PRESENTATION OF DATA

A. *Format*

A "unit" of information in this volume consists of a single sheet having a graph on one face and reference information on the back. The first five properties listed in Section III above are referred to as "point values" and are grouped together as a "unit" on a single sheet in the same manner as a graph.

B. *Pagination*

Each volume is designed to be expansible, and therefore is not compatible with conventional page numbering. The system adopted is as follows:

The body of data is arranged by materials in accordance with the Materials Index which is located in the forward portion of each volume. Furthermore, for a given small family of materials, data for the several properties are arranged in accordance with the listing given in Section III above. The Materials Index designation is given in the lower right corner of each graph or data sheet in lieu of a page number. This identification is not unique since several materials of the same family carry the same designation, but it guides the reader to the approximate location of the desired information.

Materials that do not fit into any subgroup presently listed in the Materials Index are designated by the next higher order grouping.

> Example: Nickel-Silicon alloys are not specifically identified as a family grouping in the Materials Index. These therefore, are designated by the next higher order of subdivision, namely, Nickel-Base Alloys, category IV-A in the index.

Data for such materials are located at the end of the group; that is, after those materials which do fit into a currently identified subgroup. Within this framework, where necessary, data sheets are further arranged in alphabetic order by the major alloying element. It is expected that after the initial familiarization with this arrangement, the user will be able to locate the desired information (or convince himself of its absence) with a minimum of page-by-page searching.

A unique identification of each sheet is provided by the number in the lower left corner of the sheet. The initial two digits of this number give the year when the sheet was prepared; the latter digits are merely a numerical sequence for identification purposes only and serve no other purpose.

C. *Graph Sheets*

Data extracted from various references on the same subject (material and property) are identified on each graph by means of distinctive plotting symbols. These symbols indicate the data of a given investigator, but do not necessarily imply actual test points. In numerous instances in the literature an author presents only smoothed data, either graphically or in tabular form, and it is frequently impossible to distinguish these from actual test values.

> In presenting data on thermal expansion, an investigator sometimes gives only a coefficient of expansion for a considerable temperature range. In such instances it is assumed that a linear relationship is implied, and in plotting such data the straight line may be indicated by more than the two end-points in order that the given investigator's data not be obscured by those of others.

> With regard to specific heat, some investigators present only total heat content of the material above a given datum, and make no attempt to reduce such data to specific heat. In such instances the investigator's enthalpy data were fitted with a quadratic equation of the form $\Delta H = A + BT + CT^2$ using a least-mean-square procedure to determine the coefficients. This equation was then differentiated with respect to temperature to obtain a linear variation of specific heat with temperature. Instances where this was done are so indicated.

> Curves drawn through the plotted points are deemed "most probable value" curves based on the data presented. As additional information from other investigators is added in the future, it may be necessary to modify these curves.

D. *Point Values*

The first five properties listed in Section III above are considered point functions (at standard temperature and pressure unless indicated otherwise) and are grouped in individual tables, by property, on a single sheet. Data extracted from various references are identified by distinctive plotting symbols in the same manner as points on a graph. "Most probable values," usually based only on the data presented, are given at the top of the page. In some instances where data were not available from the current survey, density and melting point information was taken from secondary (nonoriginal) sources. These appear only at the top of the sheet and are identified as to source. Melting points of binary alloys, representing the solidus line on a phase diagram, have generally not been included. Many of these are given by Hansen and Anderko in "Constitution of Binary Alloys" (Ref. 58-11).

E. *Reference Information*

1. *Symbol*

The plotting symbols are identical with, and correspond to those used on the face of a given graph or data sheet.

2. *Investigator*

The investigator, or author, of each reference is identified by name. Coauthors are included.

3. *Reference*

References are identified by hyphenated numbers such as 00-00, which serve to locate the bibliographic entry for the given source in the List of References in the Appendix. The initial two digits indicate the year of publication. The remaining number locates the specific reference within the given year.

Example: Ref. 54-7 is found in the List of References under the year 1954; the seventh entry for that year. It is an article by R. W. Powell entitled "The Thermal Conductivity of Beryllia."

References which are not dated are identified with the letters ND in place of the year of publication, such as ND-00. Undated references are listed at the end of the List of References.

4. *Range*

The column marked "Range, °R" indicates the temperature range covered by the data in the given reference.

5. *Material Composition*

This column contains any pertinent information given in a reference that serves to describe the material investigated. Primarily this consists of the chemical composition of the material, its purity, density, and common trade name when given. Where a material was identified by trade name only, the nominal composition was added.

6. *Test Method*

A general indication of the test method used by the investigator is given in this column. While test methods for a given property can be reasonably grouped into several broad categories, each investigator makes his own modifications and alterations which do not lend themselves to brief description.

7. *Remarks*

Pertinent remarks concerning the given data are included in this column. Such remarks may describe a prior treatment of the material, the environment during the test, the author's estimate of accuracy, or similar information.

MATERIALS INDEX

I. ELEMENTS (Melting temperature above 1000° F)

	Element	*Symbol*
I-A-1	Actinium	Ac
I-A-2	Aluminum	Al
I-A-3	Americium	Am
I-A-4	Antimony	Sb
I-A-5	Arsenic	As
I-A-6	Astatine	At
I-B-1	Barium	Ba
I-B-2	Berkelium	Bk
I-B-3	Beryllium	Be
I-B-4	Boron	B
I-C-1	Calcium	Ca
I-C-2	Californium	Cf
I-C-3	Carbon	C

a. Extruded Acheson graphite, multicrystalline
b. Extruded Acheson amorphous carbon
c. Extruded Acheson graphite, impregnated
d. Molded Acheson graphite, multicrystalline
e. Molded Acheson amorphous carbon
f. Molded Acheson graphite, impregnated
g. Lampblack—base carbon or graphite
h. Pyrolytic graphite
j. Natural graphite-base graphite
k. Natural graphite-base carbon
m. Diamond
n. Single crystal graphite
p. Lampblacks

I-C-4	Cerium	Ce
I-C-5	Chromium	Cr
I-C-6	Cobalt	Co
I-C-7	Copper	Cu
I-C-8	Curium	Cm
I-D-1	Dysprosium	Dy
I-E-1	Einsteinium	E
I-E-2	Erbium	Er
I-E-3	Europium	Eu

7

I. ELEMENTS (Continued)

	Element	*Symbol*
I-F-1	Fermium	Fm
I-F-2	Francium	Fr
I-G-1	Gadolinium	Gd
I-G-2	Germanium	Ge
I-G-3	Gold	Au
I-H-1	Hafnium	Hf
I-H-2	Holmium	Ho
I-J-1	Iridium	Ir
I-J-2	Iron	Fe
I-L-1	Lanthanum	La
I-L-2	Lutetium	Lu
I-M-1	Magnesium	Mg
I-M-2	Manganese	Mn
I-M-3	Mendelevium	Mv
I-M-4	Molybdenum	Mo
I-N-1	Neodymium	Nd
I-N-2	Neptunium	Np
I-N-3	Nickel	Ni
I-N-4	Niobium (Columbium)	Nb
I-N-5	Nobelium	No
I-O-1	Osmium	Os
I-P-1	Palladium	Pd
I-P-2	Platinum	Pt
I-P-3	Plutonium	Pu
I-P-4	Polonium	Po
I-P-5	Praseodymium	Pr
I-P-6	Promethium	Pm
I-P-7	Protactinium	Pa
I-R-1	Radium	Ra
I-R-2	Rhenium	Re
I-R-3	Rhodium	Rh
I-R-4	Ruthenium	Ru
I-S-1	Samarium	Sm
I-S-2	Scandium	Sc
I-S-3	Silicon	Si
I-S-4	Silver	Ag
I-S-5	Strontium	Sr
I-T-1	Tantalum	Ta
I-T-2	Technetium	Tc
I-T-3	Terbium	Tb

I. ELEMENTS (Continued)

	Element	*Symbol*
I-T-4	Thorium	Th
I-T-5	Thulium	Tm
I-T-6	Titanium	Ti
I-T-7	Tungsten	W
I-U-1	Uranium	U
I-V-1	Vanadium	V
I-Y-1	Ytterbium	Yb
I-Y-2	Yttrium	Y
I-Z-1	Zirconium	Zr

II. IRON BASE ALLOYS (Iron greatest weight fraction with one or more other elements)

A. Plain Carbon Steels (Mn < 2.5%; Si < 0.36%; P, S < 0.051% each)
1. $0.02 < C \leq 0.20\%$
2. $0.20 < C \leq 0.40\%$
3. $0.40 < C \leq 0.60\%$
4. $0.60 < C \leq 0.80\%$
5. $0.80 < C \leq 1.00\%$
6. $1.00 < C \leq 1.20\%$
7. $1.20 < C \leq 1.50\%$
8. $1.50 < C \leq 2.00\%$

B. *Cast Irons*
1. *Gray, unalloyed and low alloy* (Less than 2% total alloying elements exclusive of C, Mn < 1%, Si, P, S)
2. *Gray, alloyed* (More than 2% total alloying elements exclusive of C, Mn < 1%, Si, P, S)
3. *White, unalloyed and low alloy* (Less than 2% total alloying elements exclusive of C, Mn < 1%, Si, P, S)
4. *White, alloyed* (More than 2% total alloying elements exclusive of C, Mn < 1%, Si, P, S)
5. *Malleable, Ferritic*
6. *Malleable, Pearlitic*
7. *Nodular, Ferritic*
8. *Nodular, Pearlitic*

C. *Low Alloy Steels* (Less than 10% of any single alloying element, exclusive of C; Mn < 2.5%; Si < 0.36%; P, S < 0.051% each. Alloying elements listed in decreasing order of their weight fractions. X may be none, one, or more elements; $X = X_1 + X_2 + \ldots$)
1. Fe + Ni
2. Fe + Ni + Cr + X
3. Fe + Ni + Mo + X
4. Fe + Ni + X($X_1 \neq$ Mo, Cr)
5. Fe + Mo + X
6. Fe + Cr + X($X_1 \neq$ Mo)
7. Fe + Cr + Mo + X
8. Fe + W + X
9. Fe + Si + X

II. IRON-BASE ALLOYS (Continued)

    D. *High Alloy Steels* (More than 10% of any single alloying element exclusive of C; Mn < 2.5%; Si < 1.00%; P, S < 0.051% each. Alloying elements listed in decreasing order of their weight fraction. X may be none, one, or more elements; $X = X_1 + X_2 + \ldots$)

1. Fe + Cr
2. Fe + Cr + Ni
3. Fe + Cr + Ni + X($X_1 \neq 0$)
   a. Fe + Cr + Ni + Co + X
4. Fe + Cr + X($X_1 \neq 0$, Ni)
5. Fe + Ni
6. Fe + Ni + X($X_1 \neq 0$)
   a. Fe + Ni + Cr + X
7. Fe + Al + X
8. Fe + W + X
9. Fe + Mn + X

III. COPPER-BASE ALLOYS (Copper greatest weight fraction with one or more other elements. Alloying elements listed in decreasing order of their weight fractions. X may be none, one, or more elements.)

A. *Copper + Zinc + X*

    1. Cu + Zn + Pb + X
    2. Cu + Zn + Sn + X
    3. Cu + Zn

B. *Copper + Tin + X*

    1. Cu + Sn + Pb + X
    2. Cu + Sn + Zn + X
    3. Cu + Sn

C. *Copper + Lead + X*

D. *Copper + Nickel + X*

E. *Copper + Aluminum + X*

F. *Copper + Silicon + X*

G. *Copper + Beryllium + X*

H. *Copper + Manganese + X*

J. *Copper + Tellurium + X*

K. *Copper + Chromium + X*

L. *Copper + Zirconium + X*

IV. NICKEL-BASE, COBALT-BASE, AND REFRACTORY METAL-BASE ALLOYS (Major element greatest weight fraction with one or more other elements. Alloying elements listed in decreasing order of their weight fractions. X may be none, one, or more elements.)

A. *Nickel-Base Alloys*

   1. Ni + Cu + X
   2. Ni + Mo + X
   3. Ni + Co + X
      a. Ni + Co + Cr + X
   4. Ni + Fe + X
      a. Ni + Fe + Cr + X
   5. Ni + Cr + X
      a. Ni + Cr + Fe + X
   6. Ni + Mn + X

B. *Cobalt-Base Alloys*

   1. Co + Cr + X
   2. Co + Ni + X
   3. Co + Fe + X
   4. Co + Pd + X

C. *Tungsten-Base Alloys*

D. *Molybdenum-Base Alloys*

E. *Niobium-Base Alloys*

F. *Chromium-Base Alloys*

   1. Cr + Ni + X
   2. Cr + Mo + X

G. *Vanadium-Base Alloys*

H. *Tantalum-Base Alloys*

J. *Zirconium-Base Alloys*

   1. Zr + Sn + X
   2. Zr + Nb + X
   3. Zr + U + X

K. *Hafnium-Base Alloys*

L. *Thorium-Base Alloys*

V. LIGHT METAL ALLOYS (Including Ti alloys). Major element greatest weight fraction with one or more other elements. Alloying elements listed in decreasing order of their weight fractions. X may be none, one, or more elements; $X = X_1 + X_2 + ...$)

A. *Aluminum-Base Alloys*

1. Al + Cu + X
2. Al + Si + X
   a. Al + Si + Cu + X
   b. Al + Si + Mg + X
3. Al + Mg + X
4. Al + Zn + X
5. Al + Mn + X
6. Al + Ag + X

B. *Magnesium-Base Alloys*

1. Mg + Al + Zn + X
2. Mg + Al + X ($X_1 \neq$ Zn)
3. Mg + Rare Earth + X
4. Mg + Th + X
5. Mg + Li + X
6. Mg + Zn + X

C. *Titanium-Base Alloys*

1. Ti + Al + X
2. Ti + Mn + X
3. Ti + Mo + X
4. Ti + V + X
5. Ti + Cr + X
6. Ti + Fe + X ($X_1 \neq$ Cr)
7. Ti + Fe + Cr + X
8. Ti + O + X

D. *Beryllium-Base Alloys*

VI. OTHER METAL ALLOYS (Melting temperature above 1000° F. Major element greatest weight fraction with one or more other elements. Alloying elements listed in decreasing order of their weight fractions. X may be none, one, or more elements.)

A. *Gold-Base Alloys*

    1. Au + Cd + X
    2. Au + Co + X
    3. Au + Pd + X
    4. Au + Ni + X
    5. Au + Mn + X

B. *Silver-Base Alloys*

    1. Ag + Al + X
    2. Ag + Cd + X
    3. Ag + Cu + X
    4. Ag + Pd + X

C. *Platinum-Base Alloys*

D. *Palladium-Base Alloys*

    1. Pd + Au + X
    2. Pd + Co + X
    3. Pd + Cu + X

E. *Manganese-Base Alloys*

    1. Mn + Cu + X
    2. Mn + Ni + X

F. *Uranium-Base Alloys*
    1. U + Cr + X
    2. U + Mo + X
    3. U + Zr + X

G. *Silicon-Base Alloys*

    1. Si + Fe + X

VII. CERAMICS

A. *Oxide Ceramics* (Nominal oxide; or nominal oxide greatest weight fraction with one or other oxides. X may be none, one, or more oxides. Also see VII-B and VII-E).

1. *Aluminum Oxide + X*
   a . Aluminum oxide (alumina, corundum, sapphire)
   b . Aluminum oxide + Chromium oxide + X
2. *Beryllium Oxide + X*
   a . Beryllium oxide (beryllia, bromellite)
3. *Calcium Oxide + X*
   a . Calcium oxide (calcia, lime)
4. *Rare Earth Oxides* (Atomic Numbers 57–71 in Alphabetic Order)
   a . Cerium oxide + X (ceria)
   b . Dysprosium oxide + X (dysprosia)
   c . Erbium oxide + X (erbia)
   d . Europium oxide + X (europia)
   e. Gadolinium oxide + X (gadolinia)
   f. Holmium oxide + X
   g. Lanthanum oxide + X (lanthana)
   h. Lutetium oxide + X
   j. Neodymium oxide + X (neodymia)
   k. Praseodymium oxide + X (praseodymia)
   m. Promethium oxide + X
   n. Samarium oxide + X (samaria)
   p. Terbium oxide + X (terbia)
   q. Thulium oxide + X (thulia)
   r. Ytterbium oxide + X (ytterbia)
5. *Magnesium Oxide + X*
   a. Magnesium oxide (magnesia, periclase)
6. *Silicon Oxide + X* (silica, crystobalite, quartz; see also VII-C-6)
7. *Thorium Oxide + X* (thoria, thorianite)
8. *Titanium Oxide + X* (anatase, brookite, rutile)
9. *Hafnium Oxide + X; Zirconium Oxide + X*
   a. Hafnium oxide (hafnia)
   b. Zirconium oxide (zirconia)
10. *Uranium Oxide + X*
11. *Plutonium Oxide + X*
12.
13. Other Oxide Ceramics, in Alphabetic Order: A–I
14. Other Oxide Ceramics, in Alphabetic Order: J–R
15. Other Oxide Ceramics, in Alphabetic Order: S–Z

VII. CERAMICS (Continued)

B. *Mineral Ceramics* (Also see VII-A and VII-E)

1. Aluminosilicates, non-hydrous (mullite, kyanite, sillimanite)
2. Silicates of Ba, Be, Ca, Fe, Mg, Mn, Ni, Sr, and Zn in order listed.
3. Alkali and alkaline-earth aluminosilicates (feldspars)
   a. Barium-modified feldspar
   b. Beryllium-modified feldspar (beryl)
   c. Calcium-modified feldspar
   d. Cesium-modified feldspar
   e. Lithium-modified feldspar
      Magnesium aluminosilicate, see VII-E-3
   f. Potassium feldspar
   g. Rubidium feldspar
   h. Sodium feldspar
   j. Strontium-modified feldspar
4. Hafnium silicate; Zirconium silicate
   a. Hafnium silicate (hafnon)
   b. Zirconium silicate (zircon)
5. Borates (borax, colemanite); Phosphates
6. Hafnates; Niobates; Titanates; Zirconates
   a. Hafnates
   b. Niobates
   c. Zirconates
   d. Aluminum titanate
   e. Barium titanate
   f. Calcium titanate
   g. Iron titanate
   h. Lithium titanate
   j. Magnesium titanate
   k. Strontium titanate
   m. Zinc titanate
   n. Zirconium titanate

VII. CERAMICS (Continued)

    7. Aluminates
       a . Magnesium aluminate (spinel)
       b . Barium aluminate
       c . Beryllium aluminate
       d . Calcium aluminate
       e . Cesium aluminate
       f . Lithium aluminate
       g . Potassium aluminate
       h . Rubidium aluminate
       j . Sodium aluminate
       k . Strontium aluminate
       m. Zinc aluminate

    8. Ferrites
       a . Magnesium ferrite
       b . Barium ferrite
       c . Beryllium ferrite
       d . Calcium ferrite
       e . Cesium ferrite
       f . Lithium ferrite
       g . Potassium ferrite
       h . Rubidium ferrite
       j . Sodium ferrite
       k . Strontium ferrite
       m. Cobalt ferrite
       n . Nickel ferrite
       p . Zinc ferrite

    9. Micas (Illites)
   10. Asbestos minerals

VII. CERAMICS (Continued)

    C. *Vitreous Structures*

        1. Silicate glasses
           a . Lithium silicate glass
           b . Sodium silicate glass
           c . Potassium silicate glass
           d . Rubidium silicate glass
           e . Cesium silicate glass
           f . Beryllium silicate glass
           g . Magnesium silicate glass
           h . Calcium silicate glass
           j . Strontium silicate glass
           k . Barium silicate glass
           m. Lead silicate glass
        2. Borate glasses
        3. Phosphate glasses
        4. Arsenic oxide glasses
        5. Borosilicate glasses (pyrex)
        6. Silica glasses (fused quartz)

    D. *Covalent Ceramic Structures* (Also see Section IX)

        1. Silicon carbide + X
           a . Silicon carbide
           b . Silicon carbide + Boron carbide + X
        2. Boron carbides
        3. Alkali and alkaline earth carbides
           a . Beryllium carbide
        4. Boron nitrides
        5. Halides and oxyhalides
           a . Fluorides
        6. Sulfides; Selenides

VII. CERAMICS (Continued)

E. *Vitreous Bonded Crystalline Ceramics* (conventional ceramics; also see VII-A and VII-B)

1. Alkaline earth silicate glass bond
2. Alkali silicate glass bond
3. Magnesium aluminosilicate glass bond (cordierite, steatite, talc body)
    a . Lithium modified
    b. Sodium modified
    c . Potassium modified
    d . Rubidium modified
    e . Cesium modified
    f . Beryllium modified
    g . Calcium modified
    h . Strontium modified
    j . Barium modified
    k . Lead modified
4. Calcium aluminosilicate glass bond (porcelain)
5. Other alkaline earth aluminosilicates glass bond
6. Alkali aluminosilicate glass bond
7. Borosilicate glass bond
8. Phosphate glass bond
9. Alumina firebrick
10. Basic brick
11. Silica brick

F. *Inorganic Cements and Adhesives*

VIII. CERMETS (Nominal refractory phase is that which is greatest weight fraction of total refractory phase.)

    A. *Cermets Containing Carbides as Major Refractory Phase*

        1. Tungsten carbide as major refractory phase
        2. Titanium carbide as major refractory phase
        3. Chromium carbide as major refractory phase
        4. Hafnium carbide or Zirconium carbide as major refractory phase
        5. Silicon carbide as major refractory phase

    B. *Cermets Containing Oxides or Suboxides as Major Refractory Phase*

        1. Aluminum oxide as major refractory phase
        2. Magnesium oxide as major refractory phase
        3. Uranium oxide as major refractory phase
        4. Thorium oxide as major refractory phase
        5. Beryllium oxide as major refractory phase

    C. *Cermets Containing Borides as Major Refractory Phase*

        1. Zirconium boride as major refractory phase

    D. *Cermets Containing Silicides as Major Refractory Phase*

    E. *Cermets Containing Nitrides as Major Refractory Phase*

    F. *Cermets Containing Hydrides as Major Refractory Phase*

IX. INTERMETALLICS (Nominal intermetallic, or nominal intermetallic greatest weight fraction with one or more other intermetallics. Also see section VII-D and respective alloy system.)

A. *Carbide Systems*

1. Tungsten carbide
2. Titanium carbide
3. Chromium carbide
4. Hafnium carbide; Zirconium carbide
5. Tantalum carbide
6. Molybdenum carbide
7. Uranium carbide

B. *Silicide Systems*

1. Molybdenum silicide
2. Uranium silicide

C. *Boride Systems*

1. Magnesium boride
2. Titanium boride
3. Zirconium boride

D. *Nitride Systems*

1. Titanium nitride
2. Uranium nitride
3. Zirconium nitride

E. *Hydride Systems*

1. Lithium hydride
2. Zirconium hydride

F. *Antimonide, Arsenide, Phosphide, Telluride Systems*

1. Antimonides
2. Tellurides

G. *Intermetallics Involving a Light Metal* (Al, Be, Mg, Ti)

1. Aluminides
2. Beryllides
3. Magnesium intermetallics
4. Titanium intermetallics

IX. INTERMETALLICS (Continued)

H. *Intermetallics Involving a Rare Earth*

J. *Intermetallics Involving a Refractory Metal*

1. Chromium intermetallics
2. Cobalt intermetallics
3. Hafnium intermetallics
4. Molybdenum intermetallics
5. Nickel intermetallics
6. Niobium intermetallics
7. Tantalum intermetallics
8. Thorium intermetallics
9. Tungsten intermetallics
10. Vanadium intermetallics
11. Zirconium intermetallics

For intermetallics not listed above, see respective alloy system.

X. POLYMERIC MATERIALS (Including plastics and filled plastics)

A. *Polyesters*

1. Cellulose acetate
2. Cellulose propionate
3. Cellulose acetate butyrate
4. Cellulose nitrate
5. Ethyl cellulose
6. Polyvinyl acetals
7. Polyvinyl acetate
8. Copolyvinyl chloride-acetate
9. Isocyanates
10. Polyurethanes
11. Unsaturated polyesters

B. *TAC Polyesters (tri-allyl cyanurate)*

C. *Phenolics*

1. Phenol formaldehyde
2. Furfural formaldehyde
3. Urea formaldehyde

D. *Epoxides*

E. *Melamines*

F. *Acrylics*

G. *Polyethylene and halogenated polyethylenes*

H. *Polyamide (nylon)*

J. *Natural and Synthetic Rubber*

XI. COMPOSITE MATERIALS (The work "ceramic," as used below, includes any material which is inorganic and nonmetallic. Semiorganic materials, such as silicones, are included in the term "organic.")

A. *Composite Organic Materials; Sandwich Structures.* (Any layer may be pure, filled, or reinforced.)

    1. Plastic skin, plastic foam core
    2. Plastic skin, plastic honeycomb core
    3. Solid plastic layers

B. *Composite Metallic Materials*

    1. Metal skin, metal honeycomb core
    2. Unbonded metal layers
    3. Fusion bonded metal layers
    4. Mechanically bonded metal layers
    5. Clad metals
    6. Plated metals

C. *Composite Ceramic Materials*

D. *Composite Organic-Metallic Materials; Sandwich Structures.* (Any organic layer may be pure, filled, or reinforced.)

    1. Plastic skin, metal honeycomb core
    2. Metal skin, plastic honeycomb core
    3. Metal skin, plastic foam core
    4. Adhesive bonded metal layers

E. *Composite Metallic-Ceramic Materials*

F. *Composite Organic-Ceramic Materials; Sandwich Structures.* (Any organic layer may be pure, filled, or reinforced.)

XI. COMPOSITE MATERIALS (Continued)

G. *Composite Organic-Metallic-Ceramic Materials; Sandwich Structures.* (Any organic layer may be pure, filled, or reinforced.)

H. *Reinforced Organic Materials*

    1. Reinforced teflon
    2. Reinforced melamine formaldehyde
    3. Reinforced phenolics
    4. Reinforced diallyl phthalate
    5. Reinforced polyesters and TAC polyesters
    6. Reinforced silicones
    7. Reinforced epoxides

J. *Reinforced Ceramic Materials*

LIST OF REFERENCES

1939

1. Jaeger, F. M. and Rosenbohm, E., "The Exact Formulas for the True and Mean Specific Heats of Platinum between 0° and 1600°C ", <u>Physica</u>. Vol. 6. pp. 1123-5. (Holland)

2. Seltz, H., McDonald, H. J., and Wells, C., "Heat Capacity of Iron Carbide from 68° to 298°K and the Thermodynamic Properties of Iron Carbide", <u>Am. Inst. Mining Met. Engrs.</u> Tech. Publ. No. 1137. 11 p.

3. Cennamo, F., "The Spectral Emission of Nickel at Different Temperatures", <u>Nuovo cimento.</u> Vol. 16. pp. 253-60. (Italy)

4. Raub, Ernst and Engel, Max, "Measurements of the Reflection of Silver Alloys", <u>Z. Metallkunde.</u> Vol. 31. pp. 339-44. (Germany)

1. Awbery, J.H. and Griffiths, E., "The Thermal Capacity of Pure Iron", Proc. Roy. Soc. A. 174. pp. 1-15. (England)

2. Jaeger, F.M., Rosenbohm, E., and Zuithoff, A.J., "Exact Determination of Specific Heats at High Temperatures. XII. Specific Heat, Electrical Resistance and Thermoelectric Power of Cobalt", Rec. Trav. Chim. Vol. 59. pp. 831-56. (France)

3. Sochtig, H., "Investigations of Pure Chromium in the Region of Anomaly", Ann. Physik. Vol. 38. pp. 97-120. (Germany)

4. Persoz, B., "New Method of Measuring the True Specific Heat of Metals at High Temperatures. (Specific Heats of Platinum and Nickel)", Ann. Physique (xii). Vol. 14. pp. 237-301. (France)

5. Erfling, Hanns D., "Change of Thermal Expansion and Electrical Resistance on Manganese during Transition to the α-phase", Ann. Physik. Vol. 37. pp. 162-8. (Germany)

6. Forster, Fritz and Tschentke, G., "A Method for the Measurement of the Temperature Relationships of Electrical Resistivity and Specific Heat of Solid and Liquid Metals", Z. Metallkunde. Vol. 32 (6) pp. 191-5. (Germany)

7. Zuithoff, A.C., "The Exact Measurements of the Specific Heats of Solid Substances at High Temperatures XII. The Specific Heat of Iron-Nickel Alloys of Various Composition between 100° and 1400°C", Rec. Trav. Chim. Vol. 59 (2). pp. 131-60. (France)

8. Bartenev, G.M., "Heat Capacity of Carbon Steels", J. Tech. Phys. Vol. 10. pp. 1074-84. (USSR)

9. Seltz, H., DeWitt, B.J., and McDonald, H.J., "The Heat Capacity of Nickel Oxide from 68 to 298°K and the Thermodynamic Properties of the Oxide", Am. Chem. Soc. Vol. 62. pp. 88-9.

10. Thompson, N., "Order-disorder Transformation in the Alloy Ni_3Mn", Proc. Phys. Soc. (London). Vol. 52. pp. 217-28. (England)

11. Aoyama, Sin'iti and Ito, Tunezo, "Thermal and Electrical Conductivities of Copper-zinc Alloys at Low Temperatures", Nippon Kinzoku Gakkai-si. Vol. 4. pp. 37-40. (Japan)

12. Stockdale, D., "The Densities of the Silver-rich Zinc-Silver Alloys with an Appendix on the Calculation of Densities from Lattice Parameters", J. Inst. Metals. Vol. 66(8). pp. 287-310. (England)

13. McPherson, L., "Optical Constants of the Copper-Aluminum α-alloys", Proc. Phys. Soc. Vol. 52. pp. 210-16. (England)

14. Vieweg, R. and Gottwald, F., "The Thermal Values of Artificial Materials (Resin, Plastics, etc.)", Kunststoffe. Vol. 30. pp. 138-41. (Germany)

15. Suhrmann, R. and Bendt, W., "Irreversible Changes of Electrical Resistance and Reflectivity of of Layers of Antimony, Arsenic, Tellurium, Iron and Silver Condensed at Low Temperatures", Z. Physik. Vol. 115. pp. 17-46. (Germany)

16. Hase, R., Heierberg, R. and Walkenhorst, W., "Measurement of Thermal and Electric Conductivity of Pure Aluminum and Aluminum-Magnesium Alloys up to 400°", Aluminium. Vol. 22. pp. 631-5. (Germany)

17. Kubaschewski, O. and Schrag, Gerhard, "Specific Heats of Nickel, Bismuth and Phosphorus", Z. Elektrochem. Vol. 46. pp. 675-80 (Germany)

18. Bates, L.F. and Weston, J.C., "Thermal Expansion of Invar", Nature. Vol. 145. p. 5501.

19. Sato, Syun-iti, and Sogabe, Tatuyosi, "The Specific Heats of Copper Nitride, Niobium Nitride, Sodium Oxide and the Atomic Heat of Nitrogen", Bull. Inst. Phys. Chem. Research (Tokyo). Vol. 19. pp. 943-50. (Japan)

20. Rogener, H., "Direct-Current Resistance of Ceramic Materials", Z. Elektrochem. Vol. 46. pp. 25-7. (Germany)

1. Osborn, Robert H., "Thermal Conductivities of Tungsten and Molybdenum at Incandescent Temperatures", J. Opt. Soc. Am. Vol. 31. pp. 428-32.

2. Kelley, K. K., "The Specific Heats at Low Temperatures of Crystalline Boric Oxide, Boron Carbide, and Silicon Carbide", J. Am. Chem. Soc. Vol. 63. pp. 1137-9.

3. Hidnert, Peter, "Thermal Expansion of Electrolytic Chromium", J. Research Nat. Bur. Standards. Vol. 26 (1). pp. 81-91, Research Paper No. 1361.

4. Hidnert, Peter, "Thermal Expansion of Cast and of Swaged Chromium", J. Research Nat. Bur. Standards. Vol. 27 (2). pp. 113-24, Research Paper No. 1407.

5. Uyeno, Kozo, "Determination of the Vapor Pressure of Solid Salts. IV. The Vapor Pressures of WO_3, MoO_3, CdO, TeO_2, and Their Thermodynamic Values", J. Chem. Soc. Japan. Vol. 62. pp. $^399-4. ^3$ (Japan)

6. Nix, F. C. and MacNair, D., "Thermal Expansion of Pure Metals: Copper, Gold, Aluminum, Nickel and Iron", Phys. Rev. Vol. 60. pp. 597-605.

7. Jaeger, F. M. and Rosenbohm, E., "The Temperature Coefficient of the Electrical Resistance of Ruthenium and Its Thermoelectrical Behavior with Respect to Platinum", Proc. Acad. Sci. Amsterdam. Vol. 44. pp. 144-52. (Holland)

8. Rosenholtz, Joseph L. and Smith, Dudley, T., "Linear Thermal Expansion and Inversions of Quartz, Var. Rock Crystal", Am. Mineral. Vol. 26. pp. 103-9.

9. Navias, Louis, "Compositions and Properties of Some High-Titania Ceramics", J. Am. Ceram. Soc. Vol. 24. pp. 148-155.

10. Orlowski, H. J. and Koenig, C. J., "Thermal Expansion of Silicate Fluxes in the Crystalline and Glassy States", J. Am. Ceram. Soc. Vol. 24. pp. 80-84.

11. Squire, C. F. and Kaufmann, R. R., "The Magnetic Susceptibility of Titanium and Zirconium", J. Chem. Phys. Vol. 9. pp. 673-7.

12. Giauque, W. F. and Meads, P. F., "The Heat Capacities and Entropies of Aluminum and Copper from 15 to 300°K", J. Am. Chem. Soc. Vol. 63. pp. 1897-1901.

13. Moser, H., "Specific Heat of Silver, Nickel, β-brass, Quartz Crystals, and Quartz Glass", Physik Z. Vol. 37. pp. 737-58 (Yr. 1936), abstr. in J. Soc. Glass Tech. Vol. 25 (107) 5p. (England)

14. Jones, F. W. and Leech, P., "Preprecipitation Phenomena in Age-hardening Alloys", Nature. Vol. 147. pp. 327-8. (England)

15. Kelley, K. K., "The Specific Heats at Low Temperatures of Ferrous Silicate, Manganous Silicate and Zirconium Silicate", J. Am. Chem. Soc. Vol. 63. pp. 2750-2.

16. Kelley, K. K., "Specific Heat of Calcium Carbide at Low Temperatures", Ind. Eng. Chem., Vol. 33. pp. 1314-15.

17. Esser, H. and Eusterbrock, H., "Investigation of the Thermal Expansion of Some Metals and Alloys with an Improved Dilatometer", Arch. Eisenhuttenwesen. Vol. 14. pp. 341-355. (Germany)

18. Schneider, A. and Stoll, E. K., "Metal Vapor Pressure. I. Vapor Pressure of Magnesium over Aluminum Magnesium Alloys", Z. Elektrochem. Vol. 47. pp. 519-26. (Germany)

19. Richards, John W., "The Over-all Linear Expansion of Face-centered Cubic Metals from Absolute Zero to Their Melting Points", Univ. Microfilms (Ann Arbor, Mich.), Pub. No. 276. 30 p.

20. Johnson, B. K., "Reflecting-power Measurements in the Spectral Region 2000-1300Å", Proc. Phys. Soc. Vol. 53. pp. 258-264. (England)

21. Keesom, W. H. and Desirant, M., "The Specific Heats of Tantalum in the Normal and in the Superconductive State", Physica. Vol. 8. pp. 273-288. (Netherlands)

22. Johnson, B. K., "Reflecting-Power Measurements in the Spectral Region 2000-1300A", Proc. Phys. Soc. Vol. 53. pp. 258-264. (England)

23. Richards, John W., "The Over-All Linear Expansion of Three Face-Centered Cubic Metals (Al, Cu, Pb) from -190°C to Near Their Melting Points", Amer. Soc. Metals, Preprint. Vol. 51, 10 p.

24. Kubaschewski, O. and Wittig, F. E., "The Heat of Formation of Magnesium Telluride. The Specific Heat of Tellurium and Supremax Glass", Z. Elektrochem. Vol. 47. pp. 433-8. (Germany)

25. Southard, J. C., "The Thermal Properties of Crystalline and Glassy Boron Trioxide", J. Am. Chem. Soc. Vol. 63. pp. 3147-50

26. Hauffe, K., "The Electrical Conductivity of Uranium Oxides", Z. Physik. Chem. Vol. 48B. pp. 124-30. (Germany)

27. Miller, P. H., "The Electrical Conductivity of Zinc Oxide", Phys. Rev. Vol. 60. pp. 890-5

1. Hensel, F.R., et al., "Physical Properties of Metal Compositions with a Refractory Metal Base", Powder Metallurgy (Am. Soc. Metals). p. 483.

2. Nix, F.C. and MacNair, D.,"The Thermal Expansion of Pure Metals. II. Molybdenum, Palladium, Silver, Tantalum, Tungsten, Platinum and Lead", Phys. Rev. Vol. 61. pp. 74-48.

3. Brace, P.H., "A New Alloy for Working at High Temperature", Metal Progress. Vol. 41. pp. 354-60.

4. Erfling, H.D., "An Anomaly in the Electrical Resistance of Chromium", Ann. Physik. Vol. 41. pp. 100-2. (Germany)

5. Cleaves, Harold E. and Hiegel, John M., "Properties of High-Purity Iron", J. Research Natl. Bur. Stand. (Research Paper No. 1472). Vol. 28. pp. 643-67.

6. Wilson, A.J.C., "The Thermal Expansion of Aluminum: Further Experiments", Proc. Phys. Soc. Vol. 54 (6). pp. 487-91. (England)

7. Cherton, Robert, "Photochemistry of C_2H_2 and Heat of Vaporization of C ", Bull. Soc. Roy. Sci. Liege. Vol. 11. pp. 203-9. (Belgium)

8. Erfling, Hanns-Dieter, "Studies of Thermal Expansion of Solids at Low Temperature. III. Calcium, Columbium, Thorium, Vanadium, Silicon, Titanium", Ann. Physik. Vol. 41. pp. 467-475. (Germany)

9. Goetz, A. and Holser, A., "The Electric Resistance and Anisotropy of Artificial Graphite between 290°K and 12°K", Trans. Electrochem. Soc. Vol. 82. 6 p.

10. Foex, Marc, "Electrical Conductivity of Beryllia and of Magnesia at High Temperatures ", Compt. rend. Vol. 214. pp. 665-6. (France)

11. Moore, George E., "High Temperature Heat Content Data for Three Solid Substances", US AEC Publ. A-502. 8 p.

12. Compton, A. H., "Technological Research, Section I; Report for Month End. Dec. 15, 1942", U. S. AEC Publ. CT-393. 57 p.

13. Erfling, H. D. and Gruneisen, E.,

14. Foex, Marc, "Electrical Conductivity of Thoria at High Temperatures", Compt. rend. Vol. 215. pp. 534-6. (France)

1. Cox, Martha, "Thermal and Electrical Conductivities of W and Ta", Phys. Rev. Vol. 64. pp. 241-7.

2. Kelley, K.K., "The Specific Heat of Pure Iron at Low Temperatures", J. Chem. Phys. Vol. 11. pp. 16-18.

3. Seltz, Harry, Dunkerley, F.J., and DeWitt, B.J., "Heat Capacities and Entropies of Molybdenum and Tungsten Trioxides", J. Am. Chem Soc. Vol. 65. pp. 600-2.

4. Powell, H. and Evans, E.J., "The Hall Effect and Some Other Physical Constants of Alloys. VII. The Aluminum–Silver Series of Alloys", Phil. Mag. Vol. 34(230). pp. 145-61. (England)

5. Hidnert, Peter, "Thermal Expansion of Titanium", J. Research Natl. Bur. Standards RP1520. Vol. 30 (2). pp. 101-5.

6. Hidnert, Peter and Dickson, G., "Thermal Expansion of Some Industrial Copper Alloys", J. Research Nat. Bur. Stand. (Res. Paper No. 1550). Vol. 31 (2). pp. 77-82.

7. Bollenrath. Franz and Bungardt, Walter, "Al-Cu Alloys Containing 8 to 16% Al", Z. Metallkunde. Vol. 35. pp. 153-6. (Germany)

8. Kelley, K.K., "Specific Heats at Low Temperatures of Magnesium Orthosilicate and Magnesium Metasilicate", J. Am. Chem. Soc. Vol. 65. pp. 339-41.

9. Kelley, K.K. and Moore, G.E., "Specific Heats at Low Temperatures of Manganese Carbide and Manganese Dioxide", J. Amer. Chem. Soc. Vol. 65. pp. 782-5.

10. Rolla, L., "Contribution to the Knowledge of the Metals and Alloys of the Rare Earths", Z. Metallkunde. Vol. 35. pp. 29-42. (Germany)

11. Knapp, W.J., "Thermal Conductivity of Nonmetallic Single Crystals", J. Am. Ceram. Soc. Vol. 26. pp. 48-55.

12. Hidnert, Peter, "Thermal Expansion of Some Bronzes", J. Research Nat. Bur. Stand. Vol. 30. pp. 75-78.

13. Kubaschewski, Oswald, "Thermochemistry of Alloys. XI. Heats and Entropies of Fusion and Degree of Order of Au and Ag Alloys", Z. Physik, Chem. Vol. 192. pp. 292-308. (Germany)

14. Geller, R.F. and Bunting, E.N., "Report on the Systems Lead Oxide–Alumina–Silica", Jour. Research Nat. Bur. Stand. Vol. 31 (5). pp. 255-70.

15. Rigby, G.R., Lovell, G.H.B., and Green, A.T., Same as - Bull. British Refractories Res. Assn. No. 65. June, 1943. (England)

16. Bommer, Heinrich and Kross, Ehrhard, "The Densities of Alloys of Lanthanum with Copper, Silver and Gold", Z. anorg. Chem. Vol. 252 (1/2). pp. 62-64. (England)

17. Cornelius, H., "Thermal Expansion and Transformation Temperature in Fe Construction Materials", Luftfahrt-Forsch. Vol. 20. pp. 63-8. (Germany)

18. Seybold, A.U., "Preparation and Properties of Some Gold Alloys", U.S. AEC Publ. AECD 2434 also LADC 141. 10 p.

19. Chicago, Univ. Metallurgical Lab., "Technological Research and Development Section I. Rept. for Month Ending Jan. 15, 1943", U.S. AEC Publ. CT-422. 37 p.

20. Compton, A.H. and Allison, S.A., "Metallurgy of 94; Report for Month Ending November 6, 1943", U.S. AEC Publ. CK-1040. 7 p.

1. Kelley, K.K., "Specific Heats at Low Temperatures of Ti and TiC", Ind. Eng. Chem. Vol. 36. pp. 865-6.

2. Kelley, K.K., "Specific Heat of ZrO_2 at Low Temperatures", Ind. Eng. Chem. Vol. 36. p. 377.

3. Mikryukov, V.E. and Rabotonov, S.N., "Thermal and Electrical Conductivities of Mono- and Poly-crystalline Substances from 100°C to the Melting Point", Uchen. Zapiski Moskov Ordena Lenia Gosudarst. Uni. M. V. Lomonosova. Vol. 74. pp. 167-79. (USSR)

4. Schuman, Robert and Garrett, A.B., "The Vapor Pressure of Be at 1171-1340°K", J. Am. Chem. Soc. Vol. 66. pp. 442-4.

5. Buerschaper, Robert A., "Thermal and Electrical Conductivity of Graphite and C at Low Temperatures", J. Appl. Phys. Vol. 15. pp. 452-4.

6. Russell Jr., R. and Berberich, L.J., "Low Loss Ceramics", Electronics. Vol. 17 (5). pp. 136-42.

7. Perrot, S., "Optical Properties of Very Thin Cr Films", Ann. Phys. Vol. 19. pp. 150-207. (France)

8. Dorward, J.G. and Reed, D., "Heat Radiation and Emissivity Measurements", U.S. AEC Publ. UCRL-865. 22 p.

9. Kratz, H.R. and Raeth, C.H., "The Thermal Conductivity of Uranium", U.S. AEC Publ. CP 2315. 14 p.

10. Boelter, L.M.K., Bromberg, R. and Gier, J.T., "An Investigation of Aircraft Heaters XV. The Emissivity of Several Materials", NACA ARE No. 4A21. 17 p.

11. Nordberg, M.E. and Lillie, H.R., "Properties of Some Vycor-Brand Glasses", J. Am. Ceram. Soc. Vol. 27. p. 299

1. Demarquay, Jean, "New Method of Studying the Expansion of Bodies at Elevated Temperatures", Compt. rend. Vol. 220 (2). pp. 81-83. (France)

2. Hidnert, Peter and Dixon, George, "Some Physical Properties of Mica", J. Research Nat. Bur. Stand. Vol. 35 (4). pp. 309-53.

3. Shomate, C.H., Naylor, B.F., "High Temperature Heat Contents of Aluminum Oxide, Aluminum Sulfate, Potassium Sulfate, Ammonium Sulfate, and Ammonium Bisulfate", J. Am. Chem. Soc. Vol. 67 (1). pp. 72-5.

4. Geller, R.F. and Yavorsky, P.J., "Melting Point of Alpha-alumina", J. Research Natl. Bur. Stand. Vol. 34 (4). pp. 395-401.

5. Cueilleron, Jean, "Fusion Temperature of Boron", Compt. rend. Vol. 221 (23). pp. 698-99. (France)

6. Perry, Stanley, "Coefficient of Thermal Expansion for Aircraft Alloys over a Range from -100°F to 212°F (-73.4°C to + 100°C)", (Rept. No. CR-217). AD 108 675. 39 p.

7. Schulz, L.G., "An Experimental Confirmation of the Drude Free-electron Theory of the Optical Properties of Metals for Silver, Gold, and Copper in the Near Infrared", J. Opt. Soc. Amer. Vol. 44. pp. 540-5.

8. Schulz, L.G., "Reflectivity of Silver in the Near Infrared", Physics Rev. Vol. 93. p. 922.

9. Keller, W. H. et al., "The Casting of Thorium Metal and Some Properties of the Cast Metal", U.S. AEC Publ. CT 2951. 20 p.

10. Russell, H. W., Nelson, H. R. and Grenel, L. H. "Progress Report on the Properties of Alloys", U.S. AEC Publ. CT-2983. 28 p.

11. Powell, R. W., "Note of Existing Data for the Thermal Conductivities of Certain Metals", BR 669 13 p.

12. Fried, S., "The Crystal Structure of Neptunium Metal", U. S. AEC Publ. CN-3053. 6 p.

13. Batelle Memorial Inst., Columbus, O., "Metallurgy of Tuballoy (Uranium)", U.S. AEC Publ. CT 2700. 50 p.

14. Axilrod, Benj. M. and Koenig, Evelyn, "Properties of Some Expanded Plastics and Other Low-Density Materials", NACA TN No. 991. Natl. Bur. of Standards. 26 p.

15. Hall, G. L. and Prettyman, I. B., "The Measurement of Thermal Conductivity of Nonmetallic Solids", India Rubber World. Vol. 113. pp. 222-35.

16. Russell, H. W., Nelson, H. R. and Grenell, L. H., "Properties of Alloys, Prog. Report", U.S. AEC Publ. CT-3054. 32 p.

17. Bitsianes, G., "Alloys of Uranium and Silicon II. The Epsilon Phase", Cont. W-7405-eng-175. 32 p.

18. Rundle, R. E., Wilson, A. S. and McDonald, R. A., "The X-ray Investigation of the Uranium-Hydrogen System: The structure of UH_3", U. S. AEC Publ. AECD 2309. 14 p.

1. Kelley, K.K., Naylor, B.F., and Shomate, C.H., "The Thermodynamic Properties of Manganese", U.S. Bur. Mines Tech. Paper 686. 34 p.

2. Naylor, B.F., "The High-temperature Heat Contents of Titanium Carbide and Titanium Nitride", J. Amer. Chem. Soc. Vol. 68 (3). pp. 370-1.

3. Parke, R.M. and Bens, F.P., "Chromium-base Alloys (for Gas-turbine Blades)", A.S.T.M. Symposium on Materials for Gas Turbines, 1946. pp. 80-98. (Disc. 121-28).

4. Geller, R.F., Yavorsky, P.J., Steierman, B.L., and Creamer, A.S., "Studies of Binary and Ternary Combination of Magnesia, Calcia, Baria, Beryllia, Alumina, Thoria, and Zirconia in Relation to Their Use as Porcelains", J. Research Natl. Bur. Stand. (Research Paper No. 1703.) Vol. 36. pp. 277-312.

5. Hummel, F.A. and Henry, E.C., "Progress Report on the Investigations of Some Refractory Phosphates -- Thermal Expansions of Some Zircon-beryl Bodies", Penn. State Col. School Mineral Indus. Memo Rept. 4. PB 60 657. 7 p.

6. Naylor, B.F. and Cook, O.A., "High-temperature Heat Contents of the Metatitanates of Calcium, Iron, and Magnesium", J. Am. Chem. Soc. Vol. 68. pp. 1003-5.

7. Anderson, Scott, "Measurement of Mean Specific Heat of Plate Glass at High Temperatures", J. Am. Ceram. Soc. Vol. 29. pp. 368-70.

8. Rigby, G.R., Lovell, G.H.B., and Green, A.T., "Some Properties of the Spinels Associated with Chrome Ores", Brit. Ceram. Soc. Vol. 45 (4). pp. 137-48 (England)

9. Kornilov, I.I., Mikheev, V.S., Konenko-Gracheva, O.K., and Mints, R.S., "Equilibrium Diagram of the Ternary System Iron-chromium-aluminum", Invest. Sektora Fiz.-Khim. Anal., Inst. Obshchei i Neorg. Khim. Akad. Nauk. SSSR. Vol. 16. pp. 100-15. (U.S.S.R)

10. Pierrey, Jacques, "Study of the Thermal Expansion of Graphite", Compt. rend. Vol. 223. pp. 501-3. (France)

11. Krishnan, R.S., "Thermal Expansion of Diamond", Proc. Indian Acad. Sci. Vol. 24-A. pp. 33-44. (India)

12. Friedberg, S.A. "Investigations of Thermal and Electrical Properties of Solids at Very Low Temperatures", U.S. AEC Publ. NP-5668. 73 p.

13. Hummel, F.A. and Henry, E.C., "Physical Properties of Refractory Materials", Penn. State Coll. School Mineral Inds. Memo Rept. PB 60 660. Vol. 7. 12 p.

14. Pole, G.R., Beinlich Jr., A.W. and Gilbert, N., "Physical Properties of Some High-Temperature Refractory Compositions", J. Am. Ceram. Soc. Vol. 29. pp. 208-222.

15. Leung, Kinving, "Measurement of the Electric Resistivity of Glasses", Compt. rend. Vol. 223 (5). pp. 236-37. (France)

1. Ginnings, D. C. and Corruccini, R. J., "Heat Capacities at High Temperatures of Uranium, Uranium Trichloride and Uranium Tetrachloride ", J. Research Nat. Bur. Standards. Vol. 39. pp. 309-16.

2. Ebert, Hermann and Schulze, Alfred, "Electrical and Thermal Properties of Uranium", Metall-forschung. Vol. 2. pp. 46-49. (Germany)

3. Dahl, Andrew I. and Van Dusen, Milton S., "Resistance-temperature Relation and Thermoelectric Properties of Uranium", J. Research Nat. Bur. Stand. Vol. 39. pp. 53-8.

4. Aitchison, G. J., "Measurement by Induction Heating of the Temperature Variations of the Specific Heats of Ferromagnetic Materials", J. Sci. Instr. Vol. 24 (8). pp. 200-02.

5. Van Dusen, M. S. and Dahl, A. I., "Freezing Points of Cobalt and Nickel and a New Determination of Planck's Constant C_2 ", Science. Vol. 106. pp. 428-9.

6. Bidwell, C. C. and Hogan, C. L., "Thermal Conductivity of Aluminum; Solid and Liquid States", J. Appl. Phys. Vol. 18. pp. 776-779.

7. Hidnert, Peter and Krider, Harrison S., "Thermal Expansion of Some Copper Alloys", J. Research Nat. Bur. Stand. (Res. Paper No. 1838). Vol. 39. pp. 419-21.

8. Cornelius, H., Bungardt, W., and Bollenrath, F., "Investigations Concerning the Suitability of Heat-resisting Materials for Exhaust-gas Turbine Blades (Part 3 of 3 Parts)", Deutsche Versuchsanstalt fuer Luftfahrt, E. V. 21 p. (Germany) (Also ATI-22895, Translation, Released 1947)

9. Bunting, E. N., Shelton, G. R., and Creamer, A. S., "Properties of Barium-Strontium Titanate Di-electrics", J. Am. Ceram. Soc. Vol. 30. pp. 113-125.

10. Balz, Georg, "Electrical Behavior and Allotropy of Uranium", Metallforschung. Vol. 2. pp. 144-146. (Germany)

11. Russell Jr. Ralston and Mohr, W. C., "Characteristics of Zircon Porcelain", J. Am. Ceram. Soc. Vol. 30. pp. 32-5.

12. Armstrong, L. D. and Dauphinee, T. M., "Thermal Conductivity of Metals at High Temperatures. I--Description of the Apparatus and Measurements on Iron", Canad. J. Research. Vol. 25. pp. 357-374. (Canada)

13. Blanter, M. E., "Electrical Resistance of Iron-Chromium-Carbon Alloys at High Temperatures", J. Tech. Phys. Vol. 17. pp. 549-556. (USSR)

14. Sweeny, W. O., "Haynes Alloys for High-temperature Service", Trans. Amer. Soc. Mech. Eng. Vol. 69 (6). pp. 569-81.

15. Balz, Georg, "Electrical Behavior and Allotropy of Uranium", Metallforschung. Vol. 2. pp. 144-6. (Germany)

16. Shomate, C. H., "Heat Capacities at Low Temperatures of Titanium Dioxide (Rutile and Anatase) ", J. Am. Chem. Soc. Vol. 69. pp. 218-9.

17. Ginnings, D. C. and Corruccini, R. J., "Enthalpy, Specific Heat, and Entropy of Aluminum Oxide from 0° to 900°", J. Research Natl. Bur. Stand. (Research Paper 1797). Vol. 38, No. 6. pp. 593-600.

18. Moore, G. E. and Kelley, K. K., "High Temperature Heat Content of Uranium, Uranium Dioxide and Uranium Trioxide", J. Am. Chem. Soc. Vol. 69. pp. 2105-7.

19. Neubert, R. J., Royal, J., Van Dyken, A. R., "Structures and Properties of Artificial and Natural Graphite ", ANL - 4022 (Contr. W-710-eng-37). 57 p.

20. Rehner Jr., John, "Heat Conduction and Molecular Structure in Rubberlike Polymers", J. Polymer Sci. Vol. 2. pp. 263-74.

21. Estermann, T., Foner, A. and Randall, J. A., "Resistivity of Germanium at Low Temperatures and the Effect of Additions", Phys. Rev. Vol. 71. p. 484.

22. Jaffee, R. I. and Campbell, I. E., "The Properties of Zirconium", U. S. AEC Publ. NP 266. 27 p.

23. Argonne Natl. Lab., "Chemistry Division, Section C-II Summary Report for July, Aug. and Sept. 1946, June 2, 1947", U. S. AEC Publ. ANL4000. 127 p.

24. Argonne National Lab., "Chemistry Division, Sect. C-II, Summary Report for July through Dec. 1947 ", U. S. AEC Publ. ANL-4185 (Del.). 145 p.

25. Reysen, W. H. and Vanstrum, P. R., "Properties of 'Fluorothene", U. S. AEC Publ. AECD 2032. 8 p.

1. Bollenrath, Franz and Hauk, Viktor, "Linear Coefficients of Expansion and Electrical Resistivity of Cast Aluminum Alloys Containing Copper and Silicon", Z. Metallkunde. Vol. 39. pp. 106-8. (Germany)

2. Gordon, Paul, "A High-temperature Precision X-ray Camera. Some Measurements of the Thermal Coefficients of Expansion of Beryllium", U. S. Atomic Energy Comm. Publ. (AECD-2426). 33 p.

3. Shelton, George R., Creamer, Ansel S., and Bunting, Elmer N., "Properties of Barium-Magnesium Titanate Dielectrics", J. Am. Ceram. Soc. Vol. 31. pp. 205-212.

4. Beetle, R., McKinstry, H., Bachman, J.L., and others, "Quarterly Progress Report on the Investigation of Refractory Materials", Penn. State College School of Mineral Industries. 69 p.

5. Foex, Marc, "A Type of Transformation Common in the Lower Oxides of Manganese, Iron, Cobalt and Nickel", Compt. rend. Vol. 227. pp. 193-4. (France)

6. Knop Jr.H.W., "The Emissivity of Iron-Tungsten and Iron-Cobalt Alloys", Phys. Rev. (ii). Vol. 74 (10). pp. 1413-16.

7. King, E.G., Torgeson, D.R., and Cook, O.A., "High Temperature Heat Contents of $3CaO \cdot B_2O_3$, $2CaO \cdot B_2O_3$, $CaO \cdot B_2O_3$, and $CaO \cdot 2B_2O_3$", J. Am. Chem. Soc. Vol. 70 (6). pp. 2160-63.

8. Loriers, Jean, "Transformations of Cerium at High Temperatures", Compt. rend. Vol. 226, 11. pp. 1018-19. (France)

9. Brewer, Leo, Gilles, Paul W., and Jenkins, Francis A., "The Vapor Pressure and Heat of Sublimation of Graphite", J. Chem. Phys. Vol. 16. pp. 797-807.

10. Brewer, Leo, "The Vapor Pressure and Melting Point of Graphite", J. Chem. Phys. Vol. 16. pp. 1165-6.

11. Lyman, T., ed. Metals Handbook, 1948 edition, Am. Soc. for Metals, Cleveland, Ohio.

12. Harrower, John and Wahlin, H.B., "Phase Emissivity", Wisconsin Engr. Vol. 52. No. 8. pp. 8, 37.

13. Wahlin, H.B. and Knop Jr. H.W., "The Spectral Emissivity of Iron and Cobalt", Phys. Rev. Vol. 74. pp. 687-689.

14. Nemilov, V.A. and Rudnitsky, A.A., "Alloys of Platinum and Tungsten", Izvest. Sekt. Platiny. Vol. 21. pp. 234-8. (USSR)

15. Seifert, Ralph L., "The Spectral Emissivity and Total Emissivity of Beryllium Oxide", Phys. Rev. Vol. 73. pp. 1181-7.

16. Trice, J. B., Neely, J. J. and Teeter, C. E. "The Thermal Conductivity of a Hot Pressed Be_2 C Cylinder", NEPA 812. 12 p.

17. M. W. Kellogg Company, "6000 Pound Thrust Jet Propulsion Unit - Part II - Materials - Wiring and Calibration of Equipment", Appendix C. of Final Report (SPD 115). 14 p.

18. Ames Laboratory, "Progress Report in Metallurgy", U. S. AEC Publ. ISC-25. 35 p.

19. Wilson, A. S. and Rundle, R. E., "X-Ray Studies of Alpha, Beta, and Gamma Uranium", U. S. AEC Publ. AECD 2046. 8 p.

20. Holden, R. J., Speiser, R. and Johnston, H. L., "The Vapor Pressures of Inorganic Substances, II. Beryllium", J. Am. Chem. Soc. Vol. 70. pp. 3897-99.

21. Fine, M. E. and Ellis, W. C. "Thermal Expansion Properties of Iron-Cobalt Alloys", Bell Tel. System Tech. Publ. Monograph B-1547, 13 p. See Met. Abs. Vol. 15. p. 569.

22. Fine, M. E. and Ellis, W. C., "Thermal Expansion Properties of Iron-Cobalt Alloys", Bell Tel. System Tech. Publ. Monograph B-1547. 13 p. See Met. Abs. Vol. 15. p. 569. (Duplicate of 48-21)

23. Greiner, E. S. and Ellis, W. C., "Thermal and Electrical Properties of Ductile Titanium", Metal. Technol. AIMME Tech. Publ. No. 2466. Vol. 15. 9 p.

24. Anon., "New (Nickel) Alloy (Evanohm) Has Improved Electrical Resistance Properties", Materials and Methods. Vol. 28.pp. 62-3.

25. Baenziger, N. C., "The Crystal Structures of Some Thorium and Uranium Compounds", U. S. AEC Publ. AECD 3237, also ISC 99. 114 p.

26. Rundle, R. E., Wilson, A. S. et al., "The Crystal Structures of ThH_2 and $Zr\,H_2$", U. S. AEC Publ. AECD 2120. 9 p.

27. Zachariasen, W. H. "The Crystal Structure of Uranium Silicides and of $CeSi_2$, $NpSi_2$ and $PuSi_2$", U. S. AEC Publ. AECD 2092 (ANL-FWHZ 152).

28. Robertson, W. D. and Uhlig, H. H., "Electrical Properties of the Intermetallic Compounds MgSn and Mg_2 Pb", Am. Inst. Min. Met. Eng. Inst. Metals Div. Metals. Technol. Tech. Publ. No. 2468. Vol. 15. No. 7. 11 p.

29. Rundle, R. E., Wilson, A. S., Baenziger, N. C., "X-ray Analysis of the Uranium-Carbon System", U. S. AEC Publ. AECD 2325. 10 p.

30. Rundle, R. E., et al., "The System Uranium-Nitrogen", U. S. AEC Publ. AECD 2247. 22 p.

31. Brewer, L., Bromley, L. et al., "The Preparation and Properties of Refractory Sulfides", U. S. AEC Publ. AECD 2242 (MB-LB-18-5). 47 p.

32. Gronvold, F., "Crystal Structure of Uranium Oxide (U_3O_8)", Nature 162. 70 p.

33. Trice, J. B., Neely, J. J. and Teeter Jr., C. E., "The Heat-Capacity of Beryllium Carbide Powders", U. S. AEC Publ. AECU-19. 12 p.   also NEPA 816. 14 p.

34. Trice, J. B., Neely, J. J. and Teeter Jr., C. E., "The Heat Capacity of a Hot Pressed Beryllium Carbide Cylinder", NEPA 821. 12 p.

35. Benford, Frank, Schwarz, S. and Lloyd, G. P., "Coefficients of Reflection in the Ultraviolet of Magnesium Carbonate and Oxide", J. Optical Soc. Am. Vol. 38. pp. 964-5.

36. Malm, J. G. and Gilbreath, J. R., "The Thermal Expansion of High Density Beryllia Shapes", U. S. AEC Publ. ANL 4241. 17 p.

37. Penn. State, "Quarterly Prog. Rept. on the Investigation of Refractory Materials", U. S. AEC Publ. NP 420 Memorandum Rept. No. 16. 33 p.

38. Owens Illinois Glass Co., Research Labs., "Properties of Soda-Strontium Oxide-Alumina-Silica Glasses", J. Am. Ceramic Soc. Vol. 31. pp. 1-8.

1. Whittemore Jr., O.J., "Properties and Uses of Pure Oxide Heavy Refractories", J. Am. Ceram. Soc. Vol. 32. pp. 48-53.

2. Pallister, P.R., "The Specific Heat and Resistivity of High-Purity Iron Up to 1250°", J. Iron Steel Inst. Vol. 161. pp. 87-90. (England)

3. Smoke, E.J., "Thermal Endurance of Some Vitrified Industrial Compositions", Ceram. Age. Vol. 54. pp. 148-9.

4. Pearson, G.L. and Bardeen, J., "Electrical Properties of Pure Silicon and Silicon Alloys Containing Boron and Phosphorous", Phys. Rev. Vol. 75. pp. 865-83.

5. Michels, Walter C. and Wilford, Sally, "The Physical Properties of Titanium. I. Emissivity and Resistivity of the Commercial Metal", J. Appl. Phys. Vol. 20. pp. 1223-6.

6. Carpenter, L.G. and Reavell, Frank R., "Vaporization of Titanium", Nature. Vol. 163. p. 527.

7. Worner, H.W., "The Preparation and Some Properties of Ductile Titanium", Metallurgia. Vol. 40. (236) pp. 69-76. (England)

8. Michels, Walter, C. and Wilford, Sally E., "Spectral Emissivity and Conductivity of Titanium", Phys. Rev. Vol. 76. pp. 174-5.

9. Gordon, Paul, "A High-temperature Precision X-ray Camera. Some Measurements of the Thermal Coefficients of Expansion of Beryllium", J. Appl. Phys. Vol. 20. pp. 908-17.

10. Potter, E.V., Lukens, H.C., and Huber, R.W., "Transformation of γ to α Manganese", J. Metals. Vol. 1(7). pp. 399-404.

11. Justi, E., "Electrical Properties of Ruthenium", Z. Naturforsch. Vol. (A) 4(7). pp. 472-74. (Germany)

12. Raub, Ernst and Wolff, Karl, "Thermal Expansion Measurements of Binary Alloys Having Reversed Solubilities and of Metals Having Strong Lattice Interferences", Z. Metallkunde. Vol. 40. pp. 126-34. (Germany)

13. International Nickel Co., Inc., Development and Research Div., New York, New York, "Inconel 'X', a High Temperature Alloy--Data and Information", ATI-52025. 79 p.

14. Hummel, F.A., "Properties of Some Substances Isostructural with Silica", J. Am. Ceram. Soc. Vol. 32. pp. 320-6.

15. McKinstry, Herbert A., Hocker, Clifford F., Ricker, Richard W., and others, "Quarterly Progress Report on the Investigation of Refractory Materials - and Appendix (Memorandum Report)", USAF Contract No. 433-038-ac-16374, ATI-67 891. 61 p.

16. Trombe, Felix, "Superrefractory Oxides", Bull. Soc. Franc. Ceram. Vol. 3. pp. 18-26. (France)

17. Pierrey, J., "Dilation at High Temperature", Ann. Chim. Vol. 12(4). pp. 133-95. (France)

18. Bender, Dietrich, "The Electrical Properties of Thorium", Z. Metallkunde. Vol. 40. pp. 257-60. (Germany)

19. Gebler, Kenneth A. and Wisely, Harriet R., "Dense Cordierite Bodies", J. Am. Ceram. Soc. Vol. 32. pp. 163-65.

20. Gangler, J.J., Robards, C.F., and McNurr, J.E., "Physical Properties at Elevated Temperatures of 7 Hot Pressed Ceramics", Nat. Advisory Comm. Aeronaut. TN 1911

21. Ehrlich, Paul, "The Binary Systems Ti-N, Ti-C, Ti-B, Ti-Be", Z. anorg. Chem. Vol. 259. pp. 1-41. (Germany)

22. Blocher, John and Campbell, I.E., "Vapor Pressure of Titanium", J. Am. Chem. Soc. Vol. 71. pp. 4040-2.

23. Deutsch, George C., Repko, Andrew J., Lidman, Wm., G., "Elevated Temperature Properties of Several Titanium Carbide Base Cermets", Nat. Advisory Comm. Aeronaut. Tech. Note 1915 47 p.

24. Kikoin, A.K., "The Chromium-Tellurium Alloy", Doklady Akad. Nauk S.S.S.R. Vol. 68. pp. 481-2. (U.S.S.R.)

25. Suzuki, Taira, "The Nature of Preston-Guinier Atom-groups in an Age-hardened Aluminum-copper Alloy", Science Reports. Research Insts. Tohoku University. Vol. 1 (Series A) pp. 183-8. (Japan)

26. Shomate, C.H. and Kelley, K.K., "Heat Capacities at Low Temperatures and Entropies of Vanadium Carbide and Vanadium Nitride", J. Am. Chem. Soc. Vol. 71. pp. 314-315.

27. King, E.G., "High Temperature Heat Contents of Vanadium Carbide and Vanadium Nitride", J. Am. Chem. Soc. Vol. 71. pp. 316-17.

28. Mitchell, D.W., "Heat Contents and Heat of Formation of Magnesium Nitride--High-temperature Measurements", Ind. Eng. Chem. Vol. 41. pp. 2027-31.

29. Dahl, A.I. and Cleaves, H.E., "The Freezing Point of Uranium", J. Research Nat. Bur. Stand. Vol. 43. pp. 513-7.

30. Dahl, A.I. and Cleaves, H.E., "The Freezing Point of Uranium", AECD 2541. 8 p.

31. Simpson, O.C., Thorn, R.J., and Winslow, G.H., "The Vapor Pressure and Heat of Sublimation of Graphite", AECD 2680, Argonne Natl. Lab. 85 p.

32. Kurnakov, N.N., and Troneva, M. Ya., "A Study of the System Manganese-Nickel", Doklady Akad. Nauk. S.S.S.R. Vol. 68. pp. 73-76. (USSR)

33. Kochanovaka, A., "Investigation of Thermal Dilatation of Cubic Metals. (Aluminum and Iron)", Physica. Vol. 15. pp. 191-196. (Netherlands)

34. Best, Geo., "Emissivity of Copper and Aluminum", J. Optical Soc. Am. Vol. 39. pp. 1009-11.

35. Silverman, A., chm., Data on Chemicals for Ceramic Use. Bull. No. 118. Natl. Research Council. June, 1949.

36. Maxwell, W.A., "Properties of Certain Intermetallics as Related to Elevated-temperature Applications. I. Molybdenum Disilicide", NACA RM E9G01. 27 p.

37. Boltaks, B.I., "The Electrical Properties of the Intermetallic Compound Mg_2Sn", Doklady Akad. Nauk SSSR. Vol. 64. pp. 653-6. (USSR)

38. Fakidov, I.G., Grazhdankina, N.P. and Kikoin, A.K., "On the Electrical Conductivity of a Ferromagnetic Chromium-Tellurium Alloy", Doklady Akad. Nauk. SSSR. Vol. 68. pp. 491-2. (USSR)

39. Beamer, W.H. and Maxwell, C.R., "Physical Properties of Polonium. II. X-ray Studies and Crystal Structure", J. Chem. Phys. Vol. 17. pp. 1293-8.

40. D'Eye, R.W.M., "Preparation of Pure Thorium", AERE C-R 425. 6 p. (England)

41. Litton, F.B. and Gonser, B.W., "Composition, Structure and Properties of Iodide Titanium", Metal Progress. Vol. 44. pp. 346-7.

42. Wilson, A.S. and Rundle, R.E., "The Structure of Uranium Metal", Acta Cryst. Vol. 2, pp. 126-7.

43. Carlile, S.J., Christian, J.W. and Rume-Rothery, W., "The Equilibrium Diagram of the System Chromium-Manganese", J. Inst. Metals. Vol. 76 (No. 2). pp. 169-94. (England)

44. Brewer, L. and Mastick, D.F., "The Stability of Gaseous Ferrous Oxide", U.S. AEC Publ. URCL 534. 20 p.

45. Hausner, H.H. and Pinto, N.P., "The Powder Metallurgy of Beryllium", U.S. AEC Publ. AECD 2869. 65 p.

46. Fried, S., "The Crystal Structure of Neptunium Metal", U.S. AEC Publ. NNES. Vol. 143, p. 1085.

47. Garth, R.C. and Sailer, V.L., "Thermal Conductivity of Graphite", U.S. AEC Publ. BNL-69. 18 p.

48. Putley, E.H., "The Electrical Conductivity of Germanium", Proc. Phys. Soc. Vol. 62. pp. 284-92. (England)

49. Wilhelm, H.A. and Carlson, O.N. "The Uranium-Manganese and Uranium-Copper Alloy Systems", U.S. AEC Publ. AECD 2717. 20 p.

50. Tucker Jr., C.W., "The Crystal Structures of Metallic Uranium", U.S. AEC Publ. AECD 2716. 17 p.

51. Suzuki, Taira., "The Release of Energy Associated with Crystal Restoration Process in Cold-Worked Polycrystalline Copper", Sci. Repts. Research Insts. Tohoku. Vol. Ser. A 1. pp. 193-201 (Japan)

52. Ginnings, D.C., Douglas, T.B. and Ball, A.F., "Specific Heat of Beryllium Between 0° and 900°C", U.S. AEC Publ. NBS-5. 7 p.

53. Wilhelm, H.A. and Chiotti, P., "Thorium-Carbon System", U.S. AEC Publ. AECD 2718. 22 p.

54. Powell, R.W., Hickman, M.J. and Barber, C.R., "Some Physical Properties of Aluminum Alloys at Elevated Temperatures. I. Thermal Conductivity and Electrical Resistivity. II. Linear Thermal Expansion", Metallurgia. Vol. 41. pp. 15-21. (England)

55. Jones, F.W. and Pumphrey, W.I., "Free Energy and Metastable States in the Iron-Nickel System", J. Iron Steel Inst. Vol. 163. pp. 121-31. (England)

56. Brewer, L., Edwards, R.K. and Templeton, D.H., "The Crystal Structure of UBi", U.S. AEC Publ. AECD 2730. 15 p.

57. Rundle, R.E. and Wilson, A.S., "The Structure of Some Metal Compounds of Uranium", Acta Cryst. Vol. 2. pp. 148-50. (identically the same as U.S. AEC Publ. AECD 2388).

58. Schramm, C. H., Gordon, P. and Kaufmann, A. R., "The Alloy Systems Uranium-Tungsten, Uranium-Tantalum and Tungsten-Tantalum", U. S. AEC Publ. AECD 2686. 38 p.

59. Noeron, J. T., Blumenthal, H. and Sindeband, S. J., "Structure of Diborides of Titanium, Zirconium, Columbium, Tantalum and Vanadium", J. Metals. Vol. 1. pp. 749-51.

60. Kiessling, R., "The Binary System Chromium-Boron. I. Phase Analysis and Structure of the ζ and θ phases", Acta. Chem. Scand. Vol. 3. pp. 595-603. (Sweden)

61. Zalkin, A. and Templeton, D. H., "The Crystal Structures of CeB_4, ThB_4 and UB_4", U. S. AEC Publ. AECD 2762. 4 p.

62. Kiessling, R., "The Borides of Tantalum", Acta Chem. Scand. Vol. 3. pp. 603-15. (Sweden)

63. Maxwell, W. A., "Properties of Certain Intermetallics as Related to Elevated Temperature Applications: I. Molybdenum Disilicide", NACA RM No. E9G01. 27 p.

64. Spedding, F. H. et al., "Uranium Hydride-I", Nucleonics. pp. 4-15.

65. Brewer, L., Bromley, L. et al., "Thermodynamic Properties and Equilibrium at High Temperature of the Compounds of Plutonium", Natl. Nuclear Energy Ser. Div. IV, 14B, Transuranium Elements Pt II. pp. 861-86.

66. Zachariasen, W. H., "Crystal Structure Studies of Chlorides, Bromides and Iodides of Plutonium and Neptunium", The Transuranium Elements Research Papers, Part II, Paper 20.6. pp. 1473-85.

67. Grim, M. S. et al., "Refractories for Atomic Power Production", U. S. AEC Publ. ETL-18. 19 p.

68. Norton, F. H., Fellows, D. M. et al., "(Thermal Conductivity) Prog. Rept. for Oct. 1-Dec. 31, 1949", U. S. AEC Publ. NYO-96. 45 p.

69. Foex, Marc, "The Abnormal Electrical Properties of Vanadium Sesquioxide between -100° and +300°", Compt. rend. Vol. 229. pp. 880-2. (France)

1. Kubaschewski, Oswald, "Atomic Heats of Metals", Z. Metallk. Vol. 41. pp. 445-51. (Germany)

2. Coughlin, J.P. and King, E.G., "High-temperature Heat Contents of Some Zirconium-containing Substances", J. Am. Chem. Soc. Vol. 72. pp. 2262-5.

3. Armstrong, L.D., Grayson-Smith, H., "High-temperature Calorimetry. I. A New Adiabatic Calorimeter. II. Atomic Heats of Chromium, Manganese, and Cobalt between 0° and 800°", Can. J. Research. Vol. 28A. pp. 44-50, 51-59. (Canada)

4. Scholes, William A., "Thermal Conductivity of Bodies of High Beryllium Oxide Content", J. Am. Ceram. Soc. Vol. 33. pp. 111-17.

5. Kubaschewski, O., Brizgys, P., Huchler, O., Jauch, R., and Reinartz, K., "The Heats of Fusion and Transformation of Metals", Z. Elektrochem. Vol. 54. pp. 275-88. (Germany)

6. Speiser, Rudolph, Johnston, Herrick L., and Blackburn, Paul, "Vapor Pressure of Inorganic Substances. III. Chromium between 1283 and 1561°K", J. Am. Chem. Soc. Vol. 72. pp. 4142-3.

7. Arthur, James S. "The Specific Heats of MgO, TiO_2, and ZrO_2 at High Temperatures", J. Appl. Phys. Vol. 21. 732-3.

8. Andrew, J.H., Lee, H., Chang, P.L., Fang, B., Guenot, R., Brookes, P.E., Bourne, L., Wilson, D.V., Bhat, U.V., and Lloyd, H.K., "The Effect of Cold Work on Steel", J. Iron Steel Inst. (London). Vol. 165. pp. 145-84, and 369-95. (England)

9. Kussman, A. and Rittberg, G.G.V., "A Study of the Transformations in the System Platinum Iron", Z. Metallkunde. Vol. 41 (12). pp. 470-77. (Germany)

10. Gangler, James J., "Some Physical Properties of Eight Refractory Oxides and Carbides", J. Am. Ceram. Soc. Vol. 33 (12). pp. 367-75.

11. McKee, J.H. and Adams, A.M., "Physical Properties of Extruded and Slip-cast Zircon with Particular Reference to Thermal Shock Resistance", Trans. Brit. Ceram. Soc. Vol. 49 (9). pp. 386-407. (England)

12. Koch, W.J. and Harman, C.G., "Aluminum Titanate as a Ceramic Material", U. S. Atomic Energy Commission, Tech. Information Service, Oak Ridge, Tenn., AECD-3213. 34 p.

13. Gangler, James J., "Some Properties of Eight Refractory Oxides and Carbides", J. Am. Soc. Vol. 33 (12). pp. 367-75.

14. Sweeny, W.O., "Haynes Alloys for High-temperature Service", ATI-63034. 87 p.

15. Long, Roger, A., "Fabrication and Properties of Hot-pressed Molybdenum Disilicide", NACA, RM E50F22. 34 p.

16. Anonymous, "Characteristics, Properties and Fields of Application of 'Duralite' Alloy (Thermafond C3-INA)", Alluminio. Vol. 19(4). pp. 357-68. (Italy)

17. Anonymous, "C46": Characteristics of a New Light-metal Heat-resisting Casting Alloy", Alluminio. Vol. 19 (1). pp. 59-69. (Italy)

18. Todd, S.S., "Heat Capacities at Low Temperatures and Entropies at 208.16°K of Andalusite, Kyanite, and Silimanite", J. Am. Chem. Soc. Vol. 72. pp. 742-3.

19. Neely, J.J., Teeter, C.E., and Trice, J.B., "Thermal Conductivity and Heat Capacity of Beryllium Carbide", J. Am. Ceram. Soc. Vol. 33. pp. 363-4.

20. Allendorfer, A., "The Determination of the Melting Point of Uranium", Z. Naturforsch. Vol. 5(a)(4). pp. 234-235. (Germany)

21. Westrum, Jr., E.F., Hatcher, J.B., and Osborne, D.W., "The Entropy and Low-temperature Heat Capacities of Neptunium Dioxide", AECD-2863, ANL-EFW-34. 18 p.

22. Erway, N.D. and Simpson, O.C., "The Vapor Pressure of Americium", J. Chem. Phys. also AECD 2733. Vol. 18. pp. 953-7.

23. Marshall, A.L. and Norton, F.J., "Carbon Vapor Pressure and Heat of Vaporization", J. Am. Chem. Soc. Vol. 72. pp. 2166-71.

24. Moore, Geo.E., Allison, H.W., and Struthers, J.D., "The Vaporization of Strontium Oxide", J. Chem. Phys. Vol. 18. p. 1572.

25. Fitzsimmons, E.S., "Thermal Diffusivity of Refractory Oxides", J. Am. Ceram. Soc. Vol. 33(11) pp. 327-32.

26. Kondo, Kanzi, "Some Properties of Silicon Carbide", Rept. Inst. Sci. and Technal. Univ. Tokyo. Vol. 4. pp. 4-7. (Japan)

27. Eastman, E.D., Brewer, Leo, Bromley, LeRoy A., Gilles, Paul W., Lofgren, N.L., "Preparation and Properties of Refractory Cerium Sulfides", J. Am. Chem. Soc. Vol. 72(5). pp. 2248-50.

28. Boettcher, A., "The Ligh-Reflecting Power of Vaporized Aluminum-Silver and Aluminum-Magnesium Alloys", Z. angew. Physik. Vol. 2. pp. 340-3. (Germany)

29. Brauer, G. and Tiesler, J., "The Density and Lattice Structure of the Compounds Mg_2Pb, Mg_2Sn and Mg_2Ge", Z. anorg. Chem. Vol. 262. pp. 319-327. (Germany)

30. Brewer, Leo, Searcy, Alan W., Templeton, D.H., and Dauben, Carol H., "High Melting Silicides", J. Am. Ceramic Soc. Vol. 33. pp. 291-94.

31. Thomas, Hans, "The Electrical Resistivity of Iron-Chromium-Aluminum Alloys at High Temperature", Z. Metallkunde. Vol. 41. pp. 185-90.

32. Avery, D.G., "Some Optical Properties of Evaporated Layers of Silver, Copper and Tin", Phil. Mag. Vol. 41 (321). pp. 1018-1031. (England)

33. Thielke, N.R. and Henry, E.C., "Refractory Materials for Use in High-Temperature Areas of Aircraft", Summary Report U.S. Air Force Air Materiel Command AF Tech. Rept. No. 6080. 47 p. July, 1950.

34. Westrum Jr., E.F. and Eyring, L., "The Preparation of Some Properties of Americium Metal", U.S. AEC Publ. AEC-2980; ANL-EFW-37; PC-1235. 13 p.

35. Yamamoto, Mikio, "Densities of Nickel-Cobalt Alloys", Science Repts. Research Insts. Tohoku Univ. Ser. A 2 pp. 871-7. (Japan)

36. Cubicciotti, D., "The Reactions of Metals with Gases at High Temperatures: The Melting Point-Composition Diagram of the Zirconium-Oxygen System", U.S. AEC Publ. NP-1899. Tech. Rept. 6, II. 17 p.

37. Johnson, P.D., "Behavior of Refractory Oxides and Metals, Alone and in Combination in Vacuo at High Temperatures", J. Am. Ceram. Soc. Vol. 33. pp. 168-71.

38. Greenaway, H.T., Johnstone, S.T.M. and McQuillan, M.K., "High-Temperature Thermal Analysis Using the Tungsten Molybdenum Thermocouple (Determination of Freezing Point of Chromium)", J. Inst. Metals. Vol. 80. pp. 109-14. (England)

39. Wallman, J.C., Crane, W.W.T. and Cunningham, B.B., "The Preparation and Some Properties of Curium Metal", U.S. AEC Publ. AECD 2912. 4 p.

40. Edwards, J.W., Johnston, H.L. and Blackburn, P.E., "Vapor Pressure of Inorganic Substances. V. Tantalum between 2624° and 2943°", Tch. Rept. No. 6, Ohio State Univ. Cryog. Lab. U.S. AEC Publ. NP 1933. pp. 15.

41. Carlson, O.N., "Some Studies on the Uranium-Thorium-Zirconium Ternary Alloy System", U.S. AEC Publ. AECD 3206; ISC 102; 72 p.

42. Boody, Fred. P., "Density of Hafnium and Zirconium Metals", U.S. AEC Publ. Y-696. 8 p.

43. Mass. Inst. of Tech. "Technical Prog. Rept. for the Period April through June, '50.", U.S. AEC Publ. MIT-1052 (Pt. I) 74 p.

44. Treco, R.M., "The Thermal Expansion Characteristics of Beryllium", U.S. AEC Publ. MIT-1043 (Same as J. Metals, 2, 1274-6 (1950) 28 p.

45. Chiotti, P., "Thorium-Carbon System", U.S. AEC Publ. AECD 3072. 61 p.

46. Sennet and Scott, "The Structure of Evaporated Metal Films and Their Optical Properties", J. Optical Soc. Am. Vol. 40. pp. 203-11. (Canada).

47. Myers, R.T., "Some Properties of Tantalum", Metallurgia. Vol. 21. pp. 301-4. (England)

48. Gulbransen, E.A. and Andrew, K.F., "The Kinetics of the Reactions of Beryllium with Oxygen and Nitrogen and the Effect of Oxide and Nitride Films on Its Vapor Pressure", J. Electrochem. Soc. Vol. 97. pp. 383-395.

49. Cook, L.A., Castleman, L.S. and Johnson, W.E., "Preliminary Report on the Electrical Resistivity of Zirconium", (Naval Reactor Program, Contr. AT-11-1-GEN-14). AD 81 744. 20 p.

50. Westrum, E.F. and Eyring, L., "The Melting Point and the Density of Neptunium Metal. A Micro Melting Point Apparatus for Metals", U.S. AEC Publ. UCRL-1056. 9 p.

51. Mizushima, Sanchi, "Changes of Physical Properties and Crystal sizes of Amorphous Carbon During Graphitization Process", Proc. Fujihara Mem. Fac. Eng. Keio Univ. Vol. 3 pp. 70-4. (Japan)

52. Gordon, P. and Kaufmann, A.R., "The Alloy Systems Uranium-Aluminum and Uranium-Iron", U.S. AEC Publ. AECD 2683. 41 p.

53. Tucker Jr., C.W., "An Approximate Crystal Structure for the Beta Phase of Uranium", U.S. AEC Publ. KAPL-388. 38 p.

54. Brookhaven National Lab., "Classified Progress Report of the Reactor and Engineering Department", U.S. AEC Publ. BNL-67. 37 p. (Declassified)

55. Baenziger, N. C. et al., "Compounds of Uranium with the Transition Metals of the First Long Period", _Acta Cryst._ Vol. 3. pp. 34-40

56. Bowles, P. J. et al., "The Crystal Structure of the Compound UMn_2 and a Discussion on Laves Phases in Uranium Alloys", _U. S. AEC Publ. AERE-M/R-581._ 12 p. (England)

57. Raub, Ernst and Walter, Paul, "Transition of Ternary Gold-Copper-Zinc Solid Solutions", _Z. Metalkunde._ Vol. 41. pp. 425-33. (Germany)

58. Hunt, E. B. and Rundle, R. E., "The Structure of Thorium Dicarbide by X-ray and Neutron Diffraction; Contribution No. 111", _U. S. AEC Publ. AECD-3021._ 20 p.

59. Borie Jr., B. S. "The Crystal Structure of UAl_4", _U. S. AEC Publ. ORNL-810._ 14 p.

60. Long, Roger A., "Fabrication and Properties of Hot-Pressed Molybdenum Disilicide", _NACA RM E50F22._ 34 p.

61. Chiotti, P., "Summary of Research on Experimental Refractory Bodies of High-Melting Nitrides, Carbide and Uranium Dioxide", _U. S. AEC Publ. AECD 3204, and ISC-44._

62. Mallett, M. W., Gerds, A. F. and Vaughan, D. A., "Uranium Sesquicarbide", _U. S. AEC Publ. AECD-3060; BMI-T-19._ 17 p.

63. Phipps, T. E. et al., "The Vapor Pressure of Plutonium Halides", _U. S. AEC Publ. AECD 2609; 1949 also J. Chem. Phys._ Vol. 18. pp. 724-34.

64. Norton, F. H., Fellows, D. M. et al., "Prog. Report for Jan. 1 to Mar. 31, 1950", _U. S. AEC Publ. NYO-594._ 22 p.

65. Danforth, W. E. and Morgan, P. H., "Electrical Resistance of Thoria", _Phys. Rev._ Vol. 79. pp. 142-4.

66. Norton, F. H. et al., "Progress Report for April 1 - June 30, 1950", _U. S. AEC Publ. NYO-770._ 11 p.

67. Sheehy, John P. and Killelea, Joseph H., "Development of High Temperature Thermal Insulation for Period Starting July 1, 1950 and ending Aug. 31, 1950", _Bi-Monthly Prog. Rept. No. 7 USAF Contr. No. AF33(038)7371._ ATI 90 676. 5 p.

68. Taylor, A. and Laidler, D. S., "The Formation and Crystal Structure of Silicon Carbide", _Brit. J. Applied Phys._ Vol. 1. pp. 174-81. (England)

1. Parkinson, D. H., Simon, F. E., and Spedding, F. H., "The Atomic Heats of the Rare Earth Elements", Proc. Roy. Soc. Vol. A207. pp. 137-55. (England)

2. Rigney, C. J. and Bockstahler, L. I., "The Thermal Conductivity of Titanium between 20° and 273°K", Phys. Rev. Vol. 83. p. 220.

3. Fine, M. E., Greiner, E. S., and Ellis, W. C., "Transitions in Chromium", J. Metals. Vol. 191. pp. 56-8.

4. Whittemore, Osgood J., "Properties and Uses of Zirconia Products", Brick and Clay Record. Vol. 118, No. 3. pp. 58-9.

5. Apblett, W. R. and Pellini, W. S., "A Recording Dilatometer for High Temperatures. (Linear Expansion of Molybdenum, Tungsten, Inconel, and Vitallium)", Am. Soc. Metals Preprint. (2W). 15 p.

6. Sawada, Shozo, Ando, Rinjiro, and Nomura, Shoichiro. "Thermal Expansion and Specific Heat of Tungsten Oxide at High Temperatures", Phys. Rev. Vol. 84. pp. 1054-5.

7. Skinner, Gordon B. and Johnston, Herrick L., "Low-Temperature Heat Capacities of Inorganic Solids. VIII. Heat Capacity of Zirconium from 14 to 300°K", J. Am. Chem. Soc. Vol. 73. pp. 4549-51.

8. Horn, F. H., "The Change in Electrical Resistance of Magnesium on Melting", Phys. Rev. Vol. 84. pp. 855-6.

9. Adenstedt, H. K., "Physical, Thermal, and Electrical Properties of Hafnium and High-purity Zirconium", Am. Soc. Metals Preprint. (1W). 19 p.

10. Brewer, Leo and Searcy, Alan W., "The Gaseous Species of the Aluminum-Alumina System", J. Am. Chem. Soc. Vol. 73. pp. 5308-14.

11. Edwards, James W. and Johnston, Herrick L., "Vapor Pressure Iron between 1356°K and 1519°K and Cobalt between 1363°K and 1522°K", J. Am. Chem. Soc. Vol. 73. pp. 4729-32.

12. Edwards, James W. and Johnston, Herrick L., "The Vapor Pressures of Inorganic Substances. VI. Vanadium between 1666°K and 1882°K", J. Am. Chem. Soc. Vol. 73. pp. 4727-9.

13. Skinner, G. B., Edwards, J. W., and Johnston, H. L., "Vapor Pressure of Inorganic Substances. V. Zirconium between 1949 and 2054°K", J. Am. Chem. Soc., Vol. 73. pp. 174-6

14. Berman, R. "Thermal Conductivities of Some Dielectric Solids at Low Temperatures", Proc. Roy. Soc. (London). Vol. A208. pp. 90-108. (England)

15. Ginnings, D. C. and Douglas, T. B., "Specific Heat of Beryllium between 0° and 900°", J. Am. Chem. Soc. Vol. 83. pp. 1236-40.

16. Evans Jr., Jerry E., "Thermal Conductivity of 4 Metals and Alloys Up to 1100°F. (595°C)", NACA-RM-E50L07. 15 p.

17. Gerritsen, A. N. and Linde, J. O., "The Electrical Resistance of Silver-manganese Alloys at Low Temperatures. I. The Resistance from 273°K to 1°K", Physica. Vol. 17. pp. 573-83. (Netherlands)

18. Edwards, J. W., Speiser, R., and Johnston, H., "High-temperature Structure and Thermal Expansion of Some Metals as Determined by X-ray Diffraction Data. I. Platinum, Tantalum, Niobium, and Molybdenum", J. Appl. Phys. Vol. 22 (4). pp. 424-428.

19. Johnston, Herrick L., Hersh, Herbert N., and Kerr, Eugene C., "Low-temperature Heat Capacities of Inorganic Solids. V. The Heat Capacity of Pure Elementary Boron in Both Amorphous and Crystalline Conditions between 13 and 305°K. Some Free Energies of Formation", J. Am. Chem. Soc. Vol. 73. pp. 1112-17.

20. Nomura, Shoichiro and Sawada, Shozo, "Dielectric and Thermal Properties of Barium Lead Titanates", J. Phys. Soc. Japan. Vol. 6. pp. 36-9. (Japan)

21. Hummel, F. A., "Thermal Expansion Properties of Some Synthetic Lithia Minerals", J. Am. Ceram. Soc. Vol. 34 (8). pp. 235-39.

22. Brackbill, C. E., McKinstry, H. A., and Hummel, F. A., "Thermal Expansion of Some Glasses in the System $Li_2O-Al_2O_3-SiO_2$", J. Am. Ceram. Soc. Vol. 34. pp. 107-09.

23. Hummel, F. A. and Reid, H. W., "Thermal Expansion of Some Glasses in the System $MgO-Al_2O_3-SiO_2$", J. Am. Ceram. Soc. Vol. 34. pp. 319-21.

24. Yoshiki, B. and Matsumoto, K., "High-temperature Modification of Barium Feldspar", J. Am. Ceram. Soc. Vol. 34. pp. 283-86.

25. Bungardt, Walter and Kallenback, Rudolf, "Thermal and Electric Conductivity of Aluminum and Aluminum Alloys", Z. Metallkunde. Vol. 42. pp. 82-91. (Germany)

26. Cox, S. M., Stirling, J.F., and Kirby, P. L., "Temperature Variation of Thermal Expansion and Electrical Resistivity of a Borosilicate Glass", J. Soc. Glass Technol. Vol. 35. pp. T103-35. (England)

27. Vianney, L. R., "Thermal Conductivity of 347 Stainless Steel and Zirconium", DIC Project 6627 Feb. 15, 1951.   AD 140 931. 6 p.

28. Blackburn, A.R. and Shevlin, T. S., "Fundamental Study and Equipment for Sintering and Testing of Cermet Bodies. V. Fabrication, Testing and Properties of 30 Chromium - 70 Alumina Cermets", J. Am. Ceram. Soc. Vol. 34. pp. 327-31.

29. Blomeke, J. O., Ziegler, W. T., "Heat Content, Specific Heat and Entropy of La_2O_3, Pr_6O_{11}, and Nb_2O_3 between 30° and 900°C", J. Am. Chem. Soc. Vol. 73 (11). pp. 5099-102.

30. Todd, S. S., "Low Temperature Heat Capacities and Entropies at 298.16°K of Crystalline Calcium Orthosilicate, Zinc Orthosilicate, and Tricalcium Silicate", J. Am. Chem. Soc. Vol. 73. pp. 3277-8.

31. Deem, H. W. and Nelson, H. R., "Thermal Conductivity of Silver-Cadmium Alloys from 100°C to 400°C", U. S. AEC Publ. (BMI-77). 12 p.

32. Bochirol, Louis, "True Specific Heat of Ferrites of Zinc, Nickel, and Cobalt", Compt. rend. Vol. 232. pp. 1474-7. (France)

33. Searcy, A.W., "The Vapor Pressure of Germanium", U.S. Atomic Energy Comm. Publ. UCRL-1403. 10 p.

34. Greenaway, H.T., "Pure Chromium - Its Production and Freezing Point", Australia Dept. Supply, Aeronaut. Research Labs. Rept. No. Sm-163. pp. 1-11. (Australia)

35. Hirabayashi, Makoto, "Existence of the Superlattice $CuAu_3$", J. Phys. Soc. Japan. Vol. 6. pp. 129-30. (Japan)

36. Kalish, Herbert S., Hausner, Henry, H., Angier, Roswell P., "The Physical Properties of Sintered Zirconium", SEP-44. 32 p.

37. Hall, Lewis D., "The Vapor Pressure of Gold and the Activities of Gold in Gold-Copper Solid Solutions", J. Am. Chem. Soc. Vol. 73. pp. 757-60.

38. Redfield, T. A. and Hill, J. H. "Heat Capacity of Molybdenum", U. S. Atomic Energy Comm. Publ. ORNL-1087. 9 p.

39. Weeks, J. L., "Note Regarding the Thermal Conductivity of Synthetic Sapphire", AECU-1284. 3 p.

40. Edwards, J. W., Johnston, H. L., Blackburn, P. E., "Vapor Pressure of Inorganic Substances. IV. Tantalum between 2624 and 2943°K", J. Am. Chem. Soc. Vol. 73. pp. 172-4.

41. Gebhardt, E. and Dorner, S. "Density and Specific Volume of Liquid and Solid Gold-Silver Alloys", Z. Metallkunde. Vol. 42. pp. 353-38. (Germany)

42. Robards, C. F. and Gangler, J. J., "Some Properties of Beryllium Oxide and Beryllium Oxide—Niobium Ceramal", Natl. Advisory Comm. Aeronaut. RM E50G21. 18 p

43. Thomas, Hans, "Resistance Alloys", Z. Physik. Vol. 129. pp. 219-32. (Germany)

44. Burdick, Milton, D., Zweig, Benson, Moreland, R. Eugene, "Linear Thermal Expansion of Artificial Graphites to 1370°", J. Research Natl. Bur. Stand. Vol. 47. pp. 35-40.

45. Statton, W.O., "Phase Diagram of the BaO-TiO_2 System", J. Chem. Phys. Vol. 19(1). pp. 33-40.

46. Deem, H.W. and Lucks, C.F., "Thermal Conductivity of Boron Carbide from 100°C to 800°R", BMI-713. 8 p.

47. O'Connor, W.F., and Laszlo, T.S., Killelea, J.R., et al. "Development of High Temperature Light Weight Insulating Materials for Jet Engine Tail Cones", (USAF Contr. No. AF33(038)-7371) ATI 143 262. 84 p.

48. Ricker, R.W. and Hummel, F.A., "Reactions in the System TiO-SiO; Revision of the Phase Diagram", J. Am. Ceramic Soc. Vol. 34. pp. 271-79.

49. Bochirol, Louis, "Resistivity of Zinc, Nickel, Cobalt, Magnesium and Copper Ferrites as a Function of Temperature", Compt. rend. Vol. 233. pp. 736-8. (France)

50. Mallett, M. W., Gerdes, A. F. and Nelson, H. R. "The Uranium-Carbon System", U. S. AEC Publ. AECD-3226; BMI-63. 32 p.

51. Hoard, J. L., "On the Structure of Elementary Boron", J. Am. Chem. Soc. Vol. 72. pp. 1892-3.

52. Cubicciotti, D., "The Melting Point; Composition Diagram of the Zirconium-Oxygen System", J. Am. Chem. Soc. Vol. 73. pp. 2032-5.

53. Zachariasen, W. H., "Identification and Crystal Structure of Protactinium Metal", U. S. AEC Publ. ANL-4632. 1951.

54. Russell, R. B., "The Coefficients of Thermal Expansion for Zirconium ", U. S. AEC Publ. MIT-1073. 41 p.

55. Isobe, M., "Magnetometric Studies of Transformations in Pure Manganese", Sci. Rep. Research Inst. Tohoku Univ. Vol. 3 (A). pp. 78-81. (Japan)

56. Crane, W. W. T., "Some Physical and Chemical Properties of Curium, April 16, 1951", U. S. AEC Publ. AECD 3161. 34 p.

57. McPherson, D. J. and Hansen, M., "Phase Diagrams of Zirconium-Base Binary Alloys: Progress Rept. No. 2", U. S. AEC Publ. COO-30. 21 p.

58. Carpenter, L. G. and Mair, W. N., "The Evaporation of Titanium", Proc. Phys. Soc. (London). Vol. 64B. pp. 57-66. (England)

59. Fox, G. W., Caldwell, W. C., Carlson, J. F., et al. "Solid State Physics and Synchrotron Development Prog. Rept. in Physics for the period Jan.1,1951 to June 30, 1951", U. S. AEC Publ. ISC-175. 34 p.

60. Brewer, L. and Mastick, D. F., "The Stability of Gaseous Ferrous Oxide", J. Chem. Phys. Vol. 19. pp. 334-43.

61. Sellers, P., Fried, S., Elson, R. and Zachariasen, W., "Preparation of Some Protactinium Compounds and the Metal", U. S. AEC Publ. AECD 3167. 10 p.

62. Lampson, F. K., "Summary Report on the Electrical Properties of Armco Iron and Beryllium", U. S. AEC Publ. NEPA-1860. 9 p.

63. Searcy, A. W., "The Gaseous Species of the Boron-Boric Oxide System", U. S. AEC Publ. UCRL-1404. 10p.

64. Bing, George, Fink, F. W. and Thompson, H. B. "The Thermal and Electrical Conductivities of Zirconium and Its Alloys", U. S. AEC Publ. BMI-65. 19 p.

65. Lucks, C. F., Thompson, H. B. et al., "The Experimental Measurement of Thermal Conductivities, Specific Heats, and Densities of Metallic, Transparent and Protective Materials, Part I", USAF Tech. Rept. No. 6145-1. 135 p.

66. Tucker Jr., C. W., "The Crystal Structure of the Beta Phase of Uranium", Acta. Cryst. Vol. 4. pp. 425-31.

67. Wessel, G., "Measurement of the Vapour Pressure and Condensation Coefficient of Iron, Cadmium and Silver", Z. Physik. Vol. 130. pp. 539-48. (Germany)

68. Edwards, J. W., Johnston, H., and Blackburn, P. E., "The Vapor Pressure of Inorganic Substances. VI. Vanadium between 1666°K and 1882°K", U. S. AEC Publ. NP 3057.

69. Vero, J. A., "Dilametric Determination of the Solidus Temperature (of Aluminum Alloys)", Acta. Tecn. Acad. Sci. Vol. 2. pp. 97-113. (Hungary)

70. Masumoto, H. and Saito, H., "Effect of Heat-Treatment on the Magnetic Properties of Annealed Alloys. I. Some Physical Properties in an Annealed State", Science Rept. Research Inst., Tohoku Univ. Vol. Ser. A.3. pp. 521-34. (Japan)

71. Zacharisen, W. H., "The Crystal Structure of Plutonium Sesquicarbide", U. S. AEC Publ. ANL 4631. 9 p.

72. Florio, J. V., Rundle, R. E. and Snow, A. I., "Compounds of Thorium with Transition Metals. I. The Thorium-Manganese System", U. S. AEC Publ. AECD-3249. 35 p.

73. Crandall, W. B. and Lawrence, W. G., "Fundamental Properties of Metal-Ceramic Mixtures at High Temperatures; progress during Period Feb. 1 to Mar. 31, 1951", Periodic Status Report No. 25. NP 3044. 8 p.

74. Lemons, C. and Maisner, H., "Elevated Temperature Tests on Structural Plastic Laminates", Douglas Aircraft Co., Inc., Rept. No. DEV-709. AD 75 127. 48 p.

75. Norton, F. H. and Kingery, W. D., "The Measurement of Thermal Conductivity of Refractory Materials", U. S. AEC Publ. NYO 599. 32 p.

76. Norton F. H., Kingery, W. D. et al., "The Measurement of Thermal Conductivity of Refractory Materials. (Prog. Rept. for Oct. 1 to Dec. 31, 1950)", U. S. AEC Publ. NYO-597. 22 p.

77. Norton, F. H., "The Measurement of Thermal Conductivity of Refractory Materials", U. S. AEC Publ. NYO 598. 11 p.

78. Lander, J. J., "Experimental Heat Contents of SrO, BaO, CaO, $BaCO_3$, and $SrCO_3$ at High Temperatures. Dissociation Pressures of $BaCO_2$ and $SrCO_3$", J. Am. Chem. Soc. Vol. 73. pp. 5794-7.

79. Gaunt, J., "The Infrared Transmission of Some HF Resistant Materials", U. S. AEC Publ. AERE-C/M-120. 4 p. (England)

80. McMahon, Howard, "Thermal Radiation Characteristics of Some Glasses", J. Am. Ceramic Soc. Vol. 34. pp. 91-95.

81. Dale, A. E., Pegg, E. F. and Stanworth, J. E., "Electrical Properties of Some Lithia-Containing Glasses", J. Soc. Glass-Technol. Vol. 35. pp. 136-45. (England)

82. Erway, N. D. and Seifert, R. L., "Vapor Pressure of Beryllium Oxide", J. Electrochem. Soc. Vol. 98. pp. 83-8.

83. Chandappa, N. and Simpson, H. E., "Study of the Physical Properties of Some Sodium-Boroaluminate Glasses", Glass Ind. Vol. 32(10). pp. 505-7.

84. Oriani, R. A., "The Construction and Operation of a High-Temperature Calorimeter", U. S. AEC Publ. SO-2017; GE Res. Lab RL-586. 23 p.

85. Englander, M., "Note on Measurement of Thermal Conductivity of Sintered Uranium Dioxide", U. S. AEC Publ. CEA-79. 13 p. (France)

86. Bunting, Elmer N., Shelton, George R. et al., "Properties of Beryllium-Barium Titanate Dielectrics", J. Research Nat'l.Bur. Standards. Vol. 47. pp. 15-24.

87. Shirane, G. and Takeda, A., "Volume Change at Three Transitions in BaTiO$_3$ Ceramics", J. Phys. Soc. Vol. 6. pp. 128-9. (Japan)

88. Rhodes, R. G., "Barium Titanate Twinning at Low Temperatures", Acta.Cryst. Vol. 4. pp. 105-10. (England)

1. Weeks, James L. and Seifert, Ralph L., "The Thermal Conductivity of Synthetic Sapphire", J. Am. Ceram. Soc. Vol. 35. p. 15

2. Busey, R. H. and Giauque, W. F., "The Heat Capacity of Nickel from 15 to 300°K. Entropy and Free-Energy Functions", J. Am. Chem. Soc. Vol. 74. pp. 3157-8.

3. Craig, R. S., Wallace, W. E., Coffer, L. W., and Krier, C. A., "The Heat Capacities of Magnesium between 12° and 320°K and the Entropy of Magnesium at 25°C", U. S. AEC Publ. NYO-950. 4 p.

4. Broom, T., "The Effect of Temperature of Deformation on the Electrical Resistivity of Cold-Worked Metals and Alloys", Proc. Phys. Soc. Vol. 65B. pp. 871-81. (London)

5. Hill, R. W. and Parkinson, D. H., "The Specific Heats of Germanium and Gray Tin", Phil. Mag. Vol. 43. pp. 309-16. (England)

6. Estermann, I. and Weertman, J. R., "Specific Heat of Germanium between 20°K and 200°K", J. Chem. Phys. Vol. 20. pp. 972-6.

7. Goglia, M. J., Hawkins, G. A., and Deverall, J. E., "Determination of Thermal Conductivity of Copper and Deoxidized Copper-Iron Alloys. Apparatus and Technique", Anal. Chem. Vol. 24. pp. 493-6.

8. Weiner, L., Chiotti, P., and Wilhelm, H. A., "Temperature Dependence of Electrical Resistivity of Metals", US AEC Publ. ISC-305. 82 p. AD-18042.

9. Jones, N. C., "A Note on Fused Stabilized Zirconia: A Modern High-Temperature Refractory", J. Inst. Fuel. Vol. 25. pp. 66-7. (England)

10. Mikol, Edward P., "The Thermal Conductivity of Molybdenum over the Temperature Range 1000 to 2100°F", Reprint of Oak Ridge Natl. Lab. Rept. ORNL-1131, Tech. Rept. No. 2, Engineering Experiment Station, College of Engineering, U. of Alabama, Cont. No. W-7405-eng-26. 7 p.

11. Schwartz, Bernard, "Thermal Stress Failure of Pure Refractory Oxides", J. Am. Ceram. Soc. Vol. 35. pp. 325-33.

12. Clusius, Klaus and Schachinger, Liselotte, "Results of Low-temperature Research. IX. The Atomic Heat of Cobalt between 15 and 270°K", Z. Naturforsch. Vol. 7a pp. 185-91. (Germany)

13. Todd, S. S. and Lorenson, R. E., "Heat Capacities at Low Temperatures and Entropies, at 298.16°K of Metatitanates of Barium and Strontium", J. Am. Chem. Soc. Vol. 74. pp. 2043-5.

14. James, N. R., Legvold, S., and Spedding, F. H., "The Resistivity of Lanthanum, Cerium, Praseodymium, and Neodymium at Low Temperatures", Phys. Rev. Vol. 88(5). pp. 1092-98.

15. Wartenberg, H. V., "Alumina", Z. Anorg. u. Allgem. Chem. Vol. 269. pp. 76-85. (Germany)

16. Shapiro, E., "Vapor Pressure of Thorium Oxide from 2050 to 2250°K", J. Am. Chem. Soc. Vol. 74. p. 5233.

17. Powers, R. M. and Wilhelm, H. A., "The Titanium-Vanadium System", US AEC Publ. (ISC-228). 165 p. AD 18 838

18. Lenning, G. A., Craighead, C. M., and Jaffee, R. I., "The Effect of Hydrogen on the Mechanical Properties of Titanium", Batelle Memorial Inst., Columbus, Ohio, (Contract DA 33-019-ORD-220) Summary Rept. No. 1. 64 p. AD 7533.

19. Thewlis, J., "An X-ray Powder Study of β-Uranium", Acta Cryst. Vol. 5. pp. 790-4. (England)

20. Straumanis, M. E. and Aka, E. Z., "Lattice Parameters, Coefficients of Thermal Expansion and X-ray Atomic Weight of Purest Silicon and Germanium", J. Appl. Phys. Vol. 23 (3). pp. 330-34.

21. Geballe, T. H. and Giauque, W. F., "The Heat Capacity and Entropy of Gold from 15 to 300°K", J. Am. Chem. Soc. Vol. 74. pp. 2368-9.

22. Rinck, Emile, "Allotropic Transformations of Strontium", Compt. rend. Vol. 234. pp. 845-7. (France)

23. Trombe, Felix and Foex, Marc, "Dilatometric Study of Metallic Dysprosium", Compt. rend. Vol. 235 (2). pp. 163-65. (France)

24. Elliott, R. O. and Tate, R. E., "A Determination of the Coefficient of Thermal Expansion of Alpha Plutonium", LA-1390. 20 p.

25. Oliver, D. A. and Harris, M. A., "Some Proven Gas-turbine Steels and Related Developments", A Symposium on High-temperature Steels and Alloys for Gas Turbines. Special Report No. 43. Iron and Steel Inst., London, 1952. pp. 46-59 (England)

26. Colbeck, E. W. and Rait, J. R., "Creep-Resisting Ferritic Steels", A Symposium on High-Temperature Steels and Alloys for Gas Turbines. Special Report No. 43, Iron and Steel Inst., London, 1952. pp. 107-124. (England)

27. Kirby, H. W. and Sykes, C., "Study of the Properties of a Chromium-Nickel-Niobium Austenitic Steel", A Symposium on High-temperature Steels and Alloys for Gas Turbines. Special Report No. 43, Iron and Steel Inst., London, 1952. pp. 95-106. (England)

28. Buswell, R.W.A., Pitkin, W.R., and Jenkins, L., "Sintered Alloys for High-temperature Service in Gas Turbines", A Symposium on High-temperature Steels and Alloys for Gas Turbines, Special Report No. 43, Iron and Steel Inst., London, 1952. pp. 258-68. (England)

29. Hirabayashi, Makoto, "Superlattice of the Copper-gold System", Nippon-Kinzoka-Gakkai-Shi. Vol. 16. pp. 67-72. (Japan)

30. Schwartz, Bernard, "Beryllia, Its Physical Properties at Elevated Temperatures", (Rept. No. MIT-1083) (Contract AT (30-1)-981) STI-ATI-210 826. 17 p.

31. Durbin, E.A. and Harman, C. G., "An Appraisal of the Sintering Behavior and Thermal Expansion of Some Columbates", BMI-791 . 14 p.

32. Karkhanavala, M.D. and Hummel, F. A. "Thermal Expansion of Some Simple Glasses", J. Am. Ceram. Soc. Vol. 35. pp. 215-19.

33. Lucks, C. F. and Bing, G. F., "The Experimental Measurement of Thermal Conductivities, Specific Heats, and Densities of Metallic, Transparent, and Protective Materials", AF Technical Rept. No. 6145, pt. 2, Contract AF 33(038)20558 . AD 95 239. 32 p.

34. Durbin, E. A., Wagner, H. E and Harman, C. G., "Properties of Some Columbium Oxide-Basis Ceramics", BMI-792, Batelle Memorial Inst., Columbus, Ohio, (Contract W7405-eng-92). AD-1644. 15 p.

35. Grieco, A. and Montgomery, H. C., "Thermal Conductivity of Germanium", Phys. Rev. Vol. 86 (4). pp. 570.

36. Bennett, W. D., "Some Effects of Order Disorder in Iron-Aluminum Alloys", J. Iron Steel. Inst. Vol. 171. pp. 372-9. (England)

37. Gurland, J. and Norton, J. T., "Role of the Binder Phase in Cemented Tungsten Carbide-Cobalt Alloys", J. Metals. Vol. 4. pp. 1050-6.

38. Taylor, A. and Floyd, R. W., "The Constitution of Nickel-rich Alloys of the Nickel-titanium-aluminum System", J. Inst. Metals. (Paper No. 1411). Vol. 81. pp. 25-32. (England)

39. Laquer, Henry, L., "Low-temperature Thermal Expansion of Various Materials", U.S. Atomic Energy Comm. AECD-3706. 58 p.

40. Glaser, Frank W., Arbiter, William, Ford, Michael, J., and others, "Cemented Borides (and Appendixes I thru IV)", Summary Prog. Rept. USN Contr. No. N6-ONR-256. 146 p.

41. Burney, J.D. (P.R. Mallory Co.), "Cermets Containing $MoSi_2$ and Al_2O_3",(Proceedings of the WADC Ceramic Conference of Cermets, ed. by Murray A. Schwartz) WADC Tech. Report No. 52-327. AD-1183. 350 p.

42. Shevlin, Thomas S., "Development, Properties and Investigation of a Cermet Containing 28% Alumina and 72% Chromium", WADC Tech. Rept. No. 53-17 (Contr. AF33(616)3). 52 p.

43. Trombe, Felix and Foex, Marc, "Dilatometric Study of Metallic Gadolinium", Compt. rend. Vol. 235(1). pp. 42-4. (France)

44. Tyler, W. W., Wilson Jr., A.C., and Wolga, G. J., "Thermal Conductivity, Electrical Resistivity and Thermoelectric Power of Uranium", KAPL - 802, 25 p.

45. North, J. M., "A High-temperature Adiabatic Calorimeter and the Specific Heat of Uranium between 100 and 800°", Atomic Energy Res. Estab. Vol. M/R 1016. 19 p. (England)

46. Redmond, R. F. and Lones, J., "Enthalpies and Heat Capacities of Stainless Steel (316), Zirconium, and Lithium at Elevated Temperatures", (ORNL-1342)(Contract W7405-eng-26). AD 3665. 24 p.

47. Moskowitz, Marvin and Kates, L.W., "Thermal Expansion of Zirconium and Zirconium-Tin Alloys Up to 570°C", US AEC Contr. No. AT-30-1-Gen-366. SEP 91. 10 p.

48. Deem, H. W., Nelson, H. R., "Thermal Conductivity of Powder-metallurgy Uranium", BMI-745. 10 p.

49. Weeks, J. L. and Seifert, R. L., "Apparatus for the Measurement of the Thermal Conductivity of Solids", US AEC Pub. 1952. ANL 4938. 14 p.

50. Edwards, James W., Johnston, Herrick, L., and Blackburn, Paul E., "Vapor Pressures of Inorganic Substances. VIII. Molybdenum between 2151 and 2462°K", J. Am. Chem. Soc. Vol. 74. pp. 1539-40

51. Serebrennikov, N.N. and Gel'd, P.V., "Heat Content and Heat Capacity of Silicon at High Temperatures", Doklady Akad. Nauk. SSSR. Vol. 87. pp. 1021-4. (USSR)

52. Wittig, F.E., "The (Latent) Heat of Fusion of Aluminum and of Germanium", Z. Metallkunde. Vol. 43 (5). pp. 158-161. (Germany)

53. Johnson, R.G., Hudson, D.E., Spedding, F.H., "Mass Spectrometric Determination of Latent Heats of Metals", ISC-293, Contr. No. W7205-eng-82. 107 p. AD-28 259.

54. Volger, J., "Anomalous Specific Heat of Chromium Oxide at the Antiferromagnetic Temperature", Nature. Vol. 170. p. 1027. (England)

55. Tyler, W.W. and Wilson Jr., A.C., "Thermal Conductivity, Electric Resistivity, and Thermoelectric Power of Titanium Alloy", KAPL-803 . RC-130-B.

56. Knudsen, Friedrich P., "Physical Characteristics of Titanium Carbide Base Cermets at Elevated Temperatures", Progress Report No. 2 Natl. Bur. Standards, 1503. ATI-140 033. 17 p.

57. Adams Jr., G.B., Johnston, H.L., "Low Temperature Heat Capacities of Inorganic Solids. XI. The Heat Capacity of β-gallium Oxide from 15 to 300°K", J. Am. Chem. Soc. Vol. 74. pp. 4788-9.

58. Volger, J., "The Specific Heat of Barium Titanate between 100°K and 410°K", Phillips Research Reports. Vol. 7. No. 1. pp. 21-7. (Netherlands)

59. Todd, S.S. and Lorenson, R.E., "Heat Capacities at Low Temperatures and Entropies at 298.16°K of Orthotitanates of Barium and Strontium", J. Am. Chem. Soc. Vol. 74. pp. 3764-5.

60. Grootenhuis, P., Powell, R.W., and Tye, R.P., "Thermal and Electrical Conductivity of Porous Metals Made by Powder-Metallurgy Methods", Proc. Phys. Soc. Vol. 65(7). pp. 502-511. (England)

61. Orr, R.L. and Coughlin, J.P., "High-temperature Heat Contents of Magnesium Orthotitanate and Magnesium Dititanate", J. Am. Chem. Soc. Vol. 74. pp. 3186-7.

62. Searcy, A.W., "The Vapor Pressure of Germanium", J. Am. Chem. Soc. Vol. 74. pp. 4789-91.

63. Greiner, E.S., "Specific Heat, Latent Heat of Fusion, and Melting Point of Germanium", J. Metals. Vol. 4(10). pp. 1044.

64. Bloom, D.S., Putman, J.W., and Grant, N.J., "Melting Point and Transformation of Pure Chromium", J. Metals. Vol. 4(6). p. 626.

65. Norton, F.H., Kingery, W.D., et al., "The Measurement of Thermal Conductivity of Refractory Materials", NYO-602. 40 p.

66. Norton, F.H. and Kingery, W.D., "The Measurement of Thermal Conductivity of Refractory Materials", Mass. Inst. of Tech., Cambridge, Mass. AEC Contr. No. AT (30-1) 960 ATI- 185188. 14 p.

67. Norton, F.H. and Kingery, W.D., "The Measurement of Thermal Conductivity of Refractory Materials (and Appendixes I through III)", Tech. Progress Report of Mass. Inst. of Tech. ATI-160033, AEC Contr. No. A-T-(30-1) 960. 52 p.

68. Norton, F.H. and Kingery, W.D., "The Measurement of Thermal Conductivity of Refractory Materials", Mass. Inst. of Tech. ATI 166361 AEC Contr. No. AT(30-1) 960. 12 p.

69. McCabe, C. Law, and Birchenall, C. Ernest, "Vapor Pressure of Silver", Tech. Rept. Nov. 53. (Contr. N6ori-47-T.O.4) (Reprint from J. of Metals, P. 707-709, 5/53.) AD 56 030. 3 p.

70. Hidnert, Peter and Krider, H.S. "Thermal Expansion of Aluminum and Some Aluminum Alloys", J. Research Natl. Bur. Stand. Vol. 48. pp. 209-220.

71. Tyler, W.W. and Wilson Jr., A.C., "Thermal Conductivity, Electrical Resistivity, and Thermoelectric Power of Graphite", KAPL-P-884 (Contract W31-109-eng-52). AD-8113. 6p.

72. Doehaerd, Th., Goldfinger, P., and Waelbroeck, F., "Direct Determination of the Sublimation Energy of Carbon", J. Chem. Phys. Vol. 20. p. 757.

73. Farber, Milton and Darnell, Alfred J., "The Vaporization of Graphite Filaments", J. Am. Chem. Soc. Vol. 74. pp. 3941-2.

74. St. Pierre, P.D.S., "Note on the Melting Point of Titanium Dioxide", J. Am. Ceramic Soc. Vol. 35 (7). 188 p.

75. Hogan, C.L. and Sawyer, R.B., "The Thermal Conductivity of Metals at High Temperatures", J. Appl. Phys. Vol. 23. pp. 177-80.

76. Balluffi, R.W., Resnick, R., and Timper, A.J., "Dilatometric Studies of Zirconium-tin Alloys between 25° and 1100°", U.S. Atomic Energy Comm. SEP-90. 13 p.

77. Masumoto, H., Saiton, H., and Sugihara, M., "On the Anomaly of the Specific Heat at High Temperatures in α-phase Alloys of Copper and Zinc", Nippon Kinzoku Gakkai-Shi. Vol. 16(7). pp. 359-61. (Japan)

78. Hamjian, H.J. and Lidman, W.G., "Boron Carbide as a Base Material for a Cermet", J. Am. Ceram. Soc. Vol. 35. pp. 44-8.

79. Massengale, C.B., et al.. "Quarterly Report on Evaluation of Tests for Cermets as Components of Heat-resistant Materials", NBS Rept. 2129. AD 137 413. 24 p.

80. Colosky, Benjamin P., "Thermal Conductivity Measurements on Silica", Am. Ceram. Soc. Bull. Vol. 31. pp. 465-6.

81. Sully, A.H., Brandes, E.A., and Waterhouse, R.B., "Some Measurements of the Total Emissivity of Metals and Pure Refractory Oxides and the Variation of Emissivity with Temperature", Brit. J. Appl. Physics. Vol. 3 (3). pp. 97-101. (England)

82. Frost, Dietrich and Klauer, F., "Density Change Due to the Quenching of Borosilicate Glasses", Glastech. Ber. Vol. 25 (7). pp. 206-209. (Germany)

83. Chiotti, P., "Experimental Refractory Bodies of High-melting Nitrides, Carbides and Uranium Dioxide", J. Am. Ceram. Soc. Vol. 35 (5). pp. 123-30.

84. Glaser, Frank W., Arbiter, William, Ivanick, William, et al., "Cemented Borides", Prog. Rept. Mar. 1, '51,-Oct. 1, '51 Contr. N6-ONRa256. Task Order 1, NR 035-401. ATI-201 475. 83 p.

85. Euler, Joachim, "The Heat Conductivity of Artificial Graphite Rods at Temperatures between 3300 and 3700°K", Naturwissenschaften. Vol. 39. pp. 568-9. (Germany)

86. Rogener, H., "The Supraconductivity of Niobium Nitride", Z. Physik. Vol. 132 (4). pp. 446-7. (Germany)

87. American Electro Metal Corp., "An Investigation of Various Properties of NiAl", Amer. Electro Metal Corp., Contr. AF 33(038)-10716 Prog. Rept. No. 2-3. 5 p.

88. James, N.R., Legvold, S. and Spedding, F.H., "The Resistivity of Lanthanum, Cerium, Praseodymium and Neodymium at Low Temperatures", Phys. Rev. Vol. (ii) 88. (5). pp. 1092-1098.

89. Laquer, Henry L. and Head, Earl L., "Low Temperature Thermal Expansion of Plastics", U.S. Atomic Energy Comm. Publ. LADC-1230 rev. AECU-2116 (Contr. W7405-eng-36). AD-7185. 24 p.

90. Furukawa, G.T., McCoskey, R.E. and King, G.J., "Calorimetric Properties of Polytetrafluoroethylene (Teflon) from 0° to 365°K", J. of Res. Natl. Bu. of Standards. Vol. 49. pp. 273-8.

91. Leontis, T.E., "Properties of Magnesium-Thorium and Magnesium Thorium-Cerium Alloys", J. Metals. Vol. 4. pp. 287-94.

92. Hirabayashi, Makoto, "Superlattice of the Magnesium-Cadmium System. V. A Calorimetric Study on Fusion of the Magnesium-Cadmium Alloys", Nippon-Kinzoku-Gakkai-Shi. Vol. 16. pp. 295-300. (Japan)

93. Matsukura, T., "Change of Electrical Resistance of High-Carbon High-Chromium Steels by Heat-Treatment", Nippon-Kinzoku-Gakkai-Shi. Vol. 16. pp. 655-9. (Japan)

94. Maxwell, W.A., "Oxidation-Resistance Mechanism and Other Properties of Molybdenum Disilicide", NACA RM E52A04. 17 p.

95. Freiling, Jerome, Eckert, Roger E. and Westwater, J.W., "Thermal Conductivity of Anisotropic Materials", Ind. Eng. Chem. Vol. 44. pp. 906-10.

96. Abe, F., Kimura, K. and Saito, T., "Stainless Clad Steel. I. Manufacturing Methods and General Properties", Tetsu-to-Hagane. Vol. 38. pp. 214-9. (Japan)

97. Wyman, L.L. and Bradley, J.F., "The Temperature-Resistance Characteristics of Uranium", U.S.AEC Publ. KAPL-851. Knolls Atomic Power Lab.Schenectady, N.Y. Contr. No. W-31-109-Eng-52. AD 85 128. 21 p.

98. Sasaki, W., "Electrical Resistivity of Silicon Carbide", J. Phys. Soc. Vol. 7. No. 1. p. 107. (Japan)

99. Thorn, R.J. and Simpson, O.C., "Application of Induction Heating to the Measurement of High-Temperature Properties", U.S.AEC. Publ. AECU-2009. 21 p.

100. Crandall, W.B., "Evaluation Techniques for High Temperature Metal-Ceramic Materials", Proc. of WADC Ceramic Conf. on Cermets. WADC Tech. Rpt. No. 52-327. AD 1183. pp. 243-260.

101. Searcy, A.W., "Transition Metals Silicides and Germanides", Proc. WADC Ceramic Conference on Cermets, WADC Tech. Report No. 52-327. AD 1183. pp. 275-279.

102. Mallett, M.W., Gerds, A.F. and Nelson, H.R. "Uranium-Carbon System", U.S. AEC Publ. AECD 3326; Also J. Electrochem. Soc. Vol. 99. pp. 197-204.

103. Ames Lab., Ames, Iowa - Quarterly Summary Research Report in Chemistry for July, August and September, 1952. U.S. AEC Publ. ISC-299. 26 p.

104. Mass. Inst. of Tech. "Tech. Progress Rept. for the Period Oct., 1951 through March, 1952", U. S. AEC Publ. MIT 1086. 105 p.

105. Gibson, E. D., Loomis, B. A. and Carlson, O. N., "Thorium-Zirconium and Thorium-Hafnium Alloy Systems", Trans. Amer. Soc. Metals. Vol. 50. 22 p.

106. Danielson, G. C., Murphy, G., Peterson, D. and Rogers, B. A. " Prog. Rept. of an Investigation of the Properties of Thorium and Some of Its Alloys", U. S. AEC Publ. ISC-208. (Contr. N-7405-Eng-82). 35 p.

107. Danielson, G. C., Murphy, G. et al., "Interim Report of an Investigation of the Properties of Thorium and Some of Its Alloys", U. S. AEC Publ. ISC 200. 120 p.

108. Schuch, A. F. and Laquer, H. L., "Low Temperature Thermal Expansion of Uranium", U. S. AEC Publ. AECD 3324 also LADC 1124.

109. Gupta, A., "Dilation of Electrolytic Copper Powder Compacts", Current Sci. India. Vol. 21. pp. 127-8 (India)

110. Zachariasen, W. H., "The Crystal Structure of Neptunium Metal", U. S. AEC Publ. ACED 3336 also ANL-FWHZ-199 and ANL 4788.

111. Jones, W. M., Gordon, J. and Long, E. A., "The Heat Capacities of Uranium, Uranium Trioxide and Uranium Dioxide from 15° to 300°K", J. Chem. Phys. Vol. 20. pp. 695-9.

112. Wahlin, H. B., Zenter, R. and Martin J., "The Spectral Emissivity of Iron-Nickel Alloys", J. Applied Phys. Vol. 23. pp. 107-8.

113. Tyler, W. W., Wilson Jr., A. C. and Wolga, G. J., "Thermal Conductivity, Electrical Resistivity, and Thermoelectric Power of Uranium", U. S. AEC Publ. KAPL-802. 25 p.

114. Juel, L. H., "High Density Graphite", U. S. AEC Publ. AECD-3751. Contr. AT-(11-1)-221. 33 p.

115. Tyler, W. W. and Wilson Jr., A. C., "Thermal Conductivity, Electrical Resistivity, and Thermoelectric Power of Graphite", Phys. Rev. Vol. 89. pp. 870-5.

116. Murray, J. R., "The Preparation, Properties and Alloying Behaviour of Thorium", U. S. AERE-M/R-2242. 38 p. (England)

117. Danielson, G. C., et al., "Quarterly Report of an Investigation of the Properties of Thorium and Some of Its Alloys", U. S. AEC Publ. ISC-251 (Contr. W-7405-Eng-82). 50 p.

118. Adenstedt, H. K., Peguignot, J. R. and Rayner, J. M., "The Titanium-Vanadium System", Trans. Amer. Soc. Metals. Vol. 44. pp. 990-1003.

119. McCreight, L. R., "Thermal Expansion Measurements of Six Fuel Materials", U. S. AEC Publ. KAPL-M-LRM-7. 10 p.

120. Rhines, F. N. and Newkirk, J. B., "The Order-Disorder Transformation Viewed as a Classical Phase Change", Trans. Am. Soc. Metals. Preprint 12. 18 p.

121. Masumoto, H., Saito, H. and Kobaya, T., "The Thermal Expansion and Rigidity Modulus and Its Temperature Coefficient in the Alloys of Cobalt, Iron and Vanadium and a New Alloy Velinvar", Sci. Rept. Research Insts., Tohoku Univ. Ser. 4. pp. 255-60. (Japan)

122. Bishop, S. M., Spretnak, J. W. and Fontana, M. G., "Mechanical Properties, Including Fatigue, of Titanium-Base Alloys RC-130-B and Ti-150-A at Very Low Temperatures", Amer. Soc. Metals. Preprint. Vol. 31. 14 p.

123. Lement, B. S. and Averbach, B. L., "Thermal Expansion Coefficients of Commercial and Special Heats of Invar", Rept. No. 14 (Engineering Notes) E-230. Contr. W33-038-ac-13969 . AD 947. 2 p.

124. Teitel, R. J., "The Uranium-Lead System", Trans. AIMME. Vol. 194. p.397

125. Ferro, R., "Alloys of Uranium with Bismuth", Atti. Accad. Nazi. Lincei, Rend. Classe Sci. Fis. Mat. E Mat. Vol. 13. pp. 401-405.

126. Zachariasen, W. H., "The Crystal Structure of Plutonium Sesquicarbide", Acta. Cryst. Vol. 5. pp. 17-19.

127. Post, Benjamin and Glaser, Frank W., "Crystal Structure of ZrB_{12}", J. Metals Trans. Vol. 4. pp. 631-2.

128. Shaler, A. J., "Factors in TiC - Base Cermets", Proc. of the WADC Ceramic Conf. on Cermets ed. by M. A. Schwartz. WADC Tech. Rept. No. 52-327. AD 1183. pp. 20-29. 350 p.

129. Edwards, Russell Keith, "Studies of Materials at High Temperatures", U. S. AEC Publ. AECD - 3394. 108 p.

130. Havekotte, W. C., "Development of TiC - Base Cermets (Paper No. 2)", Proc. of the WADC Ceramic Conference on Cermets, ed. by M. A. Schwartz. U. S. AEC Publ. WADC Tech. Rept. No. 52-327. AD 11 83. pp. 11-19.

131. Lambertson, W. A. and Gunzel Jr., F. H., "Refractory Oxide Melting Points", U. S. AEC Publ. AECD-3465. 4 p.

132. Foex, Marc, Goldstaub, Stanislas et al., "The Changes in Some Properties of Vanadium Sesquioxide Near Its Transformation Points", J. recherches centre natl. recherche sci. Lab. Bellvue. Vol. 21. pp. 37-59. (France)

133. Buessem, W. R., Earhart, W. R. et al., "Refractory Materials for Use in High Temperature Areas of Aircraft", U. S. AEC Publ. NP-4971. Contr. 33-038 ac 16375 (17284) AD 24 523. 46 p.

134. Humphrey, G. L., "Some Thermodynamic Properties of Silicon Carbide", U. S. Bureau of Mines Publ. BM-RI-4888. 27 p.

135. Izumitani, Tatsuoro and Terai, Ryobei, "Fundamental Studies on New Optical Glasses. I. Fluoborate Glass", Bull. Osaka Ind. Research Inst. Vol. 3. pp. 21-4 (Japan)

1. Cosgrove, L. A. and Snyder, P. E., "High-temperature Thermodynamic Properties of Molybdenum Trioxide", J. Am. Chem. Soc. Vol. 75. pp. 1227-8.

2. Silverman, L., "Thermal Conductivity Data Presented for Various Metals and Alloys up to 900°", J. Metals. Vol. 5. pp. 631-2.

3. New Jersey Ceramic Research Station, Rutgers U., New Brunswick, "Development of Ceramic Bodies with High Thermal Conductivity", Pt. 1 of Its Quarterly Prog. Rept. No. 2, AD-13154-AD-13154(e)(Contract DA36-039-sc-42577).

4. New Jersey Ceramic Research Station, Rutgers U., New Brunswick, "Development of Ceramic Bodies with High Thermal Conductivity", Pt. 1 of Its Progress Rept. No. 1 (Contract DA 36-039-sc-42577). pp. 1-33.

5. New Jersey Ceramic Research Station; Rutgers U., New Brunswick, "Development of Ceramic Bodies with High Thermal Conductivity", Pt. 1 of Its Progress Rept. No. 3, AD-19833-AD-19838 (Contr. DA36-039-sc-42577). 26 p.

6. Deem, H. W., "Thermal Conductivity and Electrical Resistivity of Hafnium", U.S. Atomic Energy Comm. BMI-853. 12 p. AD 18033.

7. Pchapsky, T. E., "Heat Capacity and Resistance Measurements for Aluminum and Lead Wires", Acta Met. I. pp. 747-51.

8. Kothen, C. W. and Johnston, H. L., "Low-temperature Heat Capacities of Inorganic Solids. XVII. Heat Capacity of Titanium from 15 to 305°K", J. Am. Chem. Soc. Vol. 75, pp. 3101-2.

9. Tyler, W. W., Wilson Jr., A. C., and Wolga, G. J., "Thermal Conductivity, Electrical Resistivity, and Thermoelectric Power of Uranium", J. Metals.(AIME Trans. 197). Vol. 5. pp. 1238-9.

10. Schofield, T. H. and Bacon, A. E., "The Melting Point of Titanium", J. Inst. Metals. Vol. 82 (4). pp. 167-169.

11. Sawada, S., "Thermal and Electrical Properties and Crystal Structure of Tungsten Oxide at High Temperatures", Phys. Rev. Vol. 91. pp. 1010-11.

12. Sims, C. T., Gideon, D. N., and others, "Investigations of Rhenium", Battelle Memorial Inst., Columbus. Ohio (Contr. AF33(616)232). 52 p. AD-100 581.

13. Coughlin, J. P. and Orr, R. L., "High-temperature Heat Contents of Metal and Orthotitanates of Barium and Strontium", J. Am. Chem. Soc. Vol. 75. pp. 530-1.

14. DeSorbo, W., "Heat Capacity of Chromium Carbide from 13 to 300°K", J. Am. Chem. Soc. Vol. 75. pp. 1825-7.

15. Wyatt, James, L., "Electrical Resistance of Titanium Metal", J. Metals. Vol. 5. No. 7. pp. 903-905.

16. Legvold, S. and Spedding, F. H., "Magnetic and Electric Properties of Gadolinium, Dysprosium, and Erbium Metals", Revs. Mod. Phys. Vol. 25. pp. 129-30.

17. Weeks, James, L. and Seifert, Ralph A., "Apparatus for the Measurement of the Thermal Conductivity of Solids", Rev. Sci. Instruments. Vol. 24(10). pp. 1054-57.

18. Alliegro, R. A., Coffin. L. B., and Tinklepaugh, J. R., "Investigation of Methods of Producing Self Bonded and Metal Bonded Silicon Carbide", N. Y. State Coll. of Ceramics, Alfred U., Qrtly. Prog. Rept. No. 5 (Contract AF33(038) 16190) 29 p. AD-17 643.

19. Hersh, Herbert, N., "Vapor Pressure of Copper", J. Am. Chem. Soc. Vol. 75. pp. 1529-31.

20. Edwards, James W. and Johnston, Herrick L., "Vapor Pressures of Inorganic Substances. XI. Titanium between 1587 and 1764°K and Copper between 1143 and 1292°K", J. Am. Chem. Soc. Vol. 75. pp. 2467-70.

21. Johnson, R. G., Caldwell, W. C., Hudson, D. E., and Spedding, F. H., "A Mass-Spectrometric Positive-ion Technique for Determining Phase-transition Temperatures and Heats of Transformation in Metals", Phys. Rev. Vol. 91. p. 466.

22. Ahman, Donald Henry, "Metallurgy of the Rare Earths with Particular Emphasis on Cerium", Iowa State Coll. J. Sci. Vol. 27. p. 120.

23. Kojima, Takeshi and Kikuchi, Katsumi, "Metallurgical Research on Cerium Metal. VIII. On the Specific Heat of $CeCl_3$ and the Latent Heat of Fusion of $CeCl_3$ and Metallic Cerium", J. of the Electrochemical Soc. of Japan. Vol. 21(4). pp. 177-180. (Japan)

24. Hoch, Michael, Nakata, Masaru, and Johnston, Herrick, L., "Vapor Pressures of Inorganic Substances: Zirconium Dioxide", Cryogenic Lab. Ohio State U. Research Foundation, Columbus (Tech. Rept. No. TR 280-11)(Contr. N6ori-17, T.O.4). 7 p. AD-18 364.

25. Skinner, G. B. and Johnston, H. L., "Thermal Expansion of Zirconium between 298°K and 1600°K", J. Chem. Phys. Vol. 21. pp. 1383-4.

26. Reynolds, J. M., Hemstreet, H. W., and Leinhardt, T. E., "The Electrical Resistance of Graphite at Low Temperatures", Phys. Rev. Vol. 91. pp. 1152-5.

27. Domenicali, Charles A., "Research in Thermoelectricity", Quarterly Progress Report (Contract DA 36-039-sc-15460)(Rept. No. P.2292-4), AD-5400. 9 p.

28. Mauer, Floyd A. and Bolz, Leonard H., "Thermal Expansion of Cermet Components by High Temperature X-ray Diffraction", Nat. Bur. Stand., Wash., D.C. (NBS Rept. No. 3148) (Contract AF 33 (616)53-12) Progress Rept. No. 3. 39 p. AD-29 676.

29. Powell, R. W., "The Thermal and Electrical Conductivities of Beryllium", Phil. Mag. Vol. 44. pp. 645-63. (England)

30. Fine, Morris E., "Elasticity and Thermal Expansion of Germanium between -195 and 275°C", J. Appl. Phys. Vol. 24(3). pp. 338-340.

31. Barson, F., Legvold, S., and Spedding, F. H., "A Low-temperature Dilatometric Study of Some Rare-earth Metals", U. S. Atomic Energy Comm. Publ. ISC 424 AD 27 154. 64 p.

32. White, G. K. (Commonwith Sci. Inc. Research Organization, Sydney, Aus.), "Thermal Conductivity of Silver at Low Temperatures", Proc. Phys. Soc. (London). Vol. 66A. pp. 844-5. (England)

33. Griffel, Maurice and Skochdopole, Richard E., "The Heat Capacity and Entropy of Thorium from 18° to 300°K", J. Am. Chem. Soc. Vol. 75 (21). pp. 5250-51.

34. Smith Jr., Wm. T. and Oliver, G. D., "Thermodynamic Properties of Technetium and Rhenium Compounds. IV. Low Temperature Heat Capacity and Thermodynamics of Rhenium", J. Am. Chem. Soc. Vol. 75. pp. 5785-6.

35. Schoefer, E. A., "Doing More with Less Nickel. (Properties of Iron-Chromium-Nickel Alloys.)", Steel. Vol. 133 (5). pp. 134-135.

36. Sully, A. H., Brandes, E. A., and Mitchell, K. W., "The Effect of Temperatures and Purity on the Ductility and Other Properties of Chromium", J. Inst. Metals. Vol. 81. pp. 585-97. (England)

37. Nadler, Marion R., "Preparation and Properties of Calcium Zirconate", Iowa State College, Ames, Master's Thesis. 54 p.

38. Tyler, W. W., Nesbitt, L. B., and Wilson Jr., A. C., "Some Low-temperature Properties of Titanium Alloy RE-130-B and Stainless Steel", J. Metals. (AIME Trans. 197). Vol. 5. pp. 1104-5.

39. Douglas, Thomas B. and Dever, James L., "Heat Capacity of Four Alloys: Nichrome V and Stainless Steels Types 347 and 446, 0° to 900°C; Monel, 0° to 300°C", NBS Rept. No. 2302. 18 p.

40. Norton, F. H. and Kingery, W. D., "The Measurement of Thermal Conductivity of Refractory Materials", Progress Rept. Oct. 1, 1953. NYO 3648, AD 23-252. 9 p.

41. Vasilos, T., Kingery, W. D., and Norton, F. H., "The Measurement of Thermal Conductivity of Refractory Materials - Carbides and Nitrides", NYO 3649. 33 p. AD-25 397.

42. Zimmerman, William F., Plankenhorn, W. J., and Bennett, Dwight G., "Aluminum Titanate as a Porous Insulating Material for the Protection of Metal.", Illinois U., Urbana. WADC Tech. Rept. No. 53-187 (Contract W33-038-ac-14520). 17 p. AD-14 763.

43. Koenig, John H., "Improved Ceramics.", Progress Report No. IV, New Jersey Research Station, Contract DA 36-039-sc-42577. AD 29335. 159 p.

44. New Jersey Ceramic Research Station, Rutgers U., New Brunswick. "High Thermal Shock Ceramics", (Cont. DA 36-039-sc-42577)(Part II of Prog. Rept. No. 1) pp. 34-48. AD-5552(b).

45. New Jersey Ceramic Research Station, Rutgers U., New Brunswick, "Development of Dense Cordierite Bodies", (Cont. DA 36-039 sc-42577)(Part V of Prog. Rept. No. 1). pp. 70-81. AD-5552(d).

46. Deem, H. W., "Thermal Conductivity of Zirconium and Zirconium-tin Alloys", Contract W-7405-Eng-92. BMI 849. 9 p.

47. Mikryukov, V. E., "Thermal and Electric Properties of Copper Alloys", Vestnik Moskov. Univ., Ser. Mat., Mekh., Astron., Fiz. i Khim. Vol. 11(2). pp. 53-70. (U.S.S.R.)

48. Kennedy, J. D., "Cemented Chrome Carbides", Product Eng. Vol. 24. pp. 154-7.

49. Hill, R. W. and Smith, P. L., "The Specific Heat of Beryllium at Low Temperatures", Phil. Mag. Vol. 44. pp. 636-44. (England)

50. Kemp, W. R. G. and Sreedhar, A. K., "The Thermal Conductivity of Magnesium at Low Temperatures", Proc. Phys. Soc. London. Vol. 66A. pp. 1077-8. (England)

51. White, G. K., "The Thermal Conductivity of Gold at Low Temperatures", Proc. Phys. Soc. (London). Vol. 66A. pp. 559-64. (England)

52. White, G. K., "Thermal and Electrical Conductivity of Copper at Low Temperatures", Australian J. Physics. Vol. 6. pp. 397-404. (Australia)

53. Kornev, Yu. V., "Determination of the Bond Energy in the Lattice of Austenite", Doklady Akad. Nauk. S. S. S. R. Vol. 93. pp. 467-70. (USSR)

54. Arbiter, W., "New High-temperature Intermetallic Materials", Contr. AF33 (616)109 WADC-TR-53-190. AD 29 396. 52 p.

55. Osborne, Darrell W. and Westrum Jr., Edgar F., "The Heat Capacity of Thorium Dioxide from 10 to 305°K. The Heat Capacity Anomalies in Uranium Dioxide and Neptunium Dioxide", Argonne National Lab - 5085 (Contract W31-109-eng-38). AD 15 189. 12 p.

56. Saller, H. A., Rough, F. A., and Dickerson, R., "Preparation and Properties of the Eutectic Uranium-Chromium Alloy", Contract W-7405-eng-92, BMI-884. 21 p.

57. Orr, Raymond L., "High-temperature Heat Contents of Tantalum and Niobium Oxides", J. Am. Chem. Soc. Vol. 75. pp. 2808-9.

58. Westrum Jr., E. F., Hatcher, J. B., and Osborne, D. W., "The Entropy and Low-temperature Heat Capacity of Neptunium Dioxide", J. Chem. Phys. Vol. 21. pp. 419-23.

59. Ginnings, D. C. and Furukawa, G. T., "Heat Capacity Standards for the Range 14 to 1200°K", J. Am. Chem. Soc. Vol. 75. pp. 522-7.

60. Sinel'nikov, N. N., "A Vacuum Adiabatic Calorimeter and Some New Data on the $\beta \rightleftarrows \alpha$ Transition for Quartz", Doklady Akad. Nauk. S. S. S. R. Vol. 92. pp. 369-72. (U. S. S. R.)

61. Douglas, Thomas B. and Logan, William M., "Thermal Conductivity and Heat Capacity of Molten Materials. Part 3. The Heat Capacity of Molybdenum Disilicide from 0° to 900°C", Natl. Bur. Stand. Wash., D. C. WADC Tech. Rept. No. 53-201, Pt. 3 Contract AF 33(616)52-10. 13 p. AD-24 019.

62. Hirone, T., Maeda, S., Tsubokawa, I., and Tsuya, N., "A Method for the Automatic Measurement of Specific Heat", Sci. Rep. Research Inst., Tohoku Univ. Vol (A), 5, (6). pp. 512-19. (Japan)

63. Gallaher, R. B. and Kitzes, A. S., "Summary Report on Portland Cement Concretes for Shielding", U. S. Atomic Energy Comm., Tech. Inform. Service, Oak Ridge, Tenn., ORNL-1414. 30 p.

64. Tarasov, V. V. and Savitskaya, Ya. S., "Specific Heat and Structure of Silicate Glasses", Doklady Akad. Nauk. S. S. S. R. Vol. 88. pp. 1019-22. (U. S. S. R.)

65. Norton, F. H. and Kingery, W. D., "The Measurement of Thermal Conductivity of Refractory Materials", Prog. Rept. Sept. 30, 1953, (NYO-3647), AD 23 561, Contract AT(30-1)960. 61 p.

66. Norton, F. H., Kingery, W. D., et al., "The Measurement of Thermal Conductivity of Refractory Materials", Prog. Rept. Jan. 1, 1953 (NYO-3642). 12 p. AD 5142.

67. Norton, F. H., Kingery, W. D., et al. (NYO-3643). "The Measurement of Thermal Conductivity of Refractory Materials", 98 p. AD 13940.

68. Norton, F. H., Kingery, W. D., et al. "The Measurement of Thermal Conductivity of Refractory Materials", Progress Report July, 1953. 10 p. AD 16492.

69. Norton, F. H. and Kingery, W. D. "The Measurement of Thermal Conductivity of Refractory Materials", Progress Rpt. NYO-3644 AD 11 816. 18 p.

70. Trombe, Felix, "The Vapor Pressures of the Rare Earth Metals, Their Separation and Purification", Bull. Soc. Chim. France. pp. 1010-12. (France)

71. Searcy, Alan W. and Myers, Clifford, E. "The Heat of Sublimation of Boron, The Dissociation Energy of BO Gas, and the Gaseous Species of the Boron-Boric Oxide System", Purdue U. Lafayette, Ind. Tech. Rept. No. 6 (Cont. N7onr-39412). AD-17617. 8 p.

72. Griffel, M., et al., "The Heat Capacity of Gadolinium from 15 to 355°K", ISC-367. 16 p.

73. Carniglia, S. C. "Vapor-pressures of Americium Trifluoride and Americium Metal", UCRL-2389 Contr. W 7405-eng-48. AD-23 277. 76 pp.

74. Sims, C. T., Wyler, E. N., and others. "Investigations of Rhenium", Battelle Memorial Inst., Columbus, Ohio (Contr. AF33(616)232). 44 p.

75. Searcy, Allan, W. and McNees Jr., Robert A., "An X-ray Diffraction and Vapor Pressure Investigation of the Rhenium-Germanium Phase Diagram", Tech. Rept. No. 8 (Contract N7onr-39412) AD 19 324. 9 p.

76. Lyubimov, A. P. and Granovakaya, A. A., "Measurement of Low Vapor Pressures at High Temperatures. III. Measurement of the Vapor Pressure of Silver with the Aid of a Radioactive Isotope", Zhur. Fiz. Khim. Vol. 27. pp. 473-5. (Russia)

77. Searcy, A. W., and McNees Jr., R. A., "The Silicides of Rhenium", AD 5753 (Contr. N7onr-39412). 14 p.

78. Tyler, W.W. and Wilson Jr., A.C., "Thermal Conductivity, Electrical Resistivity, and Thermo-electric Power of Graphite", Phys. Rev. Vol. 89. pp. 870-5.

79. DeSorbo, W. and Tyler, W.W., "The Specific Heat of Graphite from 13° to 300°K", J. Chem. Phys. Vol. 21. pp. 1660-3.

80. Berman, R. and Poulter, J., "Specific Heat of Diamond at Low Temperatures", J. Chem. Phys. Vol. 21. pp. 1906-7.

81. DeSorbo, W., "Specific Heat of Diamond at Low Temperatures", J. Chem. Phys. Vol. 21. pp. 876-80.

82. Danielson, G.C., "Quarterly Summary Research Report in Physics for Oct., Nov., and Dec., ", ISC-322 Ames Lab., Iowa State, Contr. W-7405-eng-82. 21 p

83. Chupka, Wm. A. and Inghram, Mark, G., "The Heat of Vaporization of Carbon", J. Chem. Phys. Vol. 21. pp. 371-2.

84. Chupka, W.A. and Inghram, M.G., "Molecular Species Evaporating from a Carbon Surface", J. Chem. Phys. Vol. 21. p. 1313.

85. Rudorff, W. and Valet, G., "On the Cerium-uranium Blue and Mixed-crystals in the System CeO_2-UO_2-U_3O_8 ", Z. an org. u. allgem. Chem. Vol. 271. pp. 257-72. (Germany)

86. Sinnott, M.J., "Thermal Conductivity of Nodular Iron", J. Metals 5, AIME Trans. 197 1016. Vol. 5. p. 1016.

87. Orr, Raymond L., "High Temperature Heat Contents of Magnesium Orthosilicate and Ferrous Ortho-silicate", J. Am. Chem. Soc. Vol. 75 (3). pp. 528-29.

88. Bloom, F.K., "Color and Reflectance of Stainless Steels", Metal Progress. Vol. 63. pp. 67-72.

89. Searcy, Alan W. and Jacobson, E. Leland, "The Preparation and Properties of α and β $ThSi_2$", Tech. Report (Contr. N7onr-39412). Rept. No. 3. 12 p.

90. Berman, R. and Simon, F.E., "The Thermal Conductivity of Diamond at Low Temperatures", Proc. Roy. Soc. (London). Vol. A220. pp. 171-83. (England)

91. Elliott, R.P., Rostoker, W., and McPherson, D.J., "A Study of a Family of Laves-type Intermediate Phases", Armour Research Found., Chicago, Ill. Qrtly. Prog. Rept. No. 3. (Cont. AF 18-(600)-642). AD 28 937. 14 p.

92. Rouard, P., Male, D., and Trompette, J., "Determination of the Coefficients of Reflection, Trans-mission, and Absorption of Thin Deposits of Gold Produced by Evaporation", J. Phys. Radium. Vol. 14 (11). pp. 587-590. (France)

93. Busch, G. and Winkler, U., "Electrical Conductivity and Hall Effect of Intermetallic Compounds", Helv. Phys. Acta. Vol. 26 (3/4). pp. 395-399. (Switzerland)

94. Chiochetti, V.E. and Henry, E.C., "Electrical Conductivity of Some Commercial Refractories in the Temperature Range 600° to 1500°C", J. Am. Ceram. Soc. Vol. 36. pp. 180-84.

95. Hensler, J.R. and Henry, E.C., "Electrical Resistance of Some Refractory Oxides and Their Mix-tures in the Temperature Range 600°to 1500°C", J. Am. Ceram. Soc. Vol. 36. pp. 76-83.

96. National Bureau of Standards, Washington, D.C., "Ceramic Coatings. Effect of Composition and Temperature on Resistivity", Prog. Rept. No. 2, Proj. No-TB2-0001. NBS Rept. No. 2164. AD 46 768.

97. Marx, Paul and Dole, Malcolm, "Specific Heat of Synthetic High Polymers. V. A Study of the Order-Disorder Transition in Polytetrafluorethylene", Tech. Rept. No. 3. Contr. DA11-022-ORD-996, Proj. TB2-0001 (540). AD 98 078. 4 p.

98. Marshall, T.A., "An Apparatus for Measuring the Coefficient of Thermal Conductivity of Solids and Liquids", Brit. J. Appl. Physics. Vol. 4(4). pp. 112-114. (England)

99. Doolittle, J.S., "Measurement of Thermal Conductivity and Fire Resistance of Certain Cellular Plastic Materials", N. Car. State Coll. Raleigh. Quarterly Rept. No. 3. 4 p.

100. Esaki, Leo "Properties of Thermally Treated Germanium", Phys. Rev. Vol. 89. pp. 1026-34.

101. Lagrenaudie, J., "Properties of Boron", J. Phys. Radium. Vol. 14. pp. 14-18. (France)

102. Mansfield, R., "The Electrical Conductivity and Thermoelectric Power of Magnesium Oxide", Proc. Phys. Soc. Vol. 66B. pp. 612-14. (England)

103. Mikryukov, V.E. and Pozdnyak, N.Z., "Physicomechanical Properties of Iron-Based Materials Prepared by Powder Metallurgy", Vestnik Moskov. Univ. 8, No. 2, Ser. Fiz.-Mat. i Estestven. Nauk. No. 1. pp. 53-68. (USSR)

104. Johnson, G.H., "Influence of Impurities on Electrical Conductivity of Rutile", J. Am. Ceram. Soc. Vol. 36. pp. 97-101.

105. Joyner, Bobby L. and Bell, William C., "Effect of Partial Devitrification on the Electrical Resistivity of Sodium-Bearing Glasses", J. Am. Ceram. Soc. Vol. 36. pp. 263-6.

106. Simpson, O. C. and Thorn, R. J., "Spectral Emissivities of Graphite and Carbon", U. S. AEC Publ. ANL 4878. 57 p.

107. Thorn, R. J. and Simpson, O. C., "Spectral Emissivities of Graphite and Carbon", J. Appl. Phys. Vol. 24. pp. 633-9.

108. Levingston, H. L. and Rogers, B. A., "The Thorium-Vanadium System", U. S. AEC Publ. AECD-3602; ISC-340. 20 p.

109. Saller, H. A. and Rough, F. A., "Examination and Properties of Uranium Alloys", U. S. AEC Publ. TID 10046. 22 p.

110. Keeler, J. H., "Development of Zirconium-Base Alloys Sixteenth Quarterly Report", (Progress Rept. No. 17) U. S. AEC Publ. SO-2512. 5 p.

111. Chiotti, P., "Measurement of the Electrical Resistance of Metals and Alloys at High Temperatures", U. S. AEC Publ. ISC-434. 24 p.

112. Mardon, P. G., Robertson, J. A. L. and Ball, J. E., "An Approximate Determination of the Specific Heat of α-Plutonium", U. S. AEC Publ. AERE-M/R-1181. 11 p. (England)

113. Onstott, E. I., "Preparation of Massive Samarium Metal", LA-1622. Contr. W-7405-Eng-36. 8 p.

114. Gordan, K., Skinner, B. and Johnston, H. L., "Thermal Expansion (and Lattice Parameters) of Zirconium between 290° and 1600°K", U. S. AEC Publ. NP-3747.

115. Kemper, R. S. and Boyd, C. L., "Electrical Resistance Measurements of an Irradiated Uranium Sample", U. S. AEC Publ. HW-28309. 9 p.

116. Randolph, B. W., "Electrical Measurements on Molybdenum", U. S. AEC Publ. COO-102. pp. 24-27.

117. Kinchin, G. H., "The Electrical Properties of Graphite", Proc. Roy. Soc. (London). Vol. A217. pp. 9-26 (England)

118. Lagrenaudie, J., "Semiconducting Properties of Boron", J. Chem. Phys. Vol. 50. pp. 629-33. (France)

119. Resnick, R., Frank, L. and Balluffi, R. W., "The Alpha-Beta Transformation Temperature and Grain Growth Characteristics of Hot-Pressed Uranium", U. S. AEC Publ. SEP 216. 15 p.

120. Wilhelm, H. A., Carlson, O. N. and Lunt, H. E., "Thorium-Titanium Alloy System", U. S. AEC Publ. AECD-3603; ISC-408. 22 p.

121. Foster, K. W., "The Vapour Pressure of Actinium", U. S. AEC MLM-901. 9 p.

122. Bates, J. C., "A Comparison of the Thermal Conductivity of Irradiated and Unirradiated Uranium", RBD(W)/TN-78. 12 p. (England)

123. Bell, I. P. and McDonald, J. J., "Thermal Conductivity of Metals and Uranium Compounds -- A Review of Progress to Dec. 19, 1952", RDB(c)/TN-24. 10 p.

124. Farr, J. D., Giorgi, A., et al., "The Crystal Structure of Actinium Hydride", U. S. AEC Publ. LA-1545.

125. Brown, A. R. G., Hall, A. R. and Watt, W., "Density of Deposited Carbon", Nature Vol. 172 (4390) pp. 1145-46.

126. Mass. Inst. of Tech., "Technical Progress Report for the Period Jan. 1953 through March 1953", U. S. AEC Publ. MIT-1111. 91 p.

127. Saller, H. A. et al., "Differential Thermal-Expansion Effects in Brazed Joints", U. S. AEC Publ. BMI-863 (Rev.).

128. Le Roux, Rene, "Thermoelastic Study and Isothermal Decomposition of the Eutectoid in Aluminum Bronzes", Rev. Met. Vol. 50. pp. 558-578. (France)

129. Masumoto, H., Saito, H. and Sugihara, M., "The Anomaly of the Specific Heat at High Temperatures in α-Phase Alloys of Iron and Chromium", Sci. Rep. Research Inst. Tohoku Univ. Vol. (A)5(3). pp. 203-207. (Japan)

130. Powers, W. D. and Blalock, G. C., "Heat Capacity of Two Samples of 310 Stainless Steel and of a Brazing Compound", U. S. AEC Publ. CF-53-9-98. 9 p.

131. McCabe, C. L., Schadel Jr., H. M. and Birchenall, C. E., "Vapor Pressure of Silver over Silver-Gold Solid Solution", (Contr. N6-ori-47, T.O.4) (Reprint from Jnl. of Metals:709-711, May 53). AD 56-331. 3 p.

132. Ferro, R., "Alloys of Uranium with Bismuth", Atti. Accad. Nazi. Lincei, Rend. Classe Sci. Fis. Mat. E Mat. Vol. 14. pp. 89-94.

133. Howe, J. T., ed., "Solid State Division Quarterly Prog. Rept. for Period Ending May 10, 1952", U. S. AEC Publ. ORNI-1301. 53 p.

134. Arbiter, W., "New High-Temperature Intermetallic Materials", (Contr. AF33(616)109) WADC TR-53-190 (Pt. 2). AD 29 396. 52 p.

135. Gilles, Paul W. and Pollock, Bernard D., "The Thermodynamic Properties and Equilibrium Pressures in the Molybdenum-Boron System", (Part of Thesis). U. S. AEC Publ. AECU-2894. Contr. AT-(11-1)-83. AD 72 027. 29 p.

136. Strauss, Simon W., Richards, Lloyd, E. and Moore, Dwight, G., "Effect of Temperature on the Electrical Resistivity of Several Ceramic and Silicone-Type Coatings", Nat. Bur. Stand. Wash. D.C. (Spec. Tech. Publ. No. 153) in its Prog. Rept. No. 7. AD 29 990. 8 p.

137. Arbiter, W., "New High-Temperature Intermettalic Materials", WADC TR 53 190 (Contr. AF33 (616)-109). 85 p.

138. Lambertson, W. A. and Mueller, M. H., "Uranium Oxide Phase Equilibrium Systems. III. UO_2-ZrO_2", J. Am. Ceram. Soc. Vol. 36. pp. 365-8.

139. Shartsis, L., Capps, W. and Spinner, S., "Density and Expansivity of Alkali Borates and Density Characteristics of Some Other Binary Glasses", J. Am. Ceram. Soc. Vol. 36(2). pp. 35-43

140. Wachtman, J. B. and Maxwell, L. H., "The Plastic Deformation of Ceramic Oxide Single Crystals", Contr. AF33(038)-51-4056. AD 27 292 p. 42.

141. Sense, K. A., Snyder, M. J. and Clegg, J. W., "Vapor Pressures of Beryllium Fluoride and Zirconium Fluoride", U. S. AEC Publ. AECD 03707 (Contr. W-7405-Eng-92). AD 156 816. p. 10

142. National Bur. of Standards, "Ceramic Coatings (Effect of Composition and Temperature on Resistivity)", NBS Rept. 2428, Prog. Rept. No. 3.

143. National Bur. Stand., "Ceramics Coating (Effects of Composition and Temperature on Resistivity)", (NBS Rept. 3047) Prog. Rept. No. 6. AD 26 744. 3 p.

144. Laurent, B., "Relation Between the Physical Properties and the Structures of Certain Pure Borate Glasses", Verres et refractaires. Vol. 7(3). pp. 161-73. (France)

145. Bron, V. A. and Podnogin, A. K., "Properties of Al_2TiO_5 Translation", AEC tr-1814 (Doklady Akad. Nauk SSSR). Vol. 91. pp. 93-4. (SSSR)(USA)

146. Florinskaya, V. A., "Reflection Spectra of Ordinary and Devitrified Lead Glasses in the Infrared", Doklady Akad. Nauk. SSSR. 5 p. (USSR)

1954

1. Kingery, W. D. and Francl, J., "Thermal Conductivity. X. Data for Several Pure Oxide Materials Corrected to Zero Porosity", J. Am. Ceram. Soc. Vol. 37. pp. 107-10.

2. Francl, J. and Kingery, W. D., "Thermal Conductivity. IX. Experimental Investigation of Effect of Porosity on Thermal Conductivity", J. Am. Ceram. Soc. Vol. 37. pp. 99-107.

3. McQuarrie, Malcolm, "Thermal Conductivity. V. High-temperature Method and Results for Alumina, Magnesia, and Beryllia from 1000 to 1800°C", J. Am. Ceram. Soc. Vol. 37. pp. 84-8.

4. Kingery, W. D., "Thermal Conductivity. VI. Determination of Conductivity of Al_2O_3 by Spherical Envelope and Cylinder Methods", J. Am. Ceram. Soc. Vol. 37. pp. 88-90.

5. Adams, Milton, "Thermal Conductivity. III. Prolate Spheroid Envelope Method; Data for Al_2O_3, BeO, MgO, ThO_2, and ZrO_2", J. Am. Ceram. Soc. Vol. 37. pp. 74-9.

6. Francl, J. and Kingery, W. D., "Thermal Conductivity. IV. Apparatus for Determining Thermal Conductivity by a Comparative Method; Data for Pb, Al_2O_3, BeO, and MgO", J. Am. Ceram. Soc. Vol. 37. pp. 80-4.

7. Powell, R. W., "The Thermal Conductivity of Beryllia", Trans. Brit. Ceram. Soc. Vol. 53. pp. 389-97. (England)

8. Krishnan, K. S. and Jain, S. C., "Determination of Thermal Conductivities at High Temperatures", Brit. J. Appl. Phys. Vol. 5. pp. 426-30. (England)

9. Hagel, William C., Pound, Guy M., and Mehl, Robert F., "The Free-Energy Change of Austenite-Pearlite Transformations", Metals Research Lab., Carnegie Inst. of Tech., Pittsburgh, Pa. Contract DA 36-061-ORD-350, Proj. TB2-0001 (534). 103 p. AD-39 272.

10. Altman, H. W., Rubin, T., and Johnston, H. L., "Coefficient of Thermal Expansion of Solids at Low Temperature. III. The Thermal Expansion of Pure Metals, with the Data for Aluminum, Nickel, Titanium and Zirconium.", Cryogenic Lab., Ohio State U., Research Foundation, Tech. Rept. No. TR264-27 (Contract W33-038-2c-14794). 11 p. AD-26 970.

11. Dow Chemical Co., "Thermal and Electrical Properties of Mg Base Alloys", (Contract AF 33(616) 2337)(Rept. No. 16370)(Part 2 of Its Qrtly Rept. No. 1, AD-41 190). 11 p.

12. Craig, R. S. and Krier, C. A., "Magnesium-Cadmium Alloys. VI. Heat Capacities between 12 and 320°K and the Entropies at 25° of Magnesium and Cadmium", J. Am. Chem. Soc. Vol. 76. pp. 238-40.

13. Sidles, P. H. and Danielson, G. C., "Thermal Diffusivity of Metals at High Temperatures", J. Appl. Physics. Vol. 25. pp. 58-66.

14. Raezer, Spencer, D., "Thermal and Electrical Conductivities of AISI C-1010 Steel in the Range from 25°C to 800°C", Inst. Research, Lehigh U., Bethlehem, Pa. Tech. Rept. 1 (Contract DA-36-034-ORD-1475, Prog. TB 2-0001 (151). 48 p. AD-49 544.

15. Pallister, P. R., "The α ------→γ Transformation of High-Purity Iron", J. Iron Steel Inst. Vol. 178. pp. 346-53. (England)

16. Mauer, Floyd, A. and Bolz, Leonard, H., "Thermal Expansion of Cermet Components by High Temperature X-ray Diffraction", Natl. Bur. Stand., Wash. D. C., Prog. Rept. No. 4 (NBS Rept. No. 3445)(Contract AF 33(616)53-12). 20 p. AD-38 645.

17. Oriana, R. A. and Jones, T. S., "Apparatus for the Determination of the Solidus Temperatures of High-melting Alloys", Rev. Sci. Instr. Vol. 25. pp. 248-51.

18. Wilhelm, H. A., Carlson, O. N., and Dickinson, J. M., "Niobium-Vanadium Alloy System", Trans. Amer. Inst. Min. Met. Eng. Vol. 200(8). pp. 915-18.

19. Mauer, Floyd A. and Bolz, Leonard H., "Thermal Expansion of Cermet Compounds by High Temperature X-ray Diffraction", Natl. Bur. Stand., Wash. D. C. (NBS Rept. No. 3463)(Contract AF 33(616) 53-12) Progress Rept. No. 5. 22 p. AD-38 644.

20. Saller, H. A. and Dickerson, R. F., "Induction-melted Zirconium and Zirconium Alloys", U. S. Atomic Energy Comm. BMI-908. pp. 5-37. AD-29 367.

21. Oriana, R. A. and Murphy, W. K., "The Heat Capacity of Chromium Carbide (Cr_3C_2)", J. Am. Chem. Soc. Vol. 76. pp. 343-5.

22. Nelson, R. G. and Kato, H., "Mechanical Properties of Consumable-arc-melted Kroll-process Zirconium", U. S. Bur. Mines, Rept. Invest. No. 5063. 13 p.

23. Nordheim, Rolf and Grant, Nicholas, J., "Resistivity Anomalies in the Nickel-chromium System as Evidence of Ordering Reactions", J. Inst. Metals. Vol. 82. pp. 440-4.

24. Vasilos, T. and Kingery, W. D., "Thermal Conductivity. XI. Conductivity of Some Refractory Carbides and Nitrides", J. Am. Ceram. Soc. Vol. 37. pp. 409-414.

25. Ames, S. L. and McQuillan, A. D., "Resistivity-temperature-concentraction Relationships in the System Niobium-Titanium", Acta Met. Vol. 2. pp. 831-6. (England)

26. Rosenthal, D. and Friedmann, N. E., "Thermal Diffusivity of Metals at High Temperatures", J. Apply. Phys. Vol. 25(8). pp. 1059-1060.

27. Lucks, C. F., Matolich, J., and Van Valzor, J. A., "The Experimental Measurement of Thermal Conductivities, Specific Heats, and Densities of Metallic, Transparent and Protective Materials", Battelle Memorial Inst., Columbus, Ohio, Part III, Contract AF 33(616)311; cont. of Contract AF 33(038)205581) USAF Tech. Rept. 6145-3. 71 p.

28. Honig, Richard E., "Sublimation Studies of Silicon on the Mass Spectrometer", J. Chem. Phys. Vol. 22. pp. 1610-11.

29. Bibring, Herve and Sevilleau, Francois, "Research on the Crystal Orientation and The Allotropic Transformation of Cobalt", Compt. rend. Vol. 238-(9). pp. 1026-28. (France)

30. Hoch, Michael and Johnston, Herrick L., "The Reaction Occurring on Thoriated Cathodes", J. Am. Chem. Soc. Vol. 76. pp. 4833-5.

31. Honig, Richard E., "The Heats of Sublimation and Evaporation of Germanium", J. Chem. Phys. Vol. 22. p. 1610.

32. Rasor, N. S. and Smith, A. W., "Low Temperature Thermal and Electrical Conductivities of Normal and Neutron Irradiated Graphite", NAA-SR-862 AD-85006. 37 p.

33. Davey, P. O. and Danielson, G. C., "Thermal Conductivity of Nickel", Contract W-7405-eng-82 (ISC-518) W-7405. 24 p. AD 48833.

34. Busch, G. and Vogt, O., "Variations in the Electrical and Magnetic Properties of Antimony and Indium Antimonide at the Melting Point", Helv. Phys. Acta. Vol. 27(3). pp. 241-48. (Switzerland)

35. Griffel, M. and Skochdopole, R. E., "The Heat Capacity of Gadolinium from 15 to 355°K", Phys. Rev. Vol. 93. pp. 657-61.

36. Spedding, F. H. and Daane, A. H., "Production of Rare Earth Metals in Quantity Allows Testing of Physical Properties", J. Metals. Vol. 6(5). pp. 504-510.

37. Mauer, Floyd, A. and Bolz, Leonard H., "Thermal Expansion of Cermet Components by High Temperature X-ray Diffraction", Nat. Bur. of Stand. Progress Report 6, (NBS Rept. No. 3644) (Contract AF 33(616)53-12) AD-46 601. 20 p.

38. Sims, C. T., Craighead, C. M. Jaffee, R., et al. "Investigation of Rhenium", WADC Technical Report No. 54-371. Contr. AF 33(616)-232. AD 48 279. 138 p.

39. Altman, Howard W., Rubin, Thor, and Johnston, Herrick, L., "Coefficients of Thermal Expansion of Solids at Low Temperatures. IV. The Thermal Expansion of Type 304 Stainless Steel and Yellow Brass", TR 264-28, Contract W33-038-ac-14794, AD 31 268. 9 p.

40. Shevlin, T. S. and Hauck, C. A., "Alumina-base Cermets", AD 49092, Contr. AF33(616)472, WADC-TR-54-173 (Pt. 1). 51 p.

41. Dow Chemical Co., Midland, Mich., "Investigation of Mg Alloys and Their Properties, Parts I, II and III", (Contract AF 33(616)2337) Qrtly Rept. No. 3, AD-49802(a) - (c). 33 p.

42. Deem, H. W., Winn, R. A., and Lucks, C. F., "Thermal Conductivity and Linear Expansion of the Eutectic Uranium-Chromium Alloy", Contract W-7405-eng-92 BMI-900 (AD 85 812). 16 p.

43. Smoke, E. J. (New Jersey Ceramic Res. Station), "Thermal Expansion Properties of Some High Silica Bodies in the System Lithia-Alumina-Silica", Ceram. Age. Vol. 64(6). pp. 11-15.

44. Handwerk, J. H. and McVay, T. N., "Thermal Expansion of Some Glasses in the System Li_2O-CaO-SiO_2", ORO-126. 24 p. AD-40 879.

45. Curtis, C. E., Doney, L. M., and Johnson, J. R., "Some Properties of Hafnium Oxide, Hafnium Silicate, Calcium Hafnate and Hafnium Carbide", ORNL 1681 (Contract W7405-eng-26), AD-26812. 36 p.

46. Curtis, C. E., Doney, L. M., and Johnson, J. R., "Some Properties of Hafnium Oxide, Hafnium Silicate, Calcium Hafnate, and Hafnium Carbide", J. Am. Ceram. Soc., Vol. 37(10). pp. 458-65.

47. Quirk, John and Harmon, C. G., "Properties of a Tin Oxide-Base Ceramic Body", J. Am. Ceram. Soc. Vol. 37. pp. 24-6.

48. Harrison, D. E., McKinstry, H. A., and Hummel, F. A., "High-temperature Zirconium Phosphates", J. Am. Ceram. Soc. Vol. 37(6). pp. 277-80.

49. Lamar, R. S. and Warner, N. F., "Reaction and Fired-property Studies of Cordierite Compositions", J. Am. Ceram. Soc. Vol. 37. pp. 602-10.

50. Mikryukov, V. E. and Pozdnyak, N. Z., "The Study of the Temperature Relation of the Thermal and Electrical Conductivities of Porous Iron-copper-graphite Anti-friction Alloys", Vestnik Moskov. Univ. 9, No. 9, Ser. Viz.-Mat i Estestven Nauk No. 6. pp. 51-9

51. Mauer, Floyd A. and Bolz, Leonard H., "Thermal Expansion of Cermet Components by High Temperature X-ray Diffraction", Natl. Bur. Stand., Wash. D. C. Prog. Rept. No. 7 (NBS Rept. No. 3824) (Contract AF33(616)53-12). 16 pp.

52. Shevlin, Thomas S., "Fundamental Study and Equipment for Sintering and Testing of Cermet Bodies: VI. Fabrication, Testing and Properties of 72 Chromium-28 Alumina Cermets", J. Am. Ceram. Soc. Vol. 37. pp. 140-5.

53. Rubin, T., Altman, H. W., and Johnston, H. S., "Coefficients of Thermal Expansion of Solids at Low Temperatures. I. The Thermal Expansion of Copper from 15° to 300°K", J. Amer. Chem. Soc. Vol. 76 (21). pp. 5289-93.

54. Stansbury, E. E., Elder, G. E., and McElroy, D. L., "Calorimetric Studies of Plastic Deformation and Phase Transformations", Contract AT(40-1)-1068 (ORO-131). AD 54 475. 18 p.

55. Russell, R. B., "Coefficients of Thermal Expansion for Zirconium", Trans. Amer. Inst. Min. Met. Eng. (in J. Metals, 1954, 6). Vol. 200(9). pp. 1045-52.

56. Korev, Yu V. and Golubkin, V. N., "The Determination of the Vapor Tension and the Heat of Sublimation of Cobalt in the 1050 to 1250° Temperature Range", Doklady Akad. Nauk S. S. S. R. Vol. 99. pp. 565-7. (Russia)

57. Maykuth, D. J., Ogden, H. R., Jaffee, R. I., et al., "The Titanium-manganese, Titanium-tungsten and Titanium-tantalum Phase Diagrams", (Contract AF 33-(038)-8544). AD 49904. 94 p.

58. Assayag, Genevieve and Bizette, Henri, "An Anomaly in the Heat Capacities of CoO and CoO-NiO and CoO-CuO Solid Solutions", Compt. rend. Vol. 239. pp. 238-40. (France)

59. Knudsen, F. P., Moreland, R. E., and Geller, R. F., "Physical Characteristics of Titanium Carbide Type Cermets at Elevated Temperatures", Natl. Bur. Stand. Wash., D. C. WADC Tech. Rept. No. 54-1 (Contract AF 33(616)52-2). 70 p. AD-39 070.

60. Masumoto, Hakaru, Saito, Hideo, and Takahashi, Minoru, "The Anomaly of Specific Heat at High Temperatures in α-Phase Copper-aluminum Alloys", Nippon-Kinzoku-Gakkai, Shi (J. Japan Inst. Metals.). Vol. 18. pp. 98-100. (Japan)

61. Douglas, Thomas, B. and Logan, William M., "Heat Content of Molybdenum Disilicate from 0° to 900°C", J. Research Natl. Bur. Stand. (Research Paper No. 2520). Vol. 53. pp. 91-93.

62. Bonnickson, K. R., "High Temperature Heat Contents of Calcium and Magnesium Ferrites", J. Am. Chem. Soc. Vol. 76. pp. 1480-2.

63. Coffer, L. W. and Craig, R. S., "Magnesium-cadmium Alloys. VII. Low-temperature Heat Capacities of $MgCd_3$ and Mg_3Cd and a Test of the Third Law of Thermodynamics for the $MgCd_3$ Superlattice", J. Am. Chem. Soc. Vol. 76 pp. 241-4.

64. Kingery, W. D. and Norton, F. H., "The Measurement of Thermal Conductivity of Refractory Materials", NYO-6446, Quarterly Progress Rept. (Contract AT(30-1) 960). 7 p.

65. Ewing, C. T. and Baker, B. E., "Thermal and Related Physical Properties of Molten Materials. Part I. Thermal Conductivity and Heat Capacity of Molybdenum Disilicide", Naval Research Lab., Wash., D. C., (WADC Tech. Rept. No. 54-185. pt. 1) 27 p. AD-50 565.

66. West, E. D., Ditmars, D. A., and Ginnings, D. C., "Thermal Conductivity and Heat Capacity of Molten Materials. Part 5. The Thermal Conductivity of Molybdenum Disilicide", National Bur. Stand., Wash. D. C., (WADC Tech. Rept. No. 53-201, pt. 5) (Contract AF 33(616)52-10. 19 p. AD-49 098.

67. Serebrennikov, N. N. and Gel'd, P. V., "Heat Capacity of ζ-phase of the System Iron-silicon", Doklady Akad. Nauk S. S. S. R. Vol. 97. pp. 695-8. (U. S. S. R.)

68. Rauch, W. G., "Urania-Zirconium Cermets", Final Rept. AML 5268. 13 p.

69. New Jersey Ceramic Research Station, Rutgers U., New Brunswick "Development of Ceramic Bodies with High Thermal Conductivity", Pt. 1 of Its Prog. Rept. No. 5 AD-30 849 (Cont. DA 36-039-sc-42577). 24 p.

70. Finkelshtein, R. N. and Yamshchikova, A. T., "The Effect of Aluminum on the Interatomic Bonds of Silver", Doklady Akad. Nauk S. S. S. R. Vol. 98. pp. 781-2. (U. S. S. R.)

71. Rauh, Everett G. and Thorn, Robert J., "Vapor Pressure of Uranium", J. Chem. Phys. ANL-5203 (Contr. W-31-109-eng-38)(AD-25711). Vol. 22. pp. 1414-20.

72. Rauh, Everett, G. and Thorn, Robert J., "Vapor Pressure of Uranium", ANL-5203 (Contr. No. W-31-109-eng-38). 38 p.

73. Rose, E. Ernest, Lal, Joginder, et al., "Direct Resin Filling Materials, Coefficient of Thermal Expansion and Water Sorption of Polymethyl Methacrylate", Justi, H.D., and Son, Inc., USAF School of Aviation Medicine - Proj. No. 21 1603-0002 (Rept. 1). AD 57 939. 9 p.

74. Busch, G. and Schneider, M., "Thermal Conductivity of the Intermetallic Compound In St", Helv. Phys. Acta. Vol. 27. pp. 196-198. (Switzerland)

75. Sims, C.T., Gideon, D.N., and others, "Investigations of Rhenium", Battelle Memorial Inst. Columbus, O. (Contr. AF 33(616) 232) Qrtly. Prog. Rept. No. 7. AD 33 442.

76. Douglas, P.E., "The Vapor Pressure of Calcium I", Proc. Phys. Soc. (London). Vol. 67B. pp. 783-6. (England)

77. Tomlin, D.H., "The Vapor Pressure of Calcium II", Proc. Phys. Soc. (London). Vol. 67B. pp. 787-94. (England)

78. McIntosh, G.E. and Hamilton, D.C., "Rapid Measurements of Thermal Diffusivity", Trans. Am. Soc. Mech. Engrs. Vol. 76. pp. 407-10.

79. Lieberman, D.S., "The Study of Diffusionless Phase Changes in Solid Metals and Alloys", Contract AT(30-1)-904. 64 p.

80. Chupka, Wm. A. and Inghram, Mark G., "Direct Determination of the Heat of Sublimation of Carbon", J. Chem. Phys. Vol. 22. pp. 1472.

81. Honig, R.E., "Mass Spectrometric Study of the Molecular Sublimation of Graphite", J. Chem. Phys. Vol. 22. pp. 126-31.

82. Post, B., Glaser, F.W., and Moskowitz, D., "Transition-metal Diborides", Acta Met. Vol. 2 (1). pp. 20-25.

83. Herz, Wm. H., "Investigation of the Intermetallic Compounds of Aluminum", American Electro Metal Corp., Yonkers, N.Y. Contr. AF33(038)10716, Progress Rept. No. 6. 8 p.

84. Arbiter, William, "Investigation and Evaluation of New High Temperature Materials", Prog. Rept. No. 6. (Contr. AF33(616) 109). 28 p.

85. Krishnan, Sir K.S. and Jain, S.C., "Determinations of Thermal Conductivity (of Metals. e.g. Platinum) at High Temperature", Brit. J. Appl. Physics. Vol. 5 (12). pp. 426-430. (England)

86. Johnson, E.R., Christian, S.M., "Some Properties of Germanium-Silicon Alloys", Phys. Rev. Vol. 95 (2). pp. 560-61.

87. Kitzes, A.S. and Hullings, W.Q., "Boral-Thermal Neutron Shield", U.S. Atom. Energy Comm. AECD-3625. pp. 25-40.

88. McKinney, V.L. and Rockwell, III., T., "Boral-Thermal Neutron Shield", U.S. Atom. Energy Comm. AECD-3625. pp. 3-24.

89. Gier, J.T., "Measurement of Absolute Spectral Reflectivity from 1.0 to 15 microns", J. Opt. Soc. Amer. Vol. 44. pp. 558-562.

90. O'Brien, F.R., Covington, Perry, C., et al., "An Investigation of the Thermal Properties of Heat Resistant Plastic Laminates", Southern Research Inst. Rept. No. 1864-523-IV. Contract AF 33 (616)2045. AD 65 211. 5 p.

91. Kuchkuda, Roman W., "The Coefficient of Linear Thermal Expansion of Various Plastic Materials", Picatinny Arsenal Proj. No. TB4-7211; Tech. Rept. No. 2025. AD 34 721. 107 p.

92. Rudner, Merritt A., Graeff, Richard F., and Bertolet Jr., E.C., "Investigation of Selected Combinations of Teflon with Filler Materials for Application to Electronic Parts", Contract NObsr - 63134. Final Report. AD 45 199. 39 p.

93. Meechan, C.J. and Eggleston, R.R., "Formation Energies of Vacancies in Copper and Gold", Acta Met. Vol. 2. pp. 680-3.

94. Barzelay, Martin E., Tong, Kin Nee and Hollo, George, "Thermal Conductance of Contacts (of Aluminum Alloy and Stainless Steel)", NACA TN-3167. 47 p.

95. Comoforo, J.E. and Hatch, R.A., "Synthetic-Mica Investigations. IV. Dielectric Properties of Hot-Pressed Synthetic Mica and Other Ceramics at Temperatures up to 400°", J. Am. Ceram. Soc. Vol. 37. pp. 317-22.

96. Weigelt, W. and Haase, G., "Electrical Resistance of Magnesia Sintered in a High Vacuum", Ber. Deut. keram. Ges. Vol. 31. No. 2. pp. 45-8. (Germany)

97. Russell, R.B., "Coefficients of Thermal Expansion for Zirconium", Trans. Amer. Inst. Min. Met. Eng. Vol. 200(9) pp. 1045-52.

98. Ball, J.G., Robertson, J.A.L. et al., "Some Physical Properties of Metallic Plutonium", Nature. Vol. 173. pp. 534-35. (England)

99. Ames Lab., "Quarterly Summary Research Report in Physics for July, August and September 1954", U. S. AEC Publ. ISC-533. 14 p.

100. Johnson, H. A. and Dow Chemical Co., "Experimental Magnesium Alloys. Pt. 3. Thermal and Electrical Properties of Magnesium Base Alloys", WADC-TR-54-83 (Pt. 3) Contr. AF (600)-19147. 37 p.

101. Carlson, O. N., Kenney, D. J. and Wilhelm, H. A., "The Aluminum-Vanadium Alloy System." U. S. AEC Publ. ISC 448. 28 p.

102. Lampson, F. K., Rowe, G. H. et al., "Electrical Resistivity of Commercially Pure Titanium", U. S. AEC Publ. NEPA-1826. 10 p.

103. Bell, I. P. and Makin, S. M., "Fast Reactor -- Physical Properties of Materials of Construction, Review of Progress from Sept. 1, 1953 to April 1, 1954", (RDB(c)/TN-70). 17 p. (England)

104. Rogers, B. A. and Atkins, D. F., "The Zirconium-Columbium Diagram", U. S. AEC Publ. ISC-500. Contr. W-7405-Eng-82. 39 p.

105. Chiotti, Premo, "High-Temperature Crystal Structure of Thorium", J. Electrochem. Soc. Vol. 101. pp. 567-570.

106. Sims, C. T., Gaines, G. B. et al., "Investigations of Rhenium", U. S. AEC Publ. BMI Quarterly Prog. Rept. No. 9. Contr. AF 33(616)232. 28 p.

107. Meechan, C. J. and Eggleston, R. R., "Formation Energies of Vacancies in Copper and Gold", U. S. AEC Publ. NAA-SR-879. Contr. AT-11-1-Gen-8. 11 p.

108. Meechan, C. J. and Eggleston, R. R., "Formation Energies of Vacancies in Copper and Gold", Acta Met. Vol. 2. pp. 680-3.

109. Schelton, S. M., Dilling, E. D., et al., "Zirconium Progress Report for the Period of Sept. 15-Dec. 15, 1954", U. S. AEC Publ. USBM-C-22. 41 p.

110. Lord, W.B.H., "Some Physical Properties of Metallic Plutonium", Nature. Vol. 173. pp. 534-535. (England)

111. Faris, F. E. and Hove, J. E. et al., "Radiation Effects Quarterly Progress Rept. for Jan-March 1954", U. S. AEC Publ. NAA-SR-1013. 48 p.

112. DeVos, J. C., "A New Determination of the Emissivity of Tungsten Ribbon", Physica. Vol. 20. pp. 690-714 (Holland)

113. Grass, G., "The Optical Behaviour of Metals (Cobalt, Copper, Iron Manganese, Nickel, and Silver) at High Temperatures (but below their melting points)", Z. Metallkunde. Vol. 45. pp. 538-47. (Germany)

114. Green, E. C., Jones, D. J. and Pitkin, W. R., "Developments in High-Density (Tungsten) Alloys", Iron Steel Inst. (London) Spec. Rept. No. 58. pp. 253-6. (England)

115. Argonne Natl. Lab., "Metallurgy Division Quarterly Report for Jan., Feb. and March 1954", U. S. AEC Publ. ANL-5257 (Del.). 63 p.

116. Saller, H. A., Stacy, J. T., and Klebanow, H. L., "High-Temperature Brazing of Nichrome. V.", U. S. AEC Publ. BMI-933 (Contr. W-7405-Eng-92). p. 26

117. Anon. "Heavy Alloy (Tungsten Base Alloy)", Metal Ind. Vol. 84. pp. 427-488.

118. Masumoto, H., Saito, H. and Shinozaki, M., "Order-Disorder Transformation of the Alloys of Iron and Cobalt", Science Rept. Research Insts., Tohoku Univ. Vol. Ser. A6. pp. 523-8 (Japan)

119. Hori, Kazuo and Murchara, Masatoshi, "Aluminum Alloy Containing Titanium", Nippon Kinzoku Gakkaishi. Vol. 18. pp. 621-4. (Japan)

120. Masumoto, H., Saito, Hideo and Sagai, Yutaka, "Influence of Addition of Nickel on Thermal Expansion, Rigidity Modulus, and Temperature Coefficient of Cobalt-Iron-ChromiumAlloys. II. Alloys Added with 30% and 40% Nickel", Nippon Kinzoku Gakkaishi. Vol. 18. pp. 81-4 (Japan)

121. Troshkina, V. A. and Khomyakov, K. G., "Study of Structural Changes in Iron-Nickel-Aluminum Alloys by the Method of True Heat Capacity", J. Gen. Chem. U.S.S.R. Vol. 24. pp. 785-92. (USSR)

122. Wilkes, G. B., "Total Normal Emissivities and Solar Absorptivities of Materials", WADC Tech. Rept. No. 54-42 (Contr. W33-)33-(ac)-20486). 94 p.

123. Frost, B.R.T. and Maskrey, J. T., "The Uranium-Lead System", J. Inst. Metals. Vol. 32. p. 171.

124. Liu, Tien-Shih and Bobone, Renato, "Research in Electrical Properties of Intermetallic Compounds", U. S. AEC Publ. NP-5268; Contr. AF18(600)-774. 46 p.

125. Ellinger, F. H. et al., "The Preparation and Properties of Magnesium Hydrides", AECU 2970. 5 p.

126. Cotter, P. G. and Kohn, J. A., "Industrial-Diamond Substitutes. I. Physical and X-ray Study of Hafnium Carbide", J. Amer. Ceram. Soc. Vol. 37. pp. 415-20.

127. National Bureau of Standards, "Thermal Conductivity, and Heat Capacity Project", U. S. AEC Publ. NBS-3179. Contr. 33(616)52-10. 8 p.

128. Blumenthal, H., "Investigation of the Effect of Raw Material Production Variables on the Physical and Chemical Properties of Carbides, Nitrides and Borides", American Electro Metal Corp., Final Rept. Contr. AF33(616)-89. 126 p.

129. Blumenthal, H., "Investigation of the Effect of Raw Material Production Variables on the Physical and Chemical Properties of Carbides, Nitrides and Borides", Prog. Rept. No. 14., July 31-Aug. 31, 1954. Contr. AF33(616)-89. AD 39 839. 9 p.

130. Blunt, R. F. and Frederikse, H.P.R. et al., "III. Aluminum Antimonide", Phys. Rev. Vol. 96. pp. 578-80.

131. Hoch, Michael, and Johnston, Herrick L., "The Reaction Occurring on Thoriated Cathodes", Cryogenic Lab. Ohio State U. Research Foundation, Columbus. Tech. Rept. No. 12 (Rept. No. TR 280-12)(Contr. N6ori-17, T.O.4). 10 p.

132. National Bureau of Standards, "Quarterly Progress Report for Jan., Feb., and Mar. 1954", U. S. AEC Publ. NBS-D-128. 54 p.

133. Brady, J. G., "Apparatus for the Measurement of the Thermal Conductivity of Refractory Materials at Elevated Temperatures", J. Can. Ceram. Soc. Vol. 23. pp. 19-30. (Canada)

134. Hoch, Michael, Nakata, Masuru, and Johnston, Herrick L., "Vapor Pressures of Inorganic Substances. XII. Zirconium Dioxide", J. Am. Chem. Soc. Vol. 76. pp. 2651-2.

135. Orr, Raymond, L., "High Temperature Heat Contents of Manganese Sesquioxide and Vanadium Monoxide", J. Am. Chem. Soc. Vol. 76. pp. 857-8.

136. Dworkin, A. S., Sasmor, D. J. and Van Artsdalen, E. R., "The Thermodynamics of Boron Nitride: Low-Temperature Heat Capacity and Entropy; Heats of Combustion and Formation", J. Chem. Phys. Vol. 22. pp. 837-42.

137. Kingery, W. D. and Norton, F. H., "The Measurement of Thermal Conductivity of Refractory Materials", U. S. AEC Publ. NYO-6444 Contr. AT-(30-1)-960. 16 p.

138. Heldt, Kurt and Haase, Gunter, "Electric Resistance of Pure, Vacuum-Sintered Aluminum Oxide", Z. Angew. Phys. Vol. 6. pp. 157-60. (Germany)

139. Denton, E. P., Rawson, H. and Stanworth, J. E., "Vanadate Glasses", Nature. Vol. 173. pp. 1030-2. (England)

140. Dale, A. E., Pegg, E. F. and Stanworth, J. E., "Glasses in the Systems TeO$_2$ - MoO$_3$ and TeO$_2$ - WO$_3$", Research Correspondence Suppl. to Research (London). Vol. 7. pp. S38-9 (England)

141. Danforth, W. E., "Research on Electrical Conduction In, and Thermionic Emission from, Thorium Oxide and Similar Compounds", Bartol Research Foundation, Franklin Inst., Swarthmore, Pa. (Contr. Nonr-62800) Final Rept. 59 p.

142. Norton, F. H. and Kingery, W. D. "The Measurements of Thermal Conductivity of Refractory Materials", U. S. AEC Publ. NYO-6445. Contr. AT(30-1)-960. 8 p.

143. Gruen, Dieter, M., "Absorption Spectra and Electrical Conductivities of UO$_2$ -ThO$_2$ Solid Solutions", J. Am. Chem. Soc. Vol. 76. pp. 2117-20.

144. Norton, F. H., Kingery, W. D. et al., "The Measurement of Thermal Conductivity of Refractory Materials", U. S. AEC Publ. NYO-6442. Contr. AT(30-1)-960. 8 p.

145. National Bur. of Standards, "Ceramic Coatings (Effect of Composition and Temperature on Resistivity)", NBS Rept. No. 2305. Prog. Rept. No. 7. AD 29 990. 17 p.

146. Eichelberger, Robert L., "Lime, Bonded and Stabilized with Titanium Oxide as a Refractory for Special Applications", U. S. AEC Publ. NP-5432. Final Report 2nd Ann. Rept. Prog. Rept. No. 8. 25 p.

147. Brown Jr., Frank H., and Duwez, Pol., "The Zirconia-Titania System", J. Am. Ceram. Soc. Vol. 37. pp. 129-31.

148. Handwerk, J. H. and McVay, T. N., "Thermal Expansion of Some Glasses in the System of Li$_2$ O-B$_2$ O$_3$ -SiO$_2$", Contr. AT(40-1)-1080. U. S. AEC Publ. ORO-134. AD 54 478. 22 p.

149. Norton, F. H., Kingery, W. D. et al., "The Measurement of Thermal Conductivity of Refractory Materials", Qrtly. Prog. Rept. U. S. AEC Publ. NYO-6441. (Contr. AT(30-1)960). AD 27 184. 7 p.

150. Hartman, H. and Brand, H., "Determination of the Average Heat of Some Technically Important Glass: (Part II)", Glastech. Ber. Vol. 27(1). pp. 12-15. (Germany)

151. Gunzel Jr., Fred H. and Lambertson, W. A., "Urania Bodies: Fired Density vs. Particle Size", U.S. AEC Publ. AML-5094. Contr. W31-109-Eng-38. 14 p.

1. Baldwin, G. J., Shilts, J. L., and Coomes, E. A., "Temperature Scale for Molybdenum", Notre Dame U., Ind., (Contract Nonr-162300). 18 p.

2. Oelsen, Willy, Rieskamp, Karl Heinz, and Oelsen, Olaf, "Thermodynamic Analysis. II. The Heat-Capacity Curve of a Material from a Single Calorimetric Test", Arch. Eisenhüttenw. Vol. 26. pp. 253-66. (Germany)

3. McCarthy, Kathryn A. and Ballard, Stanley S., "Thermal Conductivity of Germanium at Ambient Temperatures", Phys. Rev. Vol. 99. p. 1104.

4. White, Guy K. and Woods, S. B., "Thermal and Electrical Conductivities of Solids at Low Temperatures", Can. J. Phys. Vol. 33. pp. 58-73. (Canada)

5. Sawyer, Raymond B., "The Investigation of Thermal and Electrical Properties of Metals at High Temperatures", Inst. of Research, Lehigh U., Bethlehem, Pa. 38 p.

6. Moss, Marvin, "Apparatus for Measuring the Thermal Conductivity of Metals in Vacuum at High Temperatures", Rev. Sci. Instr. Vol. 26. pp. 276-80.

7. Domenicali, C. A. and Otter, F. A., "Thermoelectrical Resistivity of Dilute Alloys of Silicon in Copper, Nickel, and Iron", J. Appl. Phys. Vol. 26. pp. 377-80.

8. Eriksen, V. O. and Halg, W., "Thermal Conductivity and Electrical Resistivity of Uranium", J. Nuclear Energy. Vol. 1. pp. 232-3.

9. Weeks, James L., "Thermal Conductivity of Uranium and Several Uranium Alloys", J. Metals (AIME Trans. 203). Vol. 7, p. 192.

10. Buessem, W. R. and Bush, E. A., "Thermal Fracture of Ceramic Materials under Quasi-static Thermal Stresses (Ring Test)", J. Am. Ceram. Soc. Vol. 38. pp. 27-32.

11. Searcy, Alan, W. and Freeman, Robert D., "Measurement of the Molecular Weights of Vapors at High Temperature. II. The Vapor Pressure of Germanium and the Molecular Weight of Germanium Vapor", J. Chem. Phys. Vol. 23. pp. 88-90.

12. Rasor, Ned S., "Low Temperature Thermal and Electrical Conductivity and Thermoelectric Power of Graphite", Contr. AT-11-GEN-8, (NAA-SR-1061). 23 p. AD-50 086.

13. Hugon, Lionel and Jaffray, Jean, "The Thermal Conductivity of Nickel above and below the Curie Point", Ann. Phys. Vol. 12. pp. 377-85. (French)

14. Strittmater, Richard C. and Danielson, Gordon C., "Measurements of Specific Heats by a Pulse Method", AD 96968 ISC-666 (Contract W-7405-eng-82) (OTS) Ames Lab., Ames, Iowa. 27 p.

15. Rosenfield, A. R. and Averbach, B. E., "The Effect of Stress on the Expansion Coefficient", Mass. Inst. of Tech., Cambridge (Tech. Rept. No. 5) (Contract N5ori-07824). 11 p. AD-84 886.

16. Douglas, T. B. and Dever, J. L., "Enthalpy and Specific Heat of Four Corrision-resistant Alloys (80:20 Nickel, Chromium, Stainless Steel and Monel) at High Temperatures", J. Research Nat. Bur. Stand. Vol. 54 (I). pp. 15-19.

17. King, B. W. and Suber, L. L., "Some Properties of the Oxides of Vanadium and Their Compounds", J. Am. Ceramic Soc. Vol. 38. pp. 306-13.

18. Sims, Chester T., Craighead, Charles M., and Jaffee, Robert I., "Physical and Mechanical Properties of Rhenium", J. Metals (AIME Trans 203). Vol. 7. pp. 168-78.

19. Shevlin, Thomas S. and Hauck, Charles A., "Fundamental Study and Equipment for Sintering and Testing of Cermet Bodies. VII. Fabrication, Testing, and Properties of 34 Al_2O_3 66 Cr-Mo Cermets", J. Am. Ceram. Soc. Vol. 38 (12). pp. 450-54.

20. Nadler, M. R. and Fitzsimmons, E. S., "Preparation and Properties of Calcium Zirconate", J. Am. Ceram. Soc. Vol. 38. pp. 214-217.

21. Zwetsch, A., "Thermal Expansion of Sericite", Ber. Deut. Keram. Ges. Vol. 32 (8). pp. 236-38. (Germany)

22. New Jersey Ceramic Research Station, Rutgers, U., New Brunswick," Improved Ceramics", Progress Rept. No. 2., (Contract DA 36-039-sc-64566). 88 p. AD-74 092.

23. Saller, H. A. and Rough, F. A., "The Properties of High-uranium Alloys Containing Zirconium or Chromium", Contract W-7405-end-92. 31 p.

24. Sims, C. T., Gaines, G. B., et al., "Investigations of Rhenium", Quarterly Progress Rept. No. 12., (Contract AF 33(616)232). AD 68 891. 11 p.

25. Norton, F. H. and Kingery, W. D., "The Measurements of Thermal Conductivity of Refractory Materials", NYO-6449, Quarterly Progress Report (Contract AT(30-1)-960). 16 p.

26. Bischoff, Friedrich, "Production and Examination of Some Low Melting Glasses with High Dielectric Constant", Glastech. Ber. Vol. 28 (3). pp. 98-100. (Germany)

27. Avgustink, A. and Vasil'ev, E.I., "Thermal Expansion of Certain Lithium Aluminum Silicates", Zhur. Priklad. Khim. Vol. 28 (9). pp. 939-943. (U.S.S.R.)

28. Fraser, D.B., Hallet, A.C. Hollis, "Total Contractions of Some Metals on Cooling from Room Temperature to 4°K", Congr. Intern. Froid, 9ᵉ, Paris, 1955, Compt. rend. trav. comm. I et II. Vol. 9. pp. 1064-6. (France)

29. Hirano, Kenichi, Maniwa, Hideyo, and Takagi, Yutaka, "Specific-heat Measurements on Quench-annealed Aluminum, Copper and α-phase Alloys of Copper", J. Phys. Soc. Vol. 10. pp. 909-10.

30. Bridgman, P.W., "Miscellaneous Effects of Pressure on Miscellaneous Substances", Proc. Am. Acad. Sci. Vol. 84. pp. 111-29.

31. Stull, Daniel R. and McDonald, Richard A., "The Enthalpy and Heat Capacity of Magnesium and of Type 430 Stainless Steel from 700 to 1100°K", J. Am. Chem. Soc. Vol. 77. p. 5293.

32. Clusius, Klaus and Losa, Celso Gutierrez, "Low Temperature Research. XIV. Atomic and Electronic Heats of Rhodium and Iridium between 10° and 273°K", Z. Naturforsch. Vol. 10a. p. 545. (Switzerland)

33. Skochdopole, R.E., Griffel, Maurice and Spedding, F.H., "Heat Capacity of Erbium from 15° to 320°K", J. Chem. Phys. Vol. 23. pp. 2258-63.

34. Krauss, Friedrich and Warncke, Heinz, "Specific Heat of Nickel between 180° and 1160°", Z. Metallkunde. Vol. 46. pp. 61-9. (Germany)

35. DeSorbo, Warren, "Calorimetric Investigation of a Gold-Nickel Alloy. I. Low-Temperature Heat Capacity", Acta Met. Vol. 3, 11. pp. 227-31.

36. Knudsen, F.P., Moreland, R.E., and Geller, R.F., "Physical Characteristics of Titanium Carbide Type Cermets at Elevated Temperatures", J. Am. Ceram. Soc. Vol. 38. pp. 312-23.

37. Polmear, I.J. and Hardy, H.K., "Specific Heat Measurements on Aluminum-4% Copper and Aluminum-4% Copper-Tin Alloys", J. Inst. Metals (Paper No. 1610). Vol. 83. pp. 393-4. (England)

38. Tomlinson, J.R., Domash, L., Hay, R.G., and Montgomery, C.W., "The High Temperature Heat Content of Nickel Oxide", J. Am. Chem. Soc. Vol. 77. pp. 909-10.

39. Skogen, Haven, S., "New Type of Calorimeter for the Measurement of True Heat Capacity of Ceramic Materials", Univ. Microfilms (Ann Arbor, Mich.), Publ. No. 14058. 147 p.

40. Wood, J.E., ed., "Investigation of Alloys of Magnesium and Their Properties, Part 2. Physical Properties of Mg Base Alloys", Metallic Materials: Improved Magnesium Alloys, Contract AF-33(616)2377, WADC TR 55-160, Pt. 2, Final Report. AD 90 584. 27 p.

41. Hidnert, Peter and Kirby, Richard, K., "Thermal Expansion and Phase Transformation of Low-Expanding Cobalt-Iron-Chromium Alloys", J. Research Natl. Bur. Stand. Vol. 55. pp. 29-37.

42. King, E.G., "Low Temperature Heat Capacities and Entropies at 298.16°K of Some Titanates of Aluminum, Calcium, Lithium and Zinc", J. Am. Chem. Soc. Vol. 77. pp. 2150-2.

43. Prod'homme, Micheline, "Temperature Dependence of the Specific Heat of Glasses", Compt. rend. Vol. 240. pp. 180-1. (France)

44. King, E.G., "Heat Capacities at Low Temperatures, and Entropies at 298.16°K of Crystalline Calcium and Magnesium Aluminates", J. Phys. Chem. Vol. 59. pp. 218-19.

45. Hirano, Kenichi, "Specific Heat Versus Temperature Curves of Aged Copper-Beryllium Alloys", J. Phys. Soc. Japan. Vol. 10 (8). pp. 721-2. (Japan)

46. Anonymous, "'Recidal': Properties of a New Free-Cutting High-strength Light Alloy", Allumino. Vol. 20 (5). pp. 471-88. (Italy)

47. Kingery, W.D. and Norton, F.H., "The Measurement of Thermal Conductivity of Refractory Materials", NYO-6451 Quarterly Prog. Rept. (Contr. AR (30-1)-960). AD 80 699. 16 p.

48. Hall, Tracy H., "The Melting Point of Germanium as a Function of Pressure to 180,000 Atmospheres", J. Phys. Chem. Vol. 59. pp. 1144-6.

49. Wang, C.C., "Investigation of Germanium-silicon Alloys", Sylvania Electric Products, Inc., Woburn, Mass. (Contract NObsr-63180) Final Tech. Rept. 41 p. AD-58 414.

50. Hassion, F.X., Thurmond, C.D., and Trumbore, F.A., "Melting Point of Germanium", J. Phys. Chem. Vol. 59. pp. 1076-8.

51. Petersen, David, Lyon, Ward, and Keller, W.H., "Casting of Cerium and Properties of the Cast Metal", U.S. Atomic Energy Comm., TID 5212. pp. 37-40.

52. Herrmann, K.W., Daane, A.H., and Spedding, F.H., "Physical-metallurgical Properties of Scandium, Yttrium, and the Rare Earth Metals", U. S. Atomic Energy Comm. ISC - 702. 92 p.

53. Kingery, W.D. and Norton, F.H., "The Measurement of Thermal Conductivity of Refractory Materials", NYO-6450, Quarterly Prog. Rept. (Contract AT(30-1)960). AD 73-173. 16 p.

54. Boegli, J.S. and Deissler, R.G., "Measured Effective Thermal Conductivity of Uranium Oxide Powder in Various Gases and Gas Mixtures", NACA RM E54L10. 20 p.

55. Blumenthal, Bernhard, "Melting of High-purity Uranium", J. Metals 7, AIME Trans. 203. Vol. 7 and 203. pp. 1199-1205.

56. Mokhov, V.M., Agladze, R.I., and Topchiashvili, L.I., "Thermal Expansion of Alloys of Manganese with Copper and Nickel", Fiz. Metal. I Metalloved, Akad. Nauk. SSR., Ural Filial. Vol. 1. pp. 450-4. (USSR)

57. Kingery, W.D. and Norton, F.H., "The Measurement of Thermal Conductivity of Refractory Materials", NYO-6477 Qrtly Prog. Rept. (Contr. AT(30-1) 960). AD 55 595. 14 p.

58. Mauer, F.A. and Bolz, L.H. (NBS Wash. D.C.) "Measurement of Thermal Expansion of Cermet Components of High Temperature: X-ray Diffraction", (Proj. title: Ceramic and Cermet Mat'ls) Summ. Rept. for Feb. 14, '54-Sept. 14, '55. WADC-TR 55-473 (Contr. AF33(616)53-12). AD 95 329. 63 p.

59. Sims, Chester T., Craighead, Charles M., and Jaffee, Robert I., "Physical and Mechanical Properties of Rhenium", Trans. Amer. Inst. Min. Met. Eng. (in J. Metals, 1955, 7). Vol. 203 (1). pp. 168-79. (England)

60. Kornev, Yu. V. and Golubkin, V.N., "Determination of Vapor Pressure of Solid Cobalt and Iron", Fiz. Metal. i Metalloved. Vol. 1. pp. 286-97. (USSR)

61. Hoch, Michael, "The Heat of Sublimation of Carbon", J. Phys. Chem. Vol. 59. pp. 97-9.

62. Chupka, Wm. A. and Inghram, Mark, G., "Direct Determination of the Heat of Sublimation of Carbon with the Mass Spectrometer", J. Phys. Chem. Vol. 59. pp. 100-4.

63. Assayag, P., "The Thermodynamics of Alloys of Copper and Platinum", Ann. Chim. Vol. 12. pp. 637-65. (France)

64. Groves, W.O., Hoch, M., and Johnston, H.L., "Vapor-solid Equilibria in the Titanium-Oxygen System", J. Phys. Chem. Vol. 59. pp. 127-31.

65. Herasymenko, P., "Vapor Pressure of Cadmium over Alpha Ag-Cd Alloys and Alpha and Beta Au-Cd Alloys", Final Report (Contract DA 30-069-ORD-1004, Proj. No. TB2-001. AD 62 260. 48 p.

66. DeSorbo, W., "Low Temperature Heat Capacity of Ceylon Graphite", J. Am. Chem. Soc. Vol. 77. pp. 4713-15.

67. Fischer, H.C., "Calcination of Calcite: I. Effect of Heating Rate and Temperature on Bulk Density of Calcium Oxide", Amer. Ceramic Soc. J. Vol. 38. pp. 245-251.

68. Neimark, B.E., "Experimental Determination of Some Physical Properties of Alloyed Steels", Teploenergetika. Vol. 2(3) pp. 3-10. (USSR)

69. Taylor, K.M., "Hot-pressed Boron Nitride", Ind. Eng. Chem. Vol. 47. pp. 2506-9.

70. Brown, A.R.G., "Preparation and Properties of High Temperature Pyrolytic Carbon", Rept. No. Met. 87 (Royal Aircraft Estab., Gt. Brit.) AD 79 083. 59 p. (England)

71. Rodigina, E.N., Gomel'skii, K.Z., "The Heat Content of α-aluminum Oxide (Corundum) Modification at High Temperature", Zhur. Fiz. Khim. Vol. 29. pp. 1105-12. (Russia)

72. DeVries, R.C. and Roy, R., "Phase Equilibria in the System $BaTiO_3$-$CaTiO_3$", J. Am. Ceram. Soc. Vol. 38. pp. 142-145.

73. Rase, D.E. and Roy, Rustum, "Phase Equilibria in the System BaO-TiO_2", J. Am. Ceram. Soc. Vol. 38 (2). pp. 102-13.

74. Trzebiatowski, Wlodzimierz and Drys, Miroslawa, "The System Strontium Oxide-Titanium Dioxide", Roczniki Chem. Vol. 29. pp. 964-5. (Poland)

75. Kingery, W.D., "Thermal Conductivity, XII. Temperature Dependence of Conductivity for Single-phase Ceramics", J. Am. Ceram. Soc. Vol. 38. pp. 251-5.

76. Binder, Ira and Moskowitz, David, "Cemented Borides", American Electro Metal Corporation, Yonkers, N.Y., Summary Prog. Rept. (Contr. CT N6 onr-256/1). AD 71 936. 133 p.

77. Carniglia, Stephen C. and Cunningham, B.B., "Vapor Pressures of Americium Trifluoride and Plutonium Trifluoride, Heats and Free Energies of Sublimation", J. Am. Chem. Soc. Vol. 77. pp. 1451-3.

78. Trostel Jr., Louis J., "Development and Properties of a Ceramic-fiber Base Cermet", <u>Univ. Microfilms (Ann Arbor, Mich.)</u> 106 p.

79. Markovskii, L. Ya., et al. "Structure and Properties of Beryllium Borides", <u>Zhur. Obshchei Khim.</u> Vol. 25. pp. 1045-52. (USSR)

80. Vasenin, F. I., "Thermoelectric Properties of Antimony-Tellurium Alloys", <u>Zhur. Tekh. Fiz.</u> Vol. 25. pp. 1190-7. (USSR)

81. Kuz'menko, P.P., "Some Characteristics of Alloys of the Iron-group Metals", <u>Nauk. Zapiski. Kiiv. Derzhav. Univ. in. T.G. Shevchenka 14</u>, No. 8, Zbirnik. Fiz. Fak. No.7. pp. 91-104. (USSR)

82. Zimmermann, F.J., "Total Emissivities and Absorptivities of Some Commercial Surfaces at Room and Liquid-nitrogen Temperature", <u>J. App. Phys.</u> Vol. 26. pp. 1483-8.

83. O'Brien, F.R. and Oglesby Jr., S., "Investigation of Thermal Properties of Plastic Laminates, Cores, and Sandwich Panels", WADC Tech. Rept. No. 54-306. Pt. 2. Contr. AF33(616)2045. AD 91 221. 69 p.

84. O'Brien, F.R. and Oglesby Jr., Sabert, "Investigation of Thermal Properties of Plastic Laminates", WADC Tech. Rept. No. 54-306, Pt. 1. Contr. AF33(616)2045. AD 81 159. 133 p.

85. Nopco Chemical Co., Harrison, N.J., "Investigation of Foam-in-Place Plastics for Filling Voids between Walls of Dual Wall Transit Cases", Rept. No. RADC TN-55-261. Contr. AF 30(602)1238. 21 p.

86. Pattison, J.R., "The Total Emissivity of Some Refractory Materials above 900°C", <u>Trans. Brit. Ceram. Soc.</u> Vol. 54. pp. 698-705. (England)

87. Dauphinee, T.M. and Mooser, E., "Apparatus for Measuring Resistivity and Hall Coefficient of Semi-Conductors", <u>Rev. Sci. Instruments.</u> Vol. 26. pp. 660-4.

88. Levitas, Alfred, "Electrical Properties of Germanium-Silicon Alloys", <u>Phys. Rev.</u> Vol. 99. pp. 1810-14.

89. Darnell, F.J. and Friedberg, S.A., "Some Electrical Properties of Germanium at Low Temperatures", Carnegie Inst. of Tech., Pittsburgh, Pa. Contract Nonr-76005. Tech. Rept. No. 1. 145 p.

90. Raytheon Mfg. Co., "Study of Semi-Conductor Materials and Devices", Raytheon Mfg. Co., Waltham, Mass. Quarterly Interim Tech. Rept. No. 13. (Contract NObsr-57323). 45 p.

91. Whitsett, C.R., Danielson, G.C., "Electrical Properties of Magnesium Silicide and Magnesium", Germanide U.S. AEC Publ. ISC-714. 84 p.

92. Boltaks, B.I., Konorov, P.P. and Matveev, O.A., "Electrical Properties of Cadmium Telluride", <u>Zhur. Tekh. Fiz.</u> Vol. 25. pp. 2329-35. (USSR)

93. Cunningham, B.B., "Thermodynamics of the Heavy Elements", <u>Proc. Intern. Conf. Peaceful Uses Atomic Energy, Geneva.</u> Vol. 7. pp. 225-30.

94. Konobeeyskii, S.T., "Phase Diagrams of Some Plutonium Systems", <u>Conf. Acad. Sci. USSR Peaceful Uses Atomic Energy, Session Div. Chem. Sci.</u> pp. 207-14. (Russia)

95. Snyder, T.M. and Kamm, R.L., "Some Physical Constants Important in the Design of an Atomic Power Plant", U.S. AEC Publ. C-192. (Contr. W-7401-Eng-37 (A-230)). 56 p.

96. Holland, L. and Williams, B.J., "The Effect of Aluminum Purity on the Reflectivity of Evaporated Front-Surface Mirrors", <u>J. Sci. Inst.</u> Vol. 32. p. 287

97. Powell, L.S. "The Vapor Pressure of Polonium", <u>J. Am. Chem. Soc.</u> Vol. 77. p. 3211.

98. Yoshinaga, Hiroshi, "Reflectivity of Several Crystals in the Far Infrared Region Between 20 and 200 Microns", <u>Phys. Rev.</u> Vol. 100. pp. 753-4.

99. Jette, E.R., "Some Physical Properties of Plutonium Metal", J. Chem. Physics. Vol. 23. pp. 365-8.

100. Kemp, W.R.G., Klemens, P.G. et al., "The Thermal and Electrical Conductivity of Palladium at Low Temperatures", <u>Phil. Mag. Commonwealth Sci. Ind. Res. Organization, Sydney.</u> Vol. 46. pp. 811-14.

101. Petersen, V.C. and Huber, R.W., "The Titanium-Germanium System from 0 to 30 Per Cent Germanium", <u>U.S. Bur. of Mines Publ. BM-RI-5365.</u> 23 p.

102. Mauer, Floyd, A. and Bolz, Leonard H., "Measurement of Thermal Expansion of Cermet Components of High Temperature X-Ray Diffraction", <u>WADC Tech. Rept. No. 55-473.</u> AD 95 329. 57 p.

103. Oelsen, W., Oelsen, O. and Thiel, D., "Precision Measurements of the Heat of Fusion (and Transformation) of Some Metals", <u>Z. Metallkunde.</u> Vol. 46. pp. 555-60.

104. Powell, R. W. and Tye, R. P., "Thermal-Conductivity Measurements Down to -190°: Iridium and Rhodium", Congr. Intern Froid, 9^e, Paris, 1955, Compt. rend. trav. comm. Vol. I et II. pp. 2083-7. (France)

105. Rogers, B. A. and Atkins, D. F., "The Zirconium-Columbium Diagram", J. Metals. Vol. 7. pp. 1034-41.

106. Deem, H. W. and Winn, R. A., "The Electrical Resistance of Thorium through the Allotropic Transition", U. S. AEC Publ. BMI 1052. Contr. W7405-Eng-92. AD 79 192. 8 p.

107. Rosenberg, H. M., "The Thermal Conductivity of Metals at Low Temperatures", Phil. Trans. Roy. Soc. (London). Vol. A247. pp. 441-497. (England)

108. Mauer, Floyd, A. and Bolz, Leonard H., "Thermal Expansion of Cermet Components by High Temperature X-Ray Diffraction", NBS Rept. 4685. AD 96 015. 11 p.

109. Matuyama, E., "A High-Temperature X-Ray Diffraction Powder Camera", J. Sci. Instr. Vol. 32. pp. 229-31.

110. Lehr, P. and Langeron, J. P., "Expansion Behavior of Single Crystals of Uranium", Compt. rend. Vol. 241. pp. 1130-3. (France)

111. Bostrom, W. A., Burkart, M. W. and Halteman, E. K., et al. "Development and Properties of Uranium-Base Alloys Corrosion Resistant in High Temperature Water. Part I. Alloys without Protective Cladding", U. S. AEC Publ. WAPD 127. p. 164.

112. Dayton, R. W. and Tipton Jr., C. R., "Progress Relating to Civilian Applications during Nov., 1955", U. S. AEC Publ. BMI 1057 (Del.) 70 p.

113. Sherwood, E. M. et al., "The Vapor Pressure of Rhenium", J. Electrochem. Soc. Vol. 102. pp. 650-4.

114. Horn, F. H., "Densitometric and Electrical Investigation of Boron (Impurities) in Silicon", Phys. Rev. Vol. 97. pp. 1521-25.

115. Sawyer, Raymond, B., "The Investigation of Thermal and Electrical Properties of Metals at High Temperature", U. S. AEC Publ. NP 5866. 32 p.

116. Chiba, Shoko, "Magnetic Properties and Phase Diagram of the Iron-Tellurium System", J. Phys. Soc. Japan. Vol. 10. pp. 837-42. (Japan)

117. Waldhauser, I., "Investigations on Brazing Materials Belonging to the Copper-Silver System", Kohaszati Lapok. Vol. 10. pp. 176-80. (Hungary)

118. Willmore, T. A. and Bennett, D. G., "High Alloy Content Cermets Containing Titanium Diboride as the Minor Constituent", Final Rept. for March 27, 1954, to September 1, 1955, Proj. 3066, Contr. AF33(616) 2307. (AD 99 655). WADC TR 56-137. 19 p.

119. Brink, C. and Shoemaker, D. P., "A Variation in the Sigma-Phase Structure, The Crystal Structure of the P Phase, Molybdenum-Nickel-Chromium", Acta Cryst. Vol. 8. pp. 734-5.

120. Powell, R. L. and Coffin, D. O., "Low-Temperature Thermal Conductivity of a Free-Machining Copper", Rev. Sci. Instruments. Vol. 26. p. 516.

121. Masumoto, Hakaru; Saito, Hideo; and Takahashi, Minoru, "Anomaly of Specific Heat in Alpha Phase Alloys of Copper and Aluminum", Sci. Repts. Research Insts. Tohoku Univ. Ser. A 7. pp. 465-8. (Japan)

122. Koster, W. and Knodler, A., "About the Complete Hardening of Al-Ag Alloys. X. Temperature Dependence of the Electrical Resistance", Z. Metallkunde. Vol. 46. pp. 632-9. (Germany)

123. Masumoto, Hakaru; Saito, Hideo; and Sagai, Yutaka, "Effect of Addition of Nickel on the Thermal Expansion, Rigidity Modulus, and Its Temperature Coefficient of the Alloys of Cobalt, Iron, and Chromium, Especially of Co-Elinvar. II. Additions of 30% and 40% Nickel", Sci. Rept. Research Insts. Tohoku Univ. Ser. A7. pp. 533-40. (Japan)

124. Kornilov, I. I. and Mikleev, V. S., "A New Kurnakov Compound Fe_3V in the Iron-Vanadium System", Doklady Akad. Nauk. SSSR. Vol. 104. pp. 88-90. (USSR)

125. Oelsen, Willy; Rieskamp, Karl-Heinz; and Oelsen, Olaf, "Thermodynamic Analysis. II. The Heat-Capacity Curve of a Material from a Single Calorimetric Test", Arch.Eisenhüttenw. Vol. 26. pp. 253-66. (Germany)

126. Hale, J. C. and Douglas, E. A., "The Investigation Directed Toward the Development of Ceramics with Coatings with High Reflectivities and Emissivities for Use in Aircraft Power Plants", Quarterly Progress Rept. No. 3-4. Contr. AF33(616)2376. AD 52 248.

127. Kawasaki, M., Yamaji, K. and Izumi, O., "Equilibrium of Solid Phases in Cu-Mn Binary System", Science Repts. Res. Insts. Tohoku Univ. Ser. A.7. pp. 443-54. (Japan)

128. Geach, G. A. and Jones, F. O., "Interactions in Mixtures of Hard Materials at Very High Temperatures", Plansee Proc. pp. 80-91. (Austria)

129. Grinthal, R. D., "Evaluation of New High Temperature Materials", Prog. Rept. No. 2 (Contr. No. AF33(616) 3198. AD 89 650.

130. Raeuchle, R. F. and Von Batchelder, F. W., "The Structure of MoBe$_{12}$", Acta Cryst. Vol. 8. pp. 691-4.

131. Runnalls, O.J.C. and Boucher, R.R., "The Crystal Structure of β-PuSi$_2$", Acta Cryst. Vol. 8, No. 9. p. 592.

132. Whitsett, C. R. and Danielson, G. C., "Electrical Properties of Magnesium Silicide and Magnesium Germanide", U. S. AEC Publ. ISC-714. 84 p.

133. Winkler, U., "Electric Properties of the Intermetallic Compounds Mg$_2$ Si, Mg$_2$ Ge, Mg$_2$ Sn and Mg$_2$ Pb", Helv. Phys. Acta. Vol. 28. pp. 633-66. (Switzerland)

134. Messer, Chas. E., Damon, Edwin B., and Maybury, P. C., "Solid-Liquid Equilibrium in the Lithium-Lithium Hydride System. I. Apparatus: Melting and Freezing Points of Li Hydride and Li Hydride-Rich Mixtures", U. S. AEC Publ. NYO-3958. 16 p.

135. Samsonov, G. V. and Petrash, E. V., "Various Physicochemical Properties of Alloys of Titanium Boride and Nitride", Metalloved, i Obrabotka Metallov. Vol. No. 4. pp. 19-24. (USSR)

136. Blunt, R. F., Frederikse, H.P.R. and Hosler, W. R., "Electrical and Optical Properties of Intermetallic Compounds.IV. Magnesium Stannide", Phys. Rev. Vol. 100. pp. 663-6.

137. Manowitz, R., "Thermal Conductivities of Pressed Powders", U. S. AEC Publ. MONT-164. Contr. W-35-058-Eng-71. 15 p.

138. Krikorian, Oscar Harold, "High-Temperature Studies: I. Reactions of the Refractory Silicides with Carbon and with Nitrogen. II. Thermodynamic Properties of the Carbides. III. Heat of Formation of the $3\pi_u$ State of C$_2$ from Graphite", U. S. AEC Publ. UCRL-2888. Contr. W-7405-Eng-48. AD 63 120. 136 p.

139. Nasledov, D. N. and Khalilov, A. Yu.tr. by Hope, E. R., "The Electrical Properties of InSb", (Directorate of Scientific Information Service (Canada)). (Trans. No. T 215 R of Zhur. Tech. Fiz. 26:6-14, 1955). AD 104 474. 9 p. (USSR)

140. Marx, Paul, Smith, C. W. et al., "Specific Heat of Synthetic High Polymers. IV. Polycaprolactam", J. Phys. Chem. Vol. 59. pp. 1015-19.

141. Tokuda, Taneki, "The Rate of the Sluggish Inversion of Silica Stone. Kinetics of the Polymorphous Transition of Silica", Bull. Chem. Soc. Japan. Vol. 28. pp. 435-42. (Japan)

142. Budnikov, P. P. and Tresvyatskii, S. G., "Electric Conductivity of Corundum Refractories at Elevated Temperatures", Ogneupory. Vol. 20. pp. 70-1 (USSR)

143. Parikh, N. M. and Simpson, H. E., "Germania Glasses: System Na$_2$ O-CaO-GeO$_2$", J. Am. Ceramic Soc. Vol. 35(4). pp. 99-103.

144. Burdick, M. D. and Parker, H. S., "The Effects of Crystallite Size of the Bulk Density and Strength Properties of Uranium Dioxide Specimens", U. S. AEC Publ. AECU 3189. 33 p.

145. Economos, George, "Magnetic Ceramics. II. Properties of Magnetite and Manganese Ferrite Fired in Various Atmospheres", J. Am. Ceramic. Soc. Vol. 38. pp. 292-97.

146. Reisman, Arnold and Holtzberg, Frederic, "Phase Equilibria in the System K$_2$ CO$_3$ -Nb$_2$ O$_5$ by the Method of Differential Thermal Analysis", J. Am. Chem. Soc. Vol. 77(8). pp. 2115-19.

147. National Bureau of Standards, Wash., D. C., "Quarterly Prog.Rept. to the Atomic Energy Commission for Oct., Nov. and Dec.,1954", U. S. AEC Publ. AECD-3903. 104 p.

148. Kolechkova, A. F. and Goncharov, V. V., "Heat Conductivity of Basic Refractories", Ogneupory. Vol. 20. pp. 39-44. (USSR)

149. Lengyel, Bela and Beksay, Zoltan, "Electric Conductivity of Glasses. II. Conductivity of Lithium-Sodium, Sodium-Potassium, and Potassium-Lithium Mixed Glasses", Z. Physik. Chem. (Leipzig). Vol. 204. pp. 157-64. (Germany)

150. Bielanski, A. and Deren, J., "Electrical Conductivity of Sintered MgO-Cr$_2$ O$_3$ Mixtures", Roczniki Chem. Vol. 29. pp. 1145-7. (Poland)

151. Stubblefield, Cedric T., "Thermodynamic Measurements of Rare Earth Dichlorides and Oxides - Micro-calorimeter", Univ. Microfilms (Ann Arbor, Mich.) Publ. No. 12,386. 99 p.

152. Reactor Handbook, U.S. Atomic Energy Commission Publication. McGraw Hill Book Co.

1. Lucks, C. F. and Deem, H.W., "Thermal Conductivities, Heat Capacities, and Linear Thermal Expansion of Five Materials", Battelle Memorial Inst., Columbus, Ohio WADC Tech. Rept. No. 55-496. 65 p.

2. Fieldhouse, I.B., Hedge, J.C., et al., "Measurements of Thermal Properties", Armour Research Foundation, Chicago, Ill. WADC TR 55-495, pt I. (Contract AF 33(616)-2903) 64 p.

3. Rea, Joseph Ambrose, "The Construction of a Furnace Calorimeter and the Evaluation of a Method of Thermal Analysis for Obtaining the Specific Heat of Solids at High Temperatures", Oklahoma A. and M. Coll., Stillwater, Master Thesis. 52 p.

4. Cleary, H.J., "Electrical, Thermoelectric, Hardness, and Corrosion Properties of Vanadium-base Alloys", Nuclear Metals, Inc. (U.S. Atomic Energy Commission) NMI-1161. 34 p.

5. Lambertson, W.A. and Handwerk, J.H., "The Fabrication and Physical Properties of Urania Bodies", Argonne Nat'l Lab., Lemont, Ill. (ANL-5053)(Contract W31-109-eng 38). 48 p.

6. Fieldhouse, I.B., Hedge, J.C., and Waterman, T.E., "Measurements of Thermal Properties", ARF, Chicago WADC Tech. Rept. No. 55-495, pt. 3. Contract AF 33(616) 2903 10 p.

7. Whittemore, Osgood J. and Ault, Neil N., "Thermal Expansion of Various Ceramic Materials to 1500°", J. Am. Ceram. Soc. Vol. 39. pp. 443-4.

8. Mauer, Floyd A. and Bolz, Leonard H., "Thermal Expansion of Cermet Components by High Temperature X-ray Diffraction", Nat'l Bur. Stand., Wash., D.C. (NBS Rept. No. 4884)(Contract No. AF33 (616)56-6). 23 p.

9. DePue, Leland A. and Chapin, E.J., "Electrical Resistance Study of the Effects of Oxygen on the Allotropic Transformation of Titanium", Naval Research Lab. Rept. No. 4638. 23 p.

10. Coble, R. L. and Kingery, W.D., "Effect of Porosity on Physical Properties of Sintered Alumina", J. Am. Ceram. Soc. Vol. 39(11). pp. 377-85.

11. Deardorff, D.K. and Hayes, E.T., "Melting Point Determination of Hafnium, Zirconium, and Titanium", J. Metals. Vol. 8. pp. 509-11.

12. Deegan, G.E., "Thermal and Electrical Properties of Graphite Irradiated at Temperatures from 100 to 425°K", Atomic Energy Commission. NAA-SR-1716. 77 p.

13. Pawlek, Franz and Reichel, Karl, "The Effect of Impurities on the Electrical Conductivity of Copper. I. The Electrical Conductivity of Pure Copper, Its Maximum Value, and Its Variations with Impurities", Z. Metallkunde. Vol. 47. pp. 347-56. (Germany)

14. Kemp, W.R.G., et al., "Thermal and Electrical Conductivities of Iron, Nickel, Titanium, and Zirconium at Low Temperatures", Australian J. Phys. Vol. 9. pp. 180-8. (Australia)

15. Ames, S.L. and McQuillan, A.D., "Effect of Addition Elements on the Electrical Resistivity of α-Titanium", Acta Met. Vol. 4. pp. 619-26.

16. Schindler, A.I., Smith, R.J., and Salkovitz, E.I., "Preliminary Electrical-resistivity Measurements of the Nickel-palladium Alloy System", Phys. and Chem. Solids. Vol. 1. pp. 39-41.

17. Sims, C.T., Craighead, C.M., et al., "Investigations of Rhenium", WADC-TR 54-371, suppl. 1 (Contr. AF 33(616) 232) PB 121653, AD 97301. 86 p.

18. Lang, S.M. and Knudsen, F.P., "Some Physical Properties of High Density Thorium Dioxide", J. Am. Ceram. Soc. Vol. 39 (12). pp. 415-424.

19. Ishikawa, Yoshikazu and Sawada, Shozo, "The Study of Substances Having the Ilmenite Structure", J. Phys. Soc. Japan. Vol. 11. pp. 496-501. (Japan)

20. Cleek, Given W. and Hamilton, Edgar H., "Properties of Barium Titanium Silicate Glasses", J. Research Nat. Bur. Stand. Vol. 57(6). pp. 317-23.

21. Loewen, E.G., "Thermal Properties of Titanium Alloys and Selected Tool Materials", Trans. Am. Soc. Mech. Engrs. Vol. 78. pp. 667-70.

22. Foerster, G.S., Couling, S.L., Baker, H, and Johnson, R., "Investigations of Alloys of Magnesium and Their Properties", WADC Tech. Report 56-88 (Contr. AF33(616) 2337, Task 73514) PB 121 801. AD-110 541. 84 p.

23. Bullock, G., "Thermal Changes in Steels as Shown by Resistivity", J. Iron Steel Inst. Vol. 183. pp. 362-7. (England)

24. Furukawa, G., "Thermal Properties of Al_2O_3 from 0° to 1200°", J. Research Natl. Bur. Stand. Vol. 57. pp. 67-82.

25. Allison, Floyd E., "Temperature Dependence of the Hall Coefficients in Copper Nickel Alloys", Based on a Thesis, Carnegie Inst. Tech., (Contr. Nonr - 760(04) Tech. Rept. No. 2. PB 125 888. 73 p.

26. Allison, F.E., Pugh, Emerson M., "Temperature Dependence of the Hall Coefficients in Some Copper Nickel Alloys", Phys. Rev. Vol. 102. pp. 1281-7.

27. Pattison, J.R. and Lonsdale, T.H., "The Enthalpy of a 0.12% Carbon Steel", J. Iron Steel Inst. (London). Vol. 183. pp. 284-6. (England)

28. Walker, B.E., Grand, J.A., and Miller, R.R., "High-temperature Heat Content and Heat Capacity of Al_2O_3 and $MoSi_2$", J. Phys. Chem. Vol. 60. pp. 231-3.

29. White, David and Swift, Robinson M., "Thermodynamic Properties of Magnesium Diboride and Magnesium Tetraboride", Tech. Rept. No. MCC-1023-TR-193 (Contract Noa (s) - 1023). AD 103 561. 37 p.

30. Kemp, W.R.G., Klemens, P.G., Sreedhar, A.K., and White, G.K., "The Thermal and Electrical Conductivities of Silver-Palladium and Silver-Cadmium Alloys at Low Temperatures", Proc. Roy. Soc. (London). Vol. A233. pp. 480-93. (England)

31. Grigor'ev, A.T., Panteleimonov, L.A., Kuprina, V.V., and Rybakova, L.I., "Investigation of the System Palladium-Copper-Cobalt", Zhur. Neorg. Khim. Vol. 1. pp. 1067-73 (U.S.S.R.)

32. Grigor'ev, A.T., Sokolovskaya, E.M., Budennaya, L.D., Iyutina, I.A., and Maksimova, M.V., "System Palladium-Gold-Cobalt", Zhur. Neorg. Khim. Vol. 1. pp. 1052-63. (USSR)

33. Aliev, N.A., "Application of Wiedmann-Franz Law to Copper-Aluminum Alloys", Trudy Inst. Fiz. i Mat., Akad. Nauk Azerbaidzhan. S.S.R., Ser Fiz. Vol. 8. pp. 101-13. (U.S.S.R.)

34. White, G.K. and Woods, S.B., "Thermal Conductivity of Germanium and Silicon at Low Temperatures", Phys. Rev. Vol. 103. pp. 569-71.

35. Kuprovskii, B.B. and Gel'd, P.V., "Heat Conductivity of Cast Irons", Liteinoe Proizvodstvo. Vol. 9. pp. 16-18. (U.S.S.R.)

36. Gel'd, P.V., Kuprovskii, B.B., and Serebrennikov, N.N., "Temperature Conductivity of Steels at Higher Temperatures", Teploenergetika. Vol. 3(6). pp. 45-51. (U.S.S.R.)

37. National Bureau of Standards, Wash., D.C., "Thermal Conductivity and Heat Capacity Projects", NBS Rept. No. 5761 (Contract AF 33(616)56-21), AD 101 080. 6 p.

38. Oiski, Jiro, , Awano, Mitsuru, , and Mochizuki, Takashi, "New Determination of the Temperature of Gold and Silver Points on the Thermodynamic Temperature Scale", J. Phys. Soc. Japan. Vol. 11. pp. 311-21. (Japan)

39. Gel'd, V., Serebrennikov, N.N., and Sukharev, P.M., "Thermal Expansion of Silicon and Its Alloys with Iron", Fiz. Metal. i Metalloved Akad. Nauk. SSSR Ural Filial. Vol. 2. pp. 244-53. (U.S.S.R.)

40. Ellinger, F.H., "Crystal Structure of Plutonium and the Thermal Expansion Characteristics of δ, δ', and ϵ Plutonium", J. Metals 8, AIME Trans. 206. Vol. 8. pp. 1256-59.

41. Zelikman, A.N., Gorovitz, N.N., and Prosenkova, T.E., "Vapor Pressure of Molybdenum Trioxide at High Temperature", Zhur. Noerg. Khim. Vol. 1. pp. 632-7. (U.S.S.R.)

42. Ackermann, R.J., Gilles, P.W., and Thorn, R.J., "High-temperature Thermodynamic Properties of Uranium Dioxide", J. Chem. Phys. Vol. 25. pp. 1089-97.

43. Ackermann, R.J., Thorn, R.J., and Gilles, P.W., "Vapor Pressure of Thoria", J. Am. Chem. Soc. Vol. 78. p. 1767.

44. Inghram, M.G., Berkowitz, J., and Chupka, W.A., "Mass Spectrometric Study of Vaporization of the Titanium-oxygen System", U. of Chicago Tech. Rept. 3 and 4, (Contract DA-11-022-ORD-1993) OOR-1543. AD 118 881. 27 p.

45. White, D., "The Vaporization of Magnesium Diboride", Rept. No. MCC-TR-222. 8 p.

46. Otter, F.A., "Thermoelectric Power and Electrical Resistivity of Dilute Alloys of Manganese, Palladium and Platinum in Copper, Silver, and Gold", J. Appl. Phys. Vol. 27. pp. 197-200.

47. El-Hifini, M.A. and Chao, B.T., "Measuring the Thermal Diffusivity of Metals at Elevated Temperatures", Trans. Am. Soc. Mech. Engrs. Vol. 78. pp. 813-821.

48. Paladino Jr., A.E., Swarts, E.L., et al., "Measurements of Thermal Diffusivity and Biot's Modulus for Dense Alumina between 1500° and 1800°C by an Unsteady State Method", Tech. Rept. (Contr. Nonr - 150 302) Alfred U., N.Y. (NP 6018). AD 98 567. 26 p.

49. Collins, F.M., "Dimensional Changes During Heat-treatment and Thermal Expansion of Polycrystalline Carbons and Graphite", Proceedings of the 1st and 2nd Conference on Carbon, 1953 - 1955. Waverly Press, Inc., Baltimore, Md. 222 p. pp. 177-87.

50. James, W.J. and Straumanis, M.E., "Lattice Parameter and Coefficient of Thermal Expansion of Thorium", Acta Cryst. Vol. 9. pp. 376-379.

51. Jamieson, C.P. and Mrozowski, S., "Thermal Conductivities of Polycrystalline Carbons and Graphites", Proceedings of the First and Second Conferences on Carbon, 1953, 1955, Waverly Press, Inc., Baltimore. pp. 155-66.

52. Lietz, Joachim, "The Specific Heat of Rutile and Anatase", Hamburger Beitr. Angew. Mineral u. Kristallphys. Vol. 1. pp. 229-238. (Germany)

53. Roinet, Charles, "A New Casting Alloy L'A-Z5G", Rev. Aluminium. Vol. 33(229). pp. 153-61. (France)

54. Campbell, I.E., "High Temperature Technology", John Wiley.

55. Kuczyniski, G.C., Doyama, M., and Fine, M.E., "Transformation in Disordered Gold Copper Alloys", OSR-TN-56-66. Contr. AF-18(600)-1468. AD 85 058. 31 p.

56. Ferro, Riccardo, "The Crystal Structures of Thorium Antimonides", Acta Cryst. Vol. 9. pp. 817-18. (Italy)

57. Smith, A.W. and Rasor, N.S., "Low-temperature Thermal and Electrical Conductivity of Graphite. I. Observed Dependence on Temperature, Type, Neutron Irradiation and Bromination", NAA-SR-1590 (Contr. AT 11-1-Gen-8). AD 106 065. 24 p.

58. Smith, Alan W. and Rasor, Ned S., "Observed Dependence of the Low-temperature Thermal and Electrical Conductivity of Graphite on Temperature, Type, Neutron Irradiation, and Bromination", Phys. Rev. Vol. 104. pp. 885-891.

59. Nauman, V.O., "Reflecting Power of Iron for Ultraviolet Light as a Function of Temperature in the Neighborhood of the A_3 Point", Univ. Microfilms (Ann Arbor, Mich.) Publ. No. 16199. 29 p.

60. Fabre, Denise and Romand, Jacques, "Reflection Measurements in the Far Ultraviolet with Evaporated Films of Tantalum, Tungsten, and Zirconium", Compt. rend. Vol. 242. pp. 893-6. (France)

61. Kandare, Sonja and Fabre, Denise, "Measurement of the Far Ultraviolet Reflectance of Deposits of Silicon Prepared by Vacuum Evaporation", Compt. rend. Vol. 242. pp. 1150-2. (France)

62. Marple, D.T.F., "Spectral Emissivity of Rhenium", J. Opt. Soc. Amer. Vol. 46. pp. 490-4.

63. Grigor'ev, A.T., Sokolovskaya, E.M., Budennaya, L.D., et al., "System Palladium-gold-cobalt", Zhur. Neorg. Khim. Vol. 1. pp. 1052-63. (USSR)

64. Uei, Isao, et al., "Studies on Zirconia Resistors; I. Stabilization of Zirconia and Its Electrical Conductivity", J. Ceram. Assoc. Japan. Vol. 64 (724). pp. 139-43. (Japan)

65. Noguchi, Toshio and Miyazaki, Yoshiki, "Measurement of Thermal Conductivity of Carbon Products at Room Temperature", Tanso (Carbons). Vol. 5. pp. 36-9. (Japan)

66. Betz, H.T., Olson, O.H., et al., "Determination of Emissivity and Reflectivity Data on Aircraft Structural Materials. Part I. Techniques for Measurement of Total Normal Emissivity and Reflectivity with Some Data on Copper and Nickel", WADC TR 56 222, Pt. I (Contr. AF 33(616)-3002, Task 73603). AD 110 485. 43 p.

67. Zhuralev, N.N. and Zhdanov, G.S., "Metallographic and X-Ray Examination of Germanium-rhodium Alloys", Kristallografiya. Vol. 1. pp. 205-8. (USSR)

68. Gronvold, F. and Jacobsen, E., "X-ray and Magnetic Study of Nickel Selenides in the Range NiSe and $NiSe_2$", Acta Chem. Scand. Vol. 10. pp. 1440-54. (Norway)

69. Strauss, S.W., Moore, D.G., Harrison, W.N. and Richards, L.E., "Fundamental Factors Controlling Electrical Resistivity in Vitreous Ternary Lead Silicates", Reprint from: J. Res. Nat'l Bur. Stand. Vol. 56 (3). AD 101 289. pp. 135-142.

70. Rudnitskii, A.A., "The Study of Platinum-Copper Electrical and Thermoelectrical Properties", Izvest, Sektora Fiz.-Khim. Anal., Inst. Obshchei i Neorg. Khim., Nauk. S.S.S.R. Vol. 27. pp. 171-84. (USSR)

71. Mikryukov, V.E., "Thermal and Electric Properties of Copper Alloys", Vestnik Moskov. Univ., Ser. Mat., Mekh., Astron., Fiz. i Khim., Vol. 11 (2). pp. 53-70. (USSR)

72. Lehr, P., "The Dilatometric Behavior of Pure Iron", Compt. rend. Vol. 242. pp. 632-5. (France)

73. Nakhodnova, A.P., "Electrical Conductivity of the Oxides of the Group II Metals", Zhur. Fiz. Khim. Vol. 30. pp. 1469-72. (USSR)

74. Roinet, Charles, "A New Casting Alloy L'A-Z5G", Rev. Aluminum. Vol. 33 (229). pp. 153-61. (France)

75. Hauth, W.E., "Research and Development of High Temperature, Radiation Resistant, Fixed Resistors", Contract AF 33(616) 3633 Scientific Rept. No. 1 on Phase 1. AD 105 545. 20 p.

76. Goldsmid, H.J., "The Thermal Conductivity of Bismuth Telluride", Proc. Phys. Soc. Vol. 69B. pp. 203-9. (England)

77. Trompetti, J., "Determination of the Reflection, Transmission and Absorption Coefficients for Thin Silver Films Deposited on Quartz by Evaporation", J. Phys. Radium. Vol. 17. pp. 124-8. (France)

78. Thewlis, J. and Davey, A. R., "Thermal Expansion of Diamond", Phil. Mag. Vol. (8) 1. pp. 409-14. (England)

79. Moore, H. and McMillan, P. W., "Study of Glasses Consisting of the Oxides of Elements of Low Atomic Weight ", J. Soc. Glass Technol. Vol. 40. pp. 66-161T. (England)

80. Payson, Peter, "Alloy Steel of High Expansion Coefficient", U. S. Patent No. 2,739,057. 3 p.

81. Euler, Joachim, "The Axial Temperature Distribution on the Internal Anode of a Carbon Arc and the Thermal Conductivity of Graphite at High Temperatures", Ann. Physik. Vol. 18. pp. 345-69. (Germany)

82. Dumitrescu, T., Nicolaid, M. and Iliescu, P., "Behavior at High Temperatures of Nodular Cast Irons Alloyed with Silicon", Rev. Met., Acad. Rep. Populaire Roumaine. Vol. 1. pp. 33-53. (Rumania)

83. Johnson, R. G., Hudson, D. E., Caldwell, W. C. et al., "Mass Spectrometric Study of Phase Changes in Aluminum, Praseodymium, and Neodymium", J. Chem. Phys. Vol. 25, pp. 917-25.

84. Ames Lab., "Semi-Annual Summary Research Report in Physics for January through June 1956", U. S. AEC Publ. ISC-758. 37 p.

85. Catterall, J. A., Grogan, J. D. and Pleasance, R. J. (Natl. Physical Lab., Tedington, Middlesex, England). "The System Uranium-Palladium", J. Inst. Metals. Vol. 85. pp. 63-7.

86. Spedding, F. H., Legvold, S., Daane, A. H. and Jennings, L. D. "Some Physical Properties of the Rare Earth Metals", Progr. in Low Temp. Phys. Vol. 2. pp. 368-94.

87. Samsonov, G. V., "Some Physicochemical Properties of Compounds on the Transitional Refractory Metals with Boron, Carbon and Nitrogen, and the Characteristics of Their Binary Alloys", Izvest. Sektora. Fiz. Khim. Anal. Inst. Obshchei Neorg. Khim. Akad. Nauk SSSR. Vol. 27. pp. 97-125. (USSR)

88. Barson, Fred, Legvold, S. and Spedding, F. H., "Thermal Expansion of Rare Earth Metals", U. S. AEC Publ. ISC-831. 71 p.

89. Smith, J. F., Carlson, O. N. and Vest, R. W. "Allotropic Modifications of Calcium", J. Electrochem. Soc. Vol. 103. pp. 409-13.

90. Saller, H. A., Rough, F. A. and Chubb, W., "The Properties of Uranium Containing Minor Additions of Chromium, Silicon, or Titanium", U. S. AEC Publ. BMI-1068. 28 p.

91. Edwards, A. R. and Johnstone, S. T. M., "The Constitutional Diagram of the System Chromium-Beryllium from 0 to 70 atomic Per Cent Beryllium", J. Inst. Metals. Vol. 84 (Pt. 8). pp. 313-17.

92. Hass, G. G., Hunter, W. R. and Tousey, R., "Reflectance of Evaporated Aluminum Films in the Vacuum Ultra-Violet", J. Opt. Soc. Amer. Vol. 46. pp. 1009-12.

93. Yoshida, Susumu, and Tsuya, Yuko, "Temperature Dependance of the Electrical Resistivity of the β-phase of Titanium-Molybdenum Alloys", J. Phys. Soc. Japan. Vol. 11. pp. 1206-7. (Japan)

94. Wessel, E. T., "Evaluation of Mechanical and Physical Properties of Annealed Hafnium", U. S. AEC Publ. AECU 3693. 46 p.

95. Ames, S. I. and McQuillan, A. D., "The Resistivity-Temperature-Concentration Relationships in Beta-Phase Titanium-Hydrogen Alloys", Acta Met. Vol. 4 No. 6. pp. 602-10.

96. Sagel, K., "The System Titanium-Aluminum", Z. Metallkunde. Vol. 47 No. 8.

97. Lefort, Henry, G.; Spriggs, Richard M.; Bennett, Dwight, G., "Research on Elevated Temperature Resistant Ceramic Structural Adhesives", U. S. AEC Publ. WACD Tech. Rept. 55-491 PB 121941.

98. Schofield, T. H., "Some Experiments on the Determination of the Latent Heats of Transition of Titanium and Iron", J. Inst. Metals. Vol. 85. pp. 68-70.

99. Chiotti, P., "Hanford Slug Program Semi-Annual Summary Research Report (for) July-December 1956", 19 p.

100. Griffel, Maurice, Skochdopole, R. E. and Spedding, F. H., "Heat Capacity of Dysprosium from 15 to 300°K", J. Chem. Phys. Vol. 25. pp. 75-9.

101. Riley, W. C. and Woodruff, E. M., "Thermal Expansion of Pile Graphites", U. S. AEC Publ. HW-43 395. Contr. No. W-31-109-Eng-52. 29 p.

102. Rauh, E. G., "Work Function, Ionization Potential, and Emissivity of Uranium", U. S. AEC Publ. ANL 5534 Contr. W-31-109-Eng-38. p. 21.

103. Kanai, Yasuo and Nii, Riro, "Impurity Conduction in Germanium", J. Phys. Soc. Japan. Vol. 11. pp. 83-4 (Japan)

104. Bridge, J. R., Schwartz, C. M., and Vaughan, D. A., "X-Ray Diffraction Determination of the Coefficients of Expansion of Alpha Uranium", J. of Metals. Vol. 8, sec II. pp. 1282-5.

105. Auslander, J. S. and Georgescu, I. I., "Vapor Pressure of Polonium at Room Temperature", Proc. Intern. Conf. Peaceful Uses Atomic Energy, Geneva, 1955. Vol. 7. pp. 389-91. (Switzerland)

106. Kuprovsky, B. B. and Gel'd, P. V., "Isotherms of the Thermal Conductivity of Silicon and Its Alloys with Iron at High Temperatures", Fizika Metallov i Metallovedenie. Vol. 3. pp. 182-3. (USSR)

107. Ward, L., "The Variation with Temperatures of the Spectral Emissivities of Iron, Nickel and Cobalt", Proc. Phys. Soc. Vol. 69, No. 3. pp. 339-43.

108. Heinze, D., "Temperature Dependence of the Reflectivity of Copper, Silver, Gold, Aluminum, and Nickel", Z. Physik. Vol. 144. pp. 455-75. (Germany)

109. Bruch, C. A. and Cashin, W. M., "Metallurgy Report of the Technical Department (for) March, April, May, 1956", U. S. AEC Publ. KAPL-1564 (Del). p. 45.

110. Hedge, J. C. and Fieldhouse, I. B., "Measurement of Thermal Conductivity of Uranium Oxide", Proj. No. GO22--D3. For Westinghouse Elect. Corp. Atom. Power Div. U. S. AEC Publ. AECU-3381. 12 p.

111. Fieldhouse, I. B., Hedge, J. E., et al., "Measurements of Thermal Properties", Armour Research Foundation, WADC Tech. Rept. No. 55-495, pt. 2 (Contr. AF 33(616)2903). 18 p.

112. Munster, A., Sagel, K. and Zwicker, U., "Electrical Conductivity and (Magnetic) Susceptibility of the Titanium-Aluminum System (of Alloys)", Acta Met. No. 5. Vol. 4. pp. 558-60. (Germany)

113. Smith, K. F. and Chiswik, H. H., "High Temperature Strength Zirconium and Titanium Base Alloys for Fuel Element Jacketing", U. S. AEC Publ. ANL 5339. 16 p.

114. Pollock, D. D. and Finch, D. I., "Effects of Alloying Elements on the Electrical Properties of Manganin-type Alloys", Trans. Amer. Inst. Min. Met. Eng. Vol. 206. pp. 203-10.

115. Neubert, T. J., Royal, J. and Van Dyken, A. R., "The Structure and Properties of Artificial and Natural Graphite", U. S. AEC Publ. ANL-5524. AD 90 739.

116. Joffe, A. F., "Heat Transfer in (Intermetallic-Compound) Semi-Conductors", Canad. J. Physics. Vol. 34 (12 A) pp. 1342-53. (Canada)

117. Anon. "Nimonic 100: Data on Latest Alloy of the Series", Metallurgia. Vol. 53. pp. 290-1.

118. Dayton, R. W. and Tipton, C. R., "Progress Relating to Civil Applications during April 1956", U. S. AEC Publ. BMI-1088. 82 p.

119. Boyle, R. F. and Haltemann, E. K., "Calorimetric Determination of Ordering in the U-Mo System", U. S. AEC Publ. WAPD-PWR-PMM-633. 38 p.

120. Argonne Natl. Lab., "Metallurgy Division Quarterly Report for Jan. Feb. and March 1956", U. S. AEC Publ. ANL 5563. 56 p.

121. Powell, R. W. and Tye, R. P., "The Effect of Oil Quenching and Tempering on the Thermal Conductivities and Electrical Resistivities of Three Steels", J. Iron Steel Inst. Vol. 184. pp. 10-17. (England)

122. Glaser, F. W. and Ivanick, W., "Study of the Iron-Silicon Order-Disorder Transformation", Trans. Amer. Inst. Min. Met. Vol. 206 (No. 10). pp. 1290-5.

123. Martens, Howard and Duwez, Pol., "Heat Evolved and Volume Change in the Alpha-Sigma Transformation in Chromium-Iron Alloys", J. Metals 8, AIMIE Trans. 206. p. 614.

124. Powell, R. W., "The Effect of Quenching on the Thermal Conductivities and Electrical Resistivities of Steel", J. Iron Steel Inst. (London). Vol. 184. pp. 6-10 (England)

125. Grigor'ev, A. T., Sokolovskaya, E. M. and Maksimova, M. V., "Investigation of Alloys in the System Gold-Cobalt", Zhur. Neorg. Khim. Vol. 1. pp. 1047-51. (USSR)

126. Millner, T. and Welesz, R. "Effect of Manganese Content on the Thermal Expansion Coefficient and Magnetic Properties of the So-Called Dumet Iron-Nickel Alloys", Acta Tech. Acad. Sci. Hung. Vol. 14. pp. 279-91. (Hungary)

127. Thomas, V. and Jones, D. J., "Low-Expansion Nickel-Iron Alloys Prepared by Powder Metallurgy, (Symposium on Powder Metallurgy, 1954)", Iron Steel Inst. Spec. Rept. No. 58. pp. 200-3. (England)

128. Saller, Henry A., Dickerson, Ronald F., Murr, William E., "Uranium Alloys for High-Temperature Application", U. S. AEC Publ. BMI-1098. 46 p.

129. Chiotti, P. and Carlson, O. N., "Hanford Slug Program Semi-Annual Summary Research Report for July 1 to Dec. 21, 1955", U. S. AEC Publ. ISC-709. Contr. W-7405-Eng-82. 23 p.

130. Teitel, R. J., "The Uranium-Lead System", J. Inst. Metals. Vol. 85 (No. 9). pp. 409-12.

131. Munster, A. and Sagel, K., "Critical Point of the Solid System Aluminum-Zinc", Z. Electrochem. Vol. 59. pp. 946-51. (Germany)

132. Bostrom, W. A. and Halteman, E. K., "The Metastable Gamma Phase in Uranium Base Molybdenum Alloys", U. S. AEC Publ. WADP-T-415. 32 p.

133. Smirnova, V. I. and Ormont, B. F., "Limits of Homogeneity and Dependence of Thermodynamic and Certain Other Properties of Tantalum Carbide Phases on Their Composition and Structures", Zhur. Fiz. Khim. (U. S. AEC Publ. AEC-tr-2852). Vol. 30. pp. 1327-42. (USSR)

134. Grinthal, R. D., "New High Temperature Intermetallic Materials", WADC-TR-53-190 (Pt. 5) -- AD 110 684. 65 p.

135. Rieder, Z. "Hall Constant and Magnetic Susceptibility of Transition Metal Biborides", U. S. AEC Publ. NP-6166 Contr. Nonr-1538(00). 68 p.

136. Adams, C. H., Bourke, R. et al., "Polymer Evaluation Handbook", WADC TR 56-399, Contr. AF 33(616)3034. 118 p.

137. Pietrokowsky, P., Frink, E. P. and Duwez, P., "Investigation of the Partial Constitution Diagram Ti-TiAu$_2$", Trans. Amer. Inst. Min. Met. Eng. Vol. 206. pp. 930-5.

138. Worner, H. W., "The Constitution of Titanium-Rich Alloys of Iron and Titanium", J. Inst. Metals. Vol. 79. pp. 173-88. (England)

139. Dayton, R. and Tipton, C. R., "Progress Relating to Civilian Applications during Dec. 1955", U. S. AEC Publ. BMI 1062 (Del.).

140. Cotter, P. G., Kohn, J. A. and Potter, R. A., "Physical and X-Ray Study of the Disilicides of Titanium, Zirconium and Hafnium", J. Amer. Ceram. Soc. Vol. 39. pp. 11-12.

141. Hashimoto, K. and Hirakawa, K., "The Electrical Properties of Stannous Telluride, SnTe", J. Phys. Soc. Japan. Vol. 11, No. 6. pp. 716-17. (Japan)

142. Barton, J. E. and Fulkerson, S. D., "Linear Thermal Expansion of Four Different Compositions of Be + BeO", Oak Ridge Natl. Lab. Contr. W-7405-Eng-26. U. S. AEC Publ. ORNL C.F. No. 56-11-59. 14 p.

143. Shigetomi, S. and Mori, S., "Electrical Properties of Bi$_2$Te$_3$", J. Phys. Soc. No. 9. Vol. 11. pp. 915-19. (Japan)

144. Beckman, G. and Kiessling, R., "Thermal Expansion Coefficients for Uranium Boride and β-Uranium Silicide", Nature. Vol. 178. p. 1341. (England)

145. Munster, A. and Sagel, K., "Some Electrical Properties of Titanium Nitride and Titanium Carbide", Z. Physik. Vol. 144. pp. 139-51. (Germany)

146. Kover, Francois, "The Electrical Properties of Aluminum Antimonide", Compt. rend. Vol. 243. pp. 648-50. (France)

147. Yoshinaga, H. and Oetjen, R. A., "Optical Properties of Indium Antimonide in the Region (of Wave Lengths) from 20 to 200 Microns", Phys. Rev. Vol. 101. pp. 526-31.

148. Fisher, A. and Silver, I., "Phenolic Ceramic Molded Materials with Low Coefficients of Linear Expansion for Use in P-12 Detonating Plugs", NAVORD Rept. No. 4133. AD 103 722. 18 p.

149. Carpenter, J. H. and Searcy, A. W., "Preparation, Identification, and Chemical Properties of the Niobium Germanides", J. Amer. Chem. Soc. Vol. 78 (No. 10). pp. 2079-81.

150. Smith, D. F., Brown, Duane, et al., "Low-Temperature Heat Capacity and Entropy of Molybdenum Trioxide and Molybdenum Disulfide", J. Am. Chem. Soc. Vol. 78. pp. 1533-6.

151. Zelikman, A. N. and Belyaevskaya, L. V., "The Melting Point of Molybdenite", Zhur. Neorg. Khim. Vol. 1. pp. 2239-44. (USSR)

152. Weise, E. K. and Andrews, M. C., "On the Electrical Conductivity of Some Alkaline Earth Titanates. Part II", Tech. Note No. 8, Pt. 2 OSR TN-56-125. Contr. AF33(038)12644. AD 86 001. 23 p.

153. Samsonov, G. V., Zhuravlev, N. N. and Amnuel, I. G., "Problem of the Physiochemical Properties of Boron-Carbon Alloys", U. S. AEC Publ. AEC-tr-3110 (Trans. from Fiz. Metal. i Metalloved Akad. Nauk SSSR, Ural'Filial). Vol. 3. pp. 309-19. (USSR)

154. Gilles, P. W. and Robson, H. E., "Vaporization and X-Ray Studies of Boron Carbide", Rept. No. CCC-1024-TR-191. AD 138 305. 22 p.

155. Brady, J. G. and Matthews, S., "Correlation of Data Obtained from Tests on Refractory Insulating Materials", J. Can. Ceram. Soc. Vol. 25. pp. 33-8. (Canada)

156. Belle, J. and Jones, L. J., eds., "Resume of Uranium Oxide Data - VIII", U. S. AEC Publ. WAPD-PWR-PMM-904. 100 p.

157. Shermer, H. F., "Thermal Expansion of Binary Alkaline Earth Borate Glasses", J. Research Natl. Bur. Standards. Vol. 56. pp. 73-9.

158. Moore, H. and McMillan, P. W., "Study of Glasses Consisting of the Oxides of Elements of Low Atomic Weight", J. Soc. Glass Technol. Vol. 40. pp. 66-161T. (England)

159. Danforth, W. E., "Studies in Mixed Conduction in Solids", Bartol Research Foundation, Franklin Inst., Contr. DA33-0340 ORD-1487, Proj. TB2-0001(718). 62 p.

160. Suzuki, Hiroshige; Kuwayama, Norihiko and Yamauchi, Toshivoski, "Improved Apparatus for Measuring Thermal Conductivity of Highly Conductive Hard Ceramics", J. Ceram. Assoc. Japan. Vol. 64(726). pp. 161-6. (Japan)

161. Willardson, R. K., Moody, J. W. and Goering, H. L., "The Electrical Properties of Uranium Oxides", U. S. AEC Publ. BMI-1135. Contr. W-7405-Eng-92. 42 p.

162. Augustinik, A. I. and Vasil'ev, E. I., "Thermal Expansion of Solid Solutions of Ferromagnetic Materials of the Systems $NiO-ZnO-Fe_2O_3$ and $CuO-ZnO-Fe_2O_3$", Zhru. Priklad. Khim. Vol. 29. pp. 941-4. (USSR)

163. Strauss, S. W., "Electrical Resistivity of Vitreous Ternary Lithium-Sodium Silicates", Reprint from J. of Res. of the Natl. Bur. of Stand. (R.P. No. 2665). AD 101 290. Vol. 56(4).

164. Zimmerman, Wm. F. and Allen, Alfred W., "X-Ray Thermal Expansion Measurements of Refractory Crystals", Am. Ceram. Soc. Bull. 35. Bull. 35. pp. 271-4.

165. King, E. G., "Heat Capacities at Low Temperatures and Entropies of Five Spinel Minerals", J. Phys. Chem., Vol. 60. pp. 410-12.

166. Shermer, Herman, F., "Thermal Expansion of Binary Alkali Silicate Glasses", J. Research Natl. Bur. Standards. Vol. 57(2). pp. 97-101.

167. Bruch, C. A., Cashin, W. M. and White, D. W., "Metallurgy Report of the Technical Department for Dec. 1955, Jan., Feb., 1956", U. S. AEC Publ. KAPL 1526. 29 p.

168. Vargin, V. V. and Krasotkina, N. I., "Thermal Expansion of Sodium Silicate Glasses Containing Fluorides", Doklady Akad. Nauk SSSR. Vol. 108. pp. 1133-6. (USSR)

169. Napolitano, A., Waxler, R. and Nivert Jr., J.M., "Optical Glass Technology Development", Progress Rept. Contr. AF33(616)56-17. (NBS Rept. No. 4764). AD 106-396. 8 p.

170. Moore, H. and McMillan, P.W., "Study of Glasses Consisting of the Oxides of Elements of Low Atomic Weight", J. Soc. Glass Technol. Vol. 40. pp. 66-161T. (England)

1. Saba, W.G., "The Heat Capacities of Magnesium and Cadmium between 20 and 270°C", J. Am. Chem. Soc. Vol. 79. p. 3637.

2. Boosz, H.J., "The Average Specific Heat of Hard Metals between Room Temperature and -190° ", Metall. Vol. 11. pp. 22-3. (Germany)

3. Rentschler, Russel R., "Determination of Thermal Expansivity of Zirconium Hydride ", Air Force Institute of Techn., Air University, Master's Thesis. 48 p.

4. Schofield, T.H., "The Melting Point of Niobium", Institute of Metals Journal. Vol. 85. pp. 372-74.

5. Rasor, N.S. and McClelland, J.D., "Thermal Properties of Materials--Part I, Properties of Graphite, Molybdenum and Tantalum to Their Destruction Temperatures ", WADC Tech. Rept. 56-400, Pt. 1. (Contract AF 33(616) 2909). AD 118 144. 53 p.

6. Pallister, P.R., "Specific Heat and Resistivity of Mild Steel", Iron and Steel Institute Journal. Vol. 185. pp. 474-482. (England)

7. Mark, Melvin, "Thermal Conductivity of a Plastic Honeycomb Sandwich", Modern Plastics. Vol. 34. No. 9. pp. 168, 247

8. Betz, H.T. and Olson, O.H., "Determination of Emissivity and Reflectivity Data on Structural Materials", WADC TR 56-222 Part II. Contract AF 33(616) 3002 TASK 73603. 184 p.

9. Lucks, C.F. and Deem, H.W., "Thermal Conductivities, Heat Capacities, and Linear Thermal Expansion of Five Materials, Part II. Density and Thermal Conductivity of Molten Copper", Battelle Mem. Inst. Columbus, O., (Tech. Rept. WADC-TR-55-496, Pt. 2 (Cont. AF33(616)2902) AD 118 168. 14 p.

10. Powell, R.W. and Tye, R.P., "The Influence of Heat-treatment on the Electrical Resistivity and the Thermal Conductivity of Electrodeposited Chromium", J. Inst. Metals. Vol. 85. pp. 185-95. (England)

11. Pearson, G.J., Davey, P.O., and Danielson, G. C., "Thermal Conductivity of Nickel and Uranium", Proc. Iowa Acad. Sci. Vol. 64. pp. 461-5.

12. Pupke, Gerhard, "Anisotropy of the Thermal Expansion of Iron-Nickel Alloys. I.", Z. Physik. Chem. Vol. 207. pp. 91-110. (Germany)

13. Barson, F., Legvold, S., and Spedding. F.H., "Thermal Expansion of Rare Earth Metals", Phys. Rev. Vol. 105. pp. 418-24.

14. White, G.K. and Woods, S.B., "Conductivity of Manganese", Can. J. Phys. Vol. 35. pp. 346-8.

15. White, G.K. and Woods, S.B., "Thermal and Electrical Conductivity of Rhodium, Iridium, and Platinum ", Can. J. Phys. Vol. 35. pp. 248-57. AD 128 481. (Canada)

16. Poole, D.M., Williamson, G.K., and Marples, J.A.C., "Plutonium-Thorium System", J. Inst. Metals, Paper No. 1813. Vol. 86. Pt. 4. pp. 172-6. (England)

17. Gerstein, B.C., Griffel, M., Jennings, L.D., Miller, R.E., Skochdopole, R.E., and Spedding, F.H., "Heat Capacity of Holmium from 15 to 300°K", J. Chem. Phys. Vol. 27. pp. 394-9.

18. Schindler, A.I., Smith, R.J., and Salkovitz, E.I., "The Electrical Resistivity of the Ni-Pd Alloy System between 300°K and 730°K ", NRL Rept. No. 4974 AD 138 499. 6 p.

19. Rudnitskii, A.A. and Polyakova, R.S., "Physical Properties of Ruthenium", Zhur. Neorg. Khim. Vol. 2. pp. 2758-61. (USSR)

20. Beals, R.J. and Cook, R.L., "Directional Dilation of Crystal Lattices at Elevated Temperatures", J. Am. Ceram. Soc. Vol. 40 (8). pp. 279-84.

21. Skinner, Brian J., "The Thermal Expansion of Thoria, Periclase and Diamond ", Am. Minerologist. Vol. 42. pp. 39-55.

22. Curtis, C.E. and Johnson, J.R., "Properties of Thorium Oxide Ceramics", J. Am. Ceram. Soc. Vol. 40. pp. 63-8.

23. Cline, Carl F. and Lewis, Gordon, "Development of Ultra Refractory Materials", Final Report Contr. NOrd-17175. AD 138 876. 18 p.

24. Curtis, C.E. and Johnson, J.R., "Ceramic Properties of Samarium Oxide and Gadolinium Oxide, X-ray Studies of Other Rare-earth Oxides and Some Compounds ", J. Am. Ceram. Soc. Vol. 40 (1). pp. 15-19.

25. Epelboin, Israel and Vapaille, Andre, "The Measurement of Thermal Convection of Metallic Wires of Different Kinds ", Compt. rend. Vol. 244. pp. 314-316. (France)

26. Clements, J.F. and Vyse, J., "The Thermal Conductivity of Some Refractory Materials", Trans. Brit. Ceram. Soc. Vol. 56. pp. 296-308. (England)

27. Schindler, A.I., Smith, R.J., and Salkovitz, E.I., "Electrical Resistivity of the Ni-Pd Alloy System between 300°K and 730°K", Physical Review. Vol. 108. Ser. 2. pp. 921-3.

28. Neshpor, V. S. and Samsonov, G. V., "The Problem of Brittleness of Metallic Compounds", Fiz. Metal. i Metalloved. Vol. 4. pp. 181-3. (USSR)

29. Snyder, M.J., Duckworth, W.H., "Properties of Some Refractory Uranium Compounds", BMI-1223 35, Contr. W-7405-eng-92. AD 145 106. 35 p.

30. Llewellyn, J.P., Smith, T., "The Thermal Expansion of Iron Ditelluride", Proc. Phys. Soc. Vol. B70. pp. 1113-22.

31. Ravdel, M.P., Selisskii, Ya. P., "Transitions in Ternary Ni₃Fe Solid Solutions", Doklady Akad. Nauk. Vol. 115. pp. 319-21. (USSR)

32. Baker, T.W., Spindler, W.E., and Wilkinson, D., "The Coefficient of Thermal Expansion of Zirconium Nitride", Rept. No. AERE M/M 143; IMFT/N.6. AD 132 130. 2 p. (England)

33. Kingery, W.D., "Thermal Expansion and Microstresses in Two-phase Compositions", J. Am. Ceram. Soc. Vol. 40. pp. 351-2.

34. Kothen, Charles W., "High-temperature Heat Contents of Molybdenum and Titanium and the Low-temperature Heat Capacities of Titanium", Univ. Microfilms (Ann Arbor, Mich.) Publ. No. 23697. 93 p.

35. Wallace, W.E., Craig, R.S., Saba, W.G., and Sterritt, K.F., "The Heat Capacities of Magnesium and Cadmium between 20 and 270°", U. S. Atomic Energy Comm. NYO-6334.

36. Smith, K.F. and Van Thyne, R.J., "Selected Properties of Vanadium Alloys for Reactor Application", Final Rept. on Metallurgy Program 4.10, 10 ANL 5661. AD 135 156. 31 p.

37. Powell, R. L., Roder, H.M., and Rogers, W.M., "Low Temperature Thermal Conductivity of Some Commercial Coppers", J. Appl. Phys. Vol. 28. pp. 1282-8.

38. Savitskii, E.M., Burhkanov, G.S., "Composition Diagrams of Titanium-Lanthanum and Titanium-Cerium Alloys", Zhur. Neorg. Khim. Vol. 2. pp. 2609-16. (USSR)

39. Vintaikin, E.Z., "The Determination of the Vapor Pressure of Iron over Austenite", Doklady Akad. Nauk. S.S.S.R. Vol. 117. pp. 632-4. (USSR)

40. Olette, Michel, "Measurement of the Heat Content of Silicon between 1200° and 1550°", Compt. rend. Vol. 244. pp. 1033-6. (France)

41. King, E.G., "Heat Capacities at Low Temperature and Entropies at 298.15°K, of Nickelous Oxide, Cobaltous Oxide, and Cobalt Spinel", J. Am. Ceram. Soc. Vol. 79. pp. 2399-400.

42. Bostrom, W.A. and Halteman, E.K., "Metastable Phase in Uranium-base Molybdenum Alloys", Proc. Nuclear Eng. Sci. Conf., 2nd, Philadelphia. Vol. 2. pp. 184-93.

43. Scott, J.L., "A Calorimeter Investigation of Zirconium, Titanium, and Zirconium Alloys from 60 to 960°C", ORNL-2328 Contr. No. W-7405-eng-26. AD 138 838. 122 p.

44. King, E.G., "Low Temperature Heat Capacities and Entropies at 298.15°K of Some Crystalline Silicates Containing Calcium", J. Am. Chem. Vol. 79. pp. 5437-8.

45. Walker, B.E., Ewing, C.F., and Miller, R.R., "Heat Capacity of Titanium Diboride from 30° to 700°", J. Phys. Chem. Vol. 61. pp. 1682-3.

46. Brown, A.R.G. and Gates, P.M.R., "A Titanium Vanadium Alloy", Tech. Note No. Met. 259; (JSRP Control No. 580281) AD 154 781. 13 p. (England)

47. Pell, E.M., "Solubility of Lithium in Silicon", Phys. and Chem. Solids. Vol. 3. pp. 77-81.

48. Swift, Robinson M. and White, David, "Low Temperature Head Capacities of Magnesium Diboride (MgB₂) and Magnesium Tetraboride (MgB₄)", J. Am. Chem. Soc. Vol. 79. pp. 3641-4.

49. Westrum, Edgar F. and Grimes, D.M., "Low-temperature Heat Capacity and Thermodynamic Properties of Zinc Ferrite", Phys. and Chem. Solids. Vol. 3. pp. 44-9.

50. Mikryukov, V.E., "Temperature Dependence of the Heat Conductivity and Electrica Resistance of Ti, Zr, and Zr Alloys", Vestnik Moskov Univ. Vol. 12 (5). pp. 73-80. (USSR)

51. Burlakov, V.D., "Pressure of Iron and Chromium Vapors as Determined by the Velocity of Their Evaporation in Vacuum", Fiz. Metal. i Metalloved. Vol. 5. pp. 91-101. (USSR)

52. Powell, R.L., Rogers, W.M., and Coffin, D.O., "Apparatus for Measurements of Thermal Conductivity of Solids at Low Temperatures", J. Research Natl. Bur. Standards, Res. Paper 2805. Vol. 59. pp. 349-55.

53. Charvat, F.R. and Kingery, W.D., "Thermal Conductivity. XIII. Effect of Microstructure on Conductivity of Single-phase Ceramics", J. Am. Ceram. Soc. Vol. 40. pp. 306-15.

54. Baker, H., "Investigation of Alloys of Magnesium and Their Properties. Part II. Thermal and Electrical Properties of Magnesium Base Alloys", WADC-TR-57-194 (Pt. II)(Contract AF 33(616)2337). AD 131 034. 28 p.

55. Mah, A.D., Kelley, K.K., et al., "Thermodynamic Properties of Titanium-oxygen Solutions and Compounds", Bureau of Mines, Berkeley, Calif. Rept. of Investigation No. 5316. AD 125 343. 33 p.

56. Douglas, Thomas B. and Victor, Andrew C., "Physical Properties of High Temperature Materials. Part II. The Heat Capacity of Zirconium, Several Zirconium Hydrides, and Certain Cladding Materials from 0 to 900°C; Relation to Other Thermodynamic Properties of the Zr-H System", WADC TR No. 57-374, Pt. 2 Contr. AF33(616) 56-21. AD 150 128. 75 p.

57. Sands, Donald E. and Hoard, J.L., "Rhombohedral Elemental Boron", J. Am. Chem. Soc. Vol. 79. pp. 5582-3.

58. Searcy, Alan W. and Myers, Clifford E., "The Heat of Sublimation of Boron and the Gaseous Species for the Boron-Boric Oxide System", J. Phys. Chem. AD 146 020. Vol. 61. pp. 957-60.

59. Ditmars, D.A. and Ginnings, D.C., "Thermal Conductivity of Beryllium Oxide from 40° to 750°", J. Research Natl. Bur. Stand. Res. Paper 2774. Vol. 59. pp. 93-99.

60. Hodgman, Charles D., ed., Handbook of Chemistry and Physics, 39th Edition. Chemical Rubber Publishing Co., Cleveland, Ohio.

61. Zachariasen, W.H. and Ellinger, Finley, "Crystal Structure of α-plutonium Metal", J. Chem. Phys. Vol. 27. pp. 811-12.

62. Mauer, F.A. and Bolz, L.H., "Measurement of Thermal Expansion of Cermet Components by High Temperature X-ray Diffraction", NBS Rept. No. 5837; Suppl.1 to WADC Tech. Rept. No. 55-473, AD 95 329 (Contr. AF 33(616) 56-5)(Contr. AF 33 (616) 53-12). AD 155 555. 47 p.

63. Ivanov, L.I. and Matveeva, M.P., "Apparatus for Measuring Vapor Pressure and Diffusion Constants of Metals by Isotope Exchange", Trudy Inst. Met. in A.A. Baikova. Vol. No. 1, 1957. pp. 104-7. (USSR)

64. Shimazaki, Eiichi, Matsumoto, Noboru, and Niwa, Kichizo, "The Vapor Pressure of Germanium Dioxide", Bull. Chem. Soc. Vol. 30. pp. 969-971. (Japan)

65. Berkowitz, J., Chupka, W.A., and Inghram, M.G., "Thermodynamics of the Ti-Ti_2O_3 System and the Dissociation Energy of TiO and TiO_2", J. Phys. Chem. Vol. 61. pp. 1569-72.

66. Janssen, Sylvian and Pecijare, Ordan, "The (Electrical) Resistivity of Aluminum-copper Alloys", Compt. rend. Vol. 244. pp. 2017-20. (France)

67. Sheer, Charles, Mead, Lawrence, H., et al., "Measurements of Thermal Diffusivity of Various Materials by Means of the High Intensity Electric Arc Technique", WADC Tech. Rept. 57-226. Contr. No. AF 33(616)-3669. 53 p.

68. Viting, L.M., "Study of Fe-Ni-Co System in the Region of the Metallic Compounds Ni_3Fe and FeCo. III. The Metallic Compound FeCo and the Region of Its Existence in the Fe-Co System", Zhur. Neorg. Khim. Vol. 2. pp. 845-51. (USSR)

69. Viting, L.M., "Study of the Iron-Nickel-Cobalt System in the Region of the Intermetallic Compounds Ni_3Fe, and FeCo. I. The intermetallic Compound Ni_3Fe and Its Region of Existence in the Iron-Nickel System", Zhur. Neorg. Khim. Vol. 2. pp. 367-74. (USSR)

70. Gebhardt, Erich, Seghezzi, Hans Dieter, "Apparatus for Investigating Gas-metal Systems and Measured Results of the System Tantalum-oxygen", Z. Metall K. Vol. 48. pp. 430-5. (Germany)

71. Hove, J.E., "Solid State Physics", Semi-annual Prog. Rept. July-Dec. 1956. AD 134 355. 40 p.

72. Paladino Jr., A.E., Swarts, E.L., and Crandall, W.B., "Unsteady-state Method of Measuring Thermal Diffusivity and Biot's Modulus for Alumina between 1500 and 1800°C", J. Am. Ceram. Soc. Vol. 40(10). pp. 340-45.

73. Herasymenko, P., "Vapor Pressure of Magnesium over Alpha and Beta Silver-Magnesium Alloys", New York, U., Final Rept. (Contr. DA-30-069-ORD-1405) OOR 1285. AD 128 392. 34 p.

74. Spedding, F.H., Barton, R.J., and Daane, A.H., "Vapor Pressure of Thulium Metal", J. Am. Chem. Vol. 79. pp. 5160-3.

75. Poole, D.M., Williamson, G.K., and Marples, J.A.C., "A Preliminary Investigation of the Plutonium-thorium System", AERE Rept. No. M/R 2156; HX 2827. AD 156 314. 18 p. (England)

76. Beard, A.P., Harrison, J.W., and Clark, W.B., "Preparation of Nuclear Poison and Control Alloys - Zirconium-boron Alloys", U.S. Atomic Energy Comm. KAPL - 1555. 30 p.

77. Sense, K.A., Stone, R.W., Filbert, R.B., "Vapor Pressure and Equilibrium Studies of the Sodium Fluoride-Beryllium Fluoride System", Rept. No. BMI 1186 (TID-4500, 13th ed.) Contr. No. W-7405-eng-92. AD 134 324. 30 p.

78. Sturm, W.J. and Wechsler, M.S., "Density and Resistivity Changes in Gold-cadmium upon Quenching", J. Appl. Phys. Vol. 28. pp. 1509-10.

79. Z.G., "The Dilatometric Determination of the Coefficient of Expansion of α-uranium", Atomnaya Energiya. Vol. 3. p. 272. (USSR)

80. Pelzel, E., "Copper-lead Alloys. III. The Specific Volumes of Solid and Liquid Alloys and Their Volume Configuration on Freezing", Metall. Vol. 11. pp. 954-959. (Germany)

81. Strelkov, P.G. and Novikova, S.I., "Silica Dilatometer for Low Temperatures", Pribory i Tekh. Eksperimenta. 1957 No. 5. pp. 105-10. (USSR)

82. Basmajian, J.A. and DeVries, R.C., "Phase Equilibria in the System Barium Titanate-Strontium Titanate", J. Am. Ceramic Soc. Vol. 40. pp. 373-6.

83. Drys, Miroslawa and Trzebiatowski, Wlodzimierz, "The System Strontium Oxide-Titanium Dioxide", Roczniki Chem. Vol. 31. pp. 489-96. (Poland)

84. Curtis, C.E., "Properties of Yttrium Oxide Ceramics", J. Am. Ceram. Soc. Vol. 40. pp. 274-78.

85. Smirous, K., Stourac, L., and Bednar, J., "The Semiconducting Compound SiTe", Czechoslov. J. Phys. Vol. 7. pp. 120-122. (Czechoslov.)

86. Belle, J. and Lustman, B., "Properties of UO_2", WAPD-184 (Contr. AT-11-GEN-14). 140 p.

87. Coughlin, J.P. and O'Brien, C.J., "High-temperature Heat Contents of Calcium Orthosilicates", J. Phys. Chem. Vol. 61. p. 769.

88. Larrabee, Robert Dean, "The Spectral Emissivity and Optical Properties of Tungsten", Tech. Rept. No. 328 (Contr. DA 36-039-sc-64637). AD 156 602. 81 p.

89. Ferry, Michel, "The Influence of Graphite on the Mechanical Characteristics of Gray Cast Irons Not Containing Lamellar Graphite", Fonderie. Vol. 134. pp. 113-31. (France)

90. Z.G., "Some Properties of Metallic Neptunium", Atomnaya Energiya. Vol. 3. p. 176. (USSR)

91. Kempter, C.P., Krikorian, N.H., and McGuire, J.C., "The Crystal Structure of Yttrium Nitride", J. Phys. Chem. Vol. 61. pp. 1237-8.

92. Grinthal, R.D., Bizzard, R., and Steinitz, R., "Evaluation of New High Temperature Materials", American Electro Metal Divsn. of Firth Sterling, Inc., Prog. Rpt. No. 2. AD 144 505. 26 p.

93. Somiya, Shigeyuke, Yamauchi, Toshiyoski, and Suzuki, Hiroshige, "Effects of Addition of Uranium Dioxide or Thoria on the Properties of Zirconia", Yogyo Kyokai Shi. Vol. 65. pp. 144-7. (Japan)

94. Tramposch, H. and Gerard, G., "The Physical Properties of Several Materials for Use in Photo-thermo-elastic Investigations", Tech. Rept. No. SM 57-5; OSR TN-57-282 AD 132 353. 26 p.

95. Schmidt, D.L., "Evaluation of Selectron 400 Transparent Plastic Material", WADC 57 580. AD 142 180. 25 p.

96. Muldawer, L., "Spectral Reflectivity as a Function of Temperature of β-brass Type Alloys", Rept. No. AFOSR TN 57 667 AD 136 656. 33 p.

97. Covington, P.C. and Oglesby Jr., S., "Measurements of the Thermal Properties of Various Aircraft Structural Materials", WADC TR 57-10. SRI. AD 131 032. 72 p.

98. Wisely, H.R., "Resistivity Characteristics of Some Ceramic Compositions above 1000°F", Amer. Cer. Soc. Bulletin. Vol. 36. pp. 133-136.

99. Pecijare, O., and Janssen, S., "Copper-Zinc and Copper-Tin Alloys", Compt. rend. Vol. 245. pp. 1306-9. (France)

100. Bostrom, W.A., "Electrical Resistance of Zirconium and Titanium", WAPD-T-176. (Contr. AT-11-1-GEN-14). 13 p.

101. Gast, Th., Hellwege, K.H. and Kohlhepp, E., "Thermal Conductivity of Poly(vinyl Chloride) with and without Plasticizer in the Temperature Range of 70 to 360°K", Kolloid-Z. Vol. 152. pp. 24-31. (Germany)

102. Bodor, Geza, "Determination of the Second-Order Transition Temperature of Some Polyamides", Faserforsch U. Textiltech. Vol. 8. pp. 470-1. (Germany)

103. Schwartz, H.S. and Lisle, B.J., "Effects of High Intensity Thermal Radiation on Structural Plastic Laminates", WADC Tech. Rept. No. 57-638, Pt. 1. AD 142 181. 41 p.

104. Greiner, E.S. and Gutowski, J.A., "Electrical Resistivity of Boron", J. Appl. Phys. Vol. 28. pp. 1364-1365.

105. Los, G.J., "Resistance and Magneto-Resistance of Dilute Alloys of Copper and Gold with Nickel at Low Temperatures", Physica. Vol. 23. pp. 633-40. (Holland)

106. Smith, J.H. and Street, R., "Resistivity and Magnetoresistance of Au_2Mn", Proc. Phys. Soc. Vol. B70. pp. 1089-92. (England)

107. Pecijare, O. and Janssen, S., "A Study of the Resistance of the γ_2 Phase of Copper-Aluminum Alloys", Compt. rend. Vol. 245. pp. 1228-30. (France)

108. Esin, O. A. and Zyazev, V. L., "Electrical Conductivity of Oxides of Vanadium, Lead and Copper", Zhur. Neorg. Khim. Vol. 2 (9). pp. 1998-2002. (USSR)

109. Ward, L., "The Temperature Coefficient of Reflectivity of Nickel", Proc. Phys. Soc. Vol. B 70. pp. 862-6. (England)

110. Campbell, D. A. and Schulte, H. A., "Measurement of Emissivity at Low Temperature", Jupiter Missile Prog. Tech. Rept. MT-R2J, CWO-2000035. Cont. DA-20-018- U. S. ORD-14440. AD 151 931. 42 p.

111. Gast, Th. and Granberg, G., "A Method for Dielectric Measurement of Degree of Hardening of Molded Phenol Resin", Gummi u. Asbest. Vol. 10. p. 618. (Germany)

112. Ames Lab., "Semi-Annual Summary Research Report in Physics for July through December, 1957", 60 p.

113. McCabe, C. L. and Hudson, R. G., "Free Energy of Formation of $Mn_7 C_3$ from Vapor-Pressure Measurements", Trans. Amer. Inst. Min. Met. Eng. Vol. 209. pp. 17-19.

114. Argonne Natl. Lab., "Metallurgy Division Quarterly Report for Jan., Feb. and March, 1957", U. S. AEC Publ. ANL-5717. 67 p.

115. Chiotti, P. and Carlson, O. N., "Slug Program Quarterly Report (for) April, May, June 1953", U. S. AEC Publ. ISC 398 (Del.). 32 p.

116. Waldron, M. B., "The Physical Properties and Alloying Behaviour of Plutonium Metal", Atomics. Vol. 8. pp. 383-6. (England)

117. Perova, V. I. and Knoroz, L. I., "Heat and Electric Conductivity of Certain Heat-Resistant Materials at High Temperatures", Tsentral. Nauch-Issledovatel. Inst. Tekhnol. i Mashinostroen. Vol. 79. pp. 159-74. (USSR)

118. Brocklehurst, R. E., Goode, J. M. and Vassamillet, L. F. "Coefficient of Expansion of Polonium", J. Chem. Phys. Vol. 27. p. 985.

119. Spedding, F. H., Daane, A. H. and Herrmann, K. W., "Electrical Resistivities and Phase Transformations of Lanthanum, Cerium, Praseodymium, and Neodymium", J. Metals (9), AIME Trans. (209).

120. Simmons, R. O. and Balluffi, R. W., "Low-Temperature Thermal Expansion of Copper", Phys. Rev. Vol. 108. pp. 278-80.

121. Fulk, M. M. and Reynolds, M. M. "Emissivities of Metallic Surfaces at 76°K", J. Appl. Physics.

122. Twidle, G. G., "The Spectral Reflectivity of Back-Surface and Front-Surface Aluminized Mirrors", Brit. J. Appl. Physics. Vol. 8. pp. 337-39. (England)

123. Haas, G. G., Hunter, W. R. and Tousey, R., "Influence of Purity, Substate Temperature, and Aging Conditions on the Extreme Ultra-Violet Reflections of Evaporated Aluminum", J. Opt. Soc. Amer. Vol. 47. pp. 1070-3.

124. Allen, F. G., "Emissivity at 0.65μ of Silicon and Germanium at High Temperatures", J. Appl. Physics. Vol. 28. pp. 1510-11.

125. White, G. K. and Woods, S. B., "Low-Temperature Resistivity of Transition Elements: Vanadium Niobium and Hafnium", Canad. J. Phys. Vol. 35. pp. 892-900. (Canada)

126. Tottle, C. R. "The Physical and Mechanical Properties of Niobium", J. Inst. Metals. Vol. 85. pp. 375-8. (England)

127. White, G. K. and Woods, S. B., "Low-Temperature Resistivity of the Transition Elements: Cobalt, Tungsten, and Rhenium", Canad. J. Physics. Vol. 35. pp. 656-65. (Canada)

128. Harper, A. F. A., et al., "The Thermal and Electrical Conductivity of Chromium at Low Temperatures", Phil. Mag. Vol. 2. pp. 577-83. (England)

129. Devyatkova, E. D. and Smirnov, I. A., "On the Thermal Conductivity of Germanium", Zhur. Tekhn. Fiziki. Vol. 27. pp. 1944-9. (USSR)

130. Stuckes, A. D. and Chasmar, R. P., "Measurement of the Thermal Conductivity of Semi-Conductors", Rep. Meeting on Semi-Conductors (Phys. Soc.).

131. Oelsen, W., "Thermodynamic Analysis IX. - An Air or Gas Calorimeter", Arch. Eisenhuttenwesen. Vol. 28. pp. 1-6.

132. Los, G. J., "Resistance and Magneto-Resistance of Dilute Alloys Copper and Gold with Nickel at Low Temperatures", Physica. Vol. 23. pp. 633-40. (Holland)

133. Eldred, V. W. and Curtis, G. C., "Some Properties of Neptunium Metal", Nature. Vol. 179. p. 910. (England)

134. Hidnert, P., "Thermal Expansion of Some Nickel Alloys", J. Research Natl. Bur. Standards. Vol. 58. pp. 89-92.

135. Jennings, L. D., Stanton, R. M. and Spedding, F. H., "Heat Capacity of Terbium", J. Chem. Phys. Vol. 27. pp. 909-13.

136. Haas, G. and Bradford, A. P., "Optical Properties and Oxidation of Evaporated Titanium Films", J. Opt. Soc. Amer. Vol. 47. pp. 125-9.

137. Gaines, Gordon B., and Sims, Chester T., "Electrical Resistivity and Thermoelectric Potential of Rhenium Metal", Am. Soc. Testing Materials Proc. Vol. 57. pp. 759-69.

138. Thorn, R. J. and Winslow, G. H., "Vaporization Coefficient of Graphite and Composition of the Equilibrium Vapor", J. Chem. Phys. Vol. 26. pp. 186-96.

139. Durand, R. E. and Klein, D. J., "The Effect of Reactor Irradiation at Temperatures between 400° and 700°C on the Thermal Conductivity of Graphite", U. S. AEC Publ. NAA-SR-1520. 33 p.

140. White, G. K. and Woods, S. B., "Conductivity of Alpha-Manganese", Canad. J. Physics. Vol. 35. pp. 346-8. (Canada)

141. Domenicali, C. A., "Thermo-Electric Power and Resistivity of Solid and Liquid Germanium in Vicinity of Its Melting Point", J. Appl. Phys. Vol. 28. pp. 749-53.

142. Lehr, P. and Langeron, J. P., "Dilatometric Study of Alpha-Uranium", Rev. Met. Vol. 54. pp. 257-69. (France)

143. Aas, Steinar, "Preferred Orientations in Uranium Determined by Dilatometric Studies", Tidsskr, Kjemi, Bergvesen Met. Vol. 17. pp. 77-79. (Norway)

144. Wiesner, J. B., Harvey, G. G. and Zimmerman, H. J., "Quarterly Progress Rept. No. 46 for Per. Ending May 13, 1957", U. S. AEC Publ. NP 6419, Proj. 3-99-00-100.

145. Yosim, S. J. and Milne, T. A., "Basic Chemistry of High Temperature Inorganic Systems", Semi-Annual Prog. Rept. 37 p.

146. Yosim, S. J. and Milne, T. A., "Basic Chemistry of High Temperature Inorganic Systems", Rept. No. NAA-SR-1797, Semiannual Prog. Rept. AD 123 479. 23 p.

147. Dies, K., "Study of the Mechanical Properties of Copper-Titanium and Copper-Zirconium Alloys", Metall. Vol. 11. pp. 933-41. (Germany)

148. McCreight, L. R., "Thermal Conductivity Data for Some Nuclear Fuels", U. S. AEC Publ. TID-10062. 19 p.

149. Strittmater, R. C., Pearson, G. J. and Danielson, G. C., "Measurement of Specific Heat by a Pulse Method", Proc. Iowa Acad. Sci. Vol. 64. pp. 466-70.

150. Oak Ridge National Lab., "Solid State Division Annual Progress Report for Period Ending Aug. 31, 1957", U. S. AEC Publ. ORNL-2413. 133 p.

151. Begley, R. T., "Development of Niobium Base Alloys", U. S. AEC Publ. A-2388 (WEC). 35 p.

152. Krebs, K. and Winkler, R. "The Optical Properties of the Hochheim (aluminum 3-12% silver) Alloy", Optik. Vol. 14. pp. 503-9. (Germany)

153. Lang, J. I. and Fieldhouse, I. B., "Measurement of Thermal Properties", Prog. Rept. No. 3 for Jan. Feb. and March 1957, ARF Proj. D106. Contr. AF33(616)3701. U. S. AEC Publ. NP-6258.

154. Dayton, R. W. and Tipton Jr., C. R., "Progress Relating to Civilian Applications during May 1956", U. S. AEC Publ. BMI-1094 (Del.). 86 p.

155. Del Grosso, A., "Compilation of Uranium -10 W/o Molybdenum Fuels Alloys Properties", U. S. AEC Publ. AECU 3679. 70 p.

156. Seibel, R. D. and Mason, G. L., "Thermal Properties of High Temperature Materials", WADC-TR-57-468. Contr. AF33(616)3696. AD 155 605. 64 p.

157. Bacon, G. E., Dunmur, I. W., Smith, J. H. and Street, R., "The Antiferromagnetism or Manganese-Copper Alloys", Proc. Roy. Soc. (London). Vol. A241. pp. 223-38. (England)

158. Bauer, A. A., Rough, F. A. and Dickerson, R. F., "An Investigation of Uranium Solid Solubility in Thorium", U. S. AEC Publ. BMI-1188. AD 135 063. 10 p.

159. Fulkerson, S. D. "Apparatus for Determining Linear Thermal Expansions of Materials in Vacuum or Controlled Atmospheres", U. S. AEC Publ. CF-57-7-123. 24 p.

160. Koster, Werner and Rocholl, Peter, "Conductivity and Hall Constant. I. Nickel-Chromium Alloys", Z. Metallk. Vol. 48. pp. 485-95. (Germany)

161. Teitel, R. J., "Uranium-Bismuth System", Trans. Amer. Inst. Min. Met. Eng. Vol. 209. pp. 131-6.

162. Hirabayashi, M. and Muto, Y., "Electric Resistance of $CuAu_3$ and Cu_3Au at Low Temperatures", J. Phys. Soc. Vol. 12. pp. 830-1. (Japan)

163. Dayton, R. W. and Tipton Jr. C. R., "Progress Relating to Civilian Applications during March 1956", U. S. AEC Publ. BMI-1080. 87 p.

164. Lemmon Jr. A. W., Wood, W. D. et al., "Studies Relating to the Reaction between Zirconium and Water at High Temperatures", U. S. AEC Publ. BMI-1154 Contr. W-7405-Eng-92. 123 p.

165. Hirabayashi, M., Nagasaki, S. and Kono, H., "Calorimetric Study of Cu_2Au at High Temperatures", J. Appl. Physics. Vol. 28. pp. 1070-1. (Japan)

166. Grinthal, R. D., Bizzard, R. and Steinitz, R., "Evaluation of New High Temperature Materials", Progr. Report No. 1. AD 135 860. 16 p.

167. Isserow, S., "The Uranium-Silicon Epsilon-Phase", Trans. Amer. Inst. Min. Met. Eng. Vol. 209. pp. 1236-9.

168. Suzuoka, T., "An Electrical-Resistance Study of the System $(Cr_xMn_{1-x})Sb$", J. Phys. Soc. Vol. 12. pp. 1344-7. (Japan)

169. Middleton, A. E., Herczog, A. et al., "Research on Aluminum Antimonide for Semiconductor Devices", Scientific Rept. No. 5. AD 138 886. 84 p.

170. McGlone, W. R., Dowell, A. M. and Wicklein, H. W., "Properties of Molded Plastics under Simulated Guided Missile Operating Conditions", Tech. Memo No. 479. Contr. No. AF33(038)28634 AD 139 957. 63 p.

171. Marcus, H. and Zaleski, F. V., "Expansion Characteristics of Marlex 20 and Marlex 50", Proj. Title: Materials Analysis and Evaluation Techniques. Task Title: Nuclear Radiation Applications to Engineering Measurements. WADC TR 57-92. AD 130 920. 26 p.

172. Satterhwaite, C. B. and Ure Jr., R. W., "Electrical and Thermal Properties of Bismuth Telluride", Phys. Rev. Vol. 108. pp.1164-70.

173. Stalinski, B., "Electrical Conductivity of Lanthanum Hydride", Bull. Acad. Polon. Sci. Vol. 5. pp. 1001-4. (Poland)

174. Sense, Karl A., Stone, Richard W. and Filbert Jr., Robert B., "Vapor Pressures of the Rubidium Fluoride-Zirconium Fluoride and Lithium Fluoride-Zirconium Fluoride Systems ", U. S. AEC Publ. BMI-1199.

175. Bishui, B. M. and Prasad, J., "Thermal Conductivity of Some Heat-Insulating Materials", Central Glass and Ceram. Research Inst. Bull. Vol. 4. pp. 144-9. (India)

176. Nelson, H. R., "Quarterly Report for July 1 to September 30, 1947", U. S. AEC Publ. BMI-HRN-1. 40 p.

177. Fischer, Wilhelm A., and Lorenz, Gert, "Measurements of Electrical Resistance and Thermo-electric Force of Chromium (III) Oxide at Temperatures up to 1750°", Arch Eisenhuttenw. Vol. 28. pp. 497-503. (Germany)

178. Czanderna, A. W. and Honig, J. M., "The Stoichiometry, Resistivity, and Thermoelectric Power of Cerium Dioxide Below 500°C", AFOSR-TN-57-602. 33 p.

179. National Bureau of Standards, "Optical Glass Technology Developments", NBS Report No. 5016. AD 157 030. 30 p.

180. Alfred Univ., "Study of Heat Transfer of Ceramic Materials", Final Rept. Jan. 1, 1955 - Apr. 30, 1957. 93 p.

181. Klasse, F., Heinz, A. and Hein, J., "Comparative Method for Measuring the Thermal Conductivity of Ceramic Materials", Ber. deut. keram. Ges. Vol. 35(6). pp. 183-89. (Germany)

182. Hamilton, E. H., Waxler, R. and Nivert, J. M., "Optical Glass Technology Development", NBS Rept. No. 5440. AD 139 895. 27 p.

183. Pawlowski, S., "Manufacture of Silica Products of High Refractoriness under Load and Low Porosity from Pure Izer Mountains Quartz", Prace Inst. Ministerstwa Hutnictwa. Vol. 9. pp. 241-51. (Poland)

184. Hagy, H. E. and Ritland, H. N., "Effect of Thermal History of Glass Expansion Characteristics", J. Am. Ceram. Soc. Vol. 40. pp. 436-42.

185. Cowan, J. A., "Heat Treatment and Conductivity Measurements of Sintered Zinc Oxide and Titanium Dioxide Mixtures ", EL Rept. No. 5079-1 (Engl. to Air Attache Ottawa, Rept. No. IR-481-57). AD 144 657. 15 p.

186. Stewart, James E. and Richmond, Jos. C., "Infrared Emission Spectrum of Silicon Carbide Heating Elements", J. Research Natl. Bur. Standards. Vol. 59-(6). pp. 405-9.

187.   Vickery, R. C. and Sedlacek, R., "Rare Earths in Glass Systems", AFOSR-TR-57-86. Contr. No. AF49(638)5.   AD 136 676. 43 p.

188.   Kostanyan, K. A., "Conductivity of Sodium-Calcium-Magnesium Alumino-Silicate Glasses from 100 to 1200°C", Izvest. Akad. Nauk. Armyan, S.S.R. Ser. Khim. Nauk. Vol. 10. pp. 161-72. (USSR)

189.   Ploetz, G. L., Krystyniak, C. W. and Dumes, H. E., "Thermal Expansion of Four Rare Earth Oxides", U. S. AEC Publ. KAPL-M-GLP-1. 7 p.

190.   Belle, J. and Jones, L. J., "Resume of Uranium Oxide Data. IX", U. S. AEC Publ. WAPD-TM-44. 111 p.

191.   Nelson, H. R., "Quarterly Report for July 1 to September 30, 1947", U. S. AEC Publ. BMI-HRN-1. 49 p.

192.   Mardon, P. G. and Waldron, M. B., "An Estimation of the Coefficient of Thermal Expansion of PuO_2 between 0 and 500°C", U. S. AEC Publ. AERE-M/M-171. 6 p. (England)

193.   Kuznetsov, A. K., "Certain Peculiarities in the Formation of Calcium Zirconate", Zhur. Neorg. Khim. Vol. 2. pp. 2327-33. (USSR)

194.   Yosim, S. J. and Milne, T. A., "Basic Chemistry of High Temperature Inorganic Systems", U. S. AEC Publ. NAA-SR-1797. Semi-Annual Prog. Rept. Jan.-June, 1956. N. Am. Aviation. 23 p.

195.   Grimes, D. M., Westrum Jr., E. F. and Legvold, S., "Measurement and Interpretation of Thermal and Magnetic Data on Nickel-Zinc Ferrites", Rept. No. 2262. 141-T; Tech. Rept. No. 34. AD 135 955. 37 p.

196.   Boyko, E. R. and Wisnyi, L. G., "Structure and Optical Properties of CaO · $2Al_2O_3$ and SrO · $2Al_2O_3$", U. S. AEC Publ. KAPL-1883. 19 p.

197.   Vickery, R. C. and Sedlacek, R., "Effects of Low Concentration of Rare Earth Oxides Upon Refractive Index and Density of a Lead Glass", TN2, AFOSR-TN 57-318. AD 132 389. 10 p.

198.   Duwez, P. and Loh, E., "Phase Relations in the System Zirconia-Thoria", J. Am. Ceram. Soc. Vol. 40. pp. 321-4.

199.   Wisnyi, L. G. and Pijanowski, S. W., "Thermal Stability of Uranium Dioxide", U.S. AEC KAPL-1702. p. 20.

1. Olson, O.H. and Morris, J.C., "Determination of Emissivity and Reflectivity Data on Aircraft Structural Materials", WADC TR 56-222 Part II. Sup.1 Contract AF 33(616) 3002, TASK 73606. 31 p.

2. Fieldhouse, I.B., Hedge, J.C., and Lang, J.I., "Measurements of Thermal Properties", WADC Tech. Rept. 58-274. (Contract No. AF 33(616)-3701). AD-206 892. 79 p.

3. Bentle, Gordon G., "A Physical Metallurgical Study of Thorium-rich Thorium-Uranium Alloys", NAA-SR-2069 Contract AT (11-1)-GEN-8. AD 154-822. 28 p.

4. Fieldhouse, I.B., Hedge, J.C., et al., "Thermal Properties of High Temperature Materials", WADC Tech. Rept. No. 57-487 (Contract AF 33(616)3701). AD 150 954. 79 p.

5. Lucks, C.F. and Deem, H.W., "Thermal Properties of Thirteen Metals", Am. Soc. Testing Materials, Spec. Tech. Publ. Vol. No. 227. 29 p.

6. McKeown, J.J., "High Temperature Heat Capacity and Related Thermodynamic Functions of Rare Earth Metals", Univ. Microfilms (Ann Arbor, Mich.) L.C. Card No. Mic 58-2194. 113 p.

7. Francis, R.K., McNamara, E.P., and Tinklepaugh, J.R., "The Bonding of Ceramic-Metal Laminates", Prog. Rept. No. 5. AD 154-872. 15 p.

8. Mikheev, V.S. and Pevtsov, D.M., "Phase Diagram of the Niobium-tungsten System", Zhur. Neorg. Khim. Vol. 3. pp. 861-6. (USSR)

9. Custer, Brice C., "Determination of Thermal Expansivity of Zirconium Hydride", (Rept. No. GNE-58-8); Master's Thesis, Air Force Inst. of Tech. AD 157 591. 44 p.

10. Mantell, C.L., ed. in chief., Engineering Materials Handbook. McGraw-Hill Book Co., Inc. New York.

11. Hansen, Max and Anderko, K., Constitution of Binary Alloys. McGraw-Hill Book Co., Inc., 1958. 1286 p.

12. Kornilov, I.I. and Polyakova, R.S., "Phase Diagram of the Ternary System Titanium-Niobium Molybdenum", Zhur. Neorg. Khim. Vol. 3. pp. 879-88. (USSR)

13. Cadoff, I.E., Miller, E. and Komarek, K., "Thermoelectric Properties of Intermetallic Compounds", AD 158 418. 4 p.

14. Crespi, C., "Polypropylene - A Promising New Plastic", Materials. Vol. 47 (1). pp. 110-114.

15. Schultz, A.W. and Wong, A.K., "Thermal Conductivity of Teflon, Kel-F and Duroid 5600 at Elevated Temperatures", WAL Rept. No. TR 397/10. AD 154 351. 13 p.

16. Ball, J.G. et al. "The Crystal Structures of Plutonium: The Delta and Epsilon Phases", U.S. AEC Publ. AERE-M/R 2416. 16 p. (England)

17. Dempsey, E. and Kay, A.E., "Some Investigations of Plutonium Metal", J. Inst. Metals. Vol. 86. pp. 379-84. (England)

18. Dean, D.J., Kav, A.E. and Loasby, R.G., "Note on the Specific Heat of Plutonium Metal", J. Inst. Metals. Vol. 86. p. 464. (England)

19. Fried, S., Westrum, E.F. et al., "The Microscale Preparation and Micrometallurgy of Plutonium Metal", J. Inorg. Nuclear Chem. Vol. 5. pp. 182-9.

20. Wade, W.R., "Measurements of Total Hemispherical Emissivity of Various Oxidized Metals at High Temperature", NACA-TN 4206. 44 p.

21. Deem, H.W., Wood, W.D. and Lucks, C.F., "The Relation between Electrical and Thermal Conductivities of Titanium Alloys", Trans. Met. Soc. AIME 212. pp. 520-3.

22. Hirano, K.I.. "Specific Heat of Antiferromagnetic Phase in Manganese-Rich Copper-Manganese Binary Alloys", Acta. Met. Vol. 6. p. 64.

23. Von Batchelder, F.W. and Raeuchle, R.F., "The Tetragonal MBe_{12} Structure of Silver, Palladium, Platinum and Gold", Acta. Cryst. Vol. 11. p. 122.

24. Stradley, J.G. and Shevlin, T.S., "Alumina-Base Cermets", WADC TR 54-173. Pt. 5. Contr. AF33(616)472. AD 156 810. 15 p.

25. Truesdale, R.S., Swica, J.J. and Tinklepaugh, J.R., "Metal Fiber Reinforced Ceramics", WADC TR 58-452. AD 207 079. 36 p.

1. Olson, O. H. and Morris, J. C., "Determination of Emissivity and Reflectivity Data on Aircraft Structural Materials. Part III: Techniques for Measurement of Total Normal Emissivity, Normal Spectral Emissivity at 0.665 Microns, Solar Absorptivity and Presentation of Results", WADC TR 56-222, Pt III. Contract No. AF 33(616)-3002, Project No. 7360.

2. HANDBOOK -- Hodgman, Charles D., Weast, Robt. C. et al., ed. Handbook of Chemistry and Physics, 41st Edition, Chemical Rubber Publishing Co., Cleveland, Ohio.

1. Rasor, N. S. (Personal communication, D137, re: SPECIFIC HEAT -- TANTALUM) <u>WADC TR 59-439</u>.

1. Rasor, N. S. (Personal communication, D137, re: SPECIFIC HEAT -- TANTALUM) <u>WADC TR 59-439</u>.

1. Murray, P. and Thackray, R. W., "The Thermal Expansion of Sintered UO_2 ", Rept. No. AERE M/M 22. 4 p. (England)

2. Chupka, W. A., Berkowitz, J. and Inghram, M. G., "Thermodynamics of the $Zr-ZrO_2$ System; The Dissociation Energies of ZrO and ZrO_2 ", In cooperation with Argonne Natl. Lab., Lemont, Ill. Sponsored by OOR. AD 107 062. 12 p.

3. Berkowitz, J., Inghram, M. G. and Chupka, W. A., "Polymeric Gaseous Species in the Sublimation of Molybdenum Trioxide", In cooperation with Argonne Natl. Lab., Lemont, Ill. Sponsored by OOR. AD 107 063. 14 p.

4. Ellerbeck, E. J., "Non-Metallic Materals", Special Rept. No. D2-1471, Contr. AF33(600)31802. AD 138 376. 103 p. (No date)

Investigator	Ref.	Materials Index Classification
Aas, S.	57-143	I-U-1
Abe, F.	52-96	II-A-1; XI-B-5
Ackermann, R.J.	56-42	VII-A-10
	56-43	VII-A-7
Adams, A. M.	50-11	VII-B-4-b
Adams, C.H.	56-136	X-E, F; X
Adams Jr., G.B.	52-57	VII-A-13
Adams, M.	54-5	VII-A-1-a; VII-A-2-a; VII-A-5-a; VII-A-7; VII-A-9-b
Adenstedt, H.K.	51-9	I-H-1; I-Z-1
	52-118	IV-G; V-C-4
Agladze, R.L.	55-56	I-M-2; IV-A-6; VI-E-1, 2
Ahmann, D.H.	53-22	I-C-4; I-N-1
Aka, E.Z.	52-20	I-G-2; I-S-3
Alfred University	57-180	VII-A-1-a
Aliev, N.A.	56-33	III-E; V-A-1
Allen, A.W.	56-164	VII-A-5-a; VII-B-7-a
Allen, F.G.	57-124	I-G-2; I-S-3
Allendorfer, A.	50-20	I-U-1
Alliegro, R.A.	53-18	I-C-5; I-J-2; I-N-3; I-S-3; IV-A-2; IV-B-I; VII-A-5; VII-D-1-a; VII-D-1
Allison, F.E.	56-25	IV-A-1
	56-26	IV-A-1
Allison, H.W.	50-24	VII-A-15
Allison, S.A.	49-20	VII-A-11
Altman, H.W.	54-10	I-A-2; I-N-3; I-T-6; I-Z-1
	54-39	II-D-3; III-A-3
	54-53	I-C-7
American Electro Metal Corp.	52-87	IX-G-1
Ames Laboratory	48-18	I-L-1; I-N-1
	52-103	I-C-4; I-D-1; I-L-1; I-N-1; I-P-5
	54-99	I-D-1; I-U-1
	56-63	I-A-2; I-D-1; I-P-5
	56-84	I-A-2; I-S-1; I-T-5; I-Y-1
	57-112	I-E-3
Ames, S.L.	54-25	I-N-4; I-T-6; IV-E; V-C
	56-15	I-T-6; V-C-1; V-C-8; V-C
	56-95	I-T-6; V-C; IX-E
Amnuel, I.G.	56-153	VII-D-2
Anderson, S.	46-7	VII-C-1-b
Andrew, J.H.	50-8	II-A-1, 2, 3, 4, 5, 6
Andrew, K.F.	50-48	I-B-3; XI-E
Andrews, M.C.	56-152	VII-B-6-e, f, j, k
Angier, R.P.	51-36	I-Z-1
Anonymous	48-24	IV-A-5
	50-16	V-A-1
	50-17	V-A-1
	54-117	IV-C
	55-46	V-A-3
	56-117	IV-A-3-a; IV-A-3
Aoyama, S.	40-11	I-C-7; III-A-3
Apblett, W.R.	51-5	I-M-4; I-T-7; II-D-3; II-D-6-a; IV-A-4-a; IV-A-5-a; IV-B-1, 3
Arbiter, W.	52-40	VIII-C-1
	52-84	VIII-C-1; IX-C-3; IX-J-11
	53-54	VIII-E; IX-B
Arbiter, W.	53-134	VIII-E
	53-137	VIII-B
	54-84	VIII-B, D; IX-B
Argonne National Laboratory	47-23	I-C-3-a; I-C-3; VII-A-2-a
	47-24	I-C-3
Argonne National Laboratory	54-115	IV-J; V-C-1
	56-120	VI-F; VI
	57-114	I-U-1; VI-F-2; VI-F

Armstrong, L.D.	47-12	I-J-2
	50-3	I-C-5, 6; I-M-2
Arthur, J.S.	50-7	V-A-1, 5; VII-A-5-a; VII-A-8; VII-A-9-b
Assayag, G.	54-58	VII-A-13
Assayag, P.	55-63	VII-A-13
Atkins, D.F.	54-104	I-N-4; I-Z-1
	55-105	I-N-4; I-Z-1
Augustinik, A.I.	56-162	VII-B-8-n, p
Ault, N.N.	56-7	VII-A-1-a; VII-A-3-a; VII-A-9-b; VII-A-1, 3, 5, 7, 8; VII-B-3-c; VII-B-4-b; VII-B-6-d; VII-B-7-a; VII-B-7; VII-C-6; VII-D-1-a; VII-D-5-a; VII-D-2, 7
Aŭslander, J.S.	56-105	I-P-4
Averbach, B.L.	52-123	II-D-5
Averbach, B.E.	55-15	II-A-1; II-D-6
Avery, D.G.	50-32	I-S-4
Avgustink, A.	55-27	VII-E-6
Awano, M.	56-38	I-G-3; I-S-4
Awbery, J.H.	40-1	I-J-2
Axilrod, B.M.	45-14	X-A-1; X-F, J
Bacon, A.E.	53-10	I-J-2; I-N-3; I-P-2; I-T-6
Bacon, G.E.	57-157	VI-E-1
Baenziger, N.C.	48-25	VI-F; VII-A-10; IX-J-2
	48-29	IX-A-7
	50-55	VI-F-IX-J-2, 5
Baker, B.E.	54-65	II-D-3; V-B-1; VII-A-1-a; IX-B-1
Baker, H.	56-22	V-B-4
	57-54	I-M-1; V-B-1, 2, 3, 4, 6
Baker, T.W.	57-32	IX-D-3
Baldwin, G.J.	55-1	I-M-4
Ball, A.F.	49-52	I-B-3
Ball, J.G.	53-112	I-P-3
	54-98	I-P-3
	58-16	I-P-3
Ballard, S.S.	55-3	I-G-2
Balluffi, R.W.	52-76	I-Z-1; IV-J-1
	53-119	I-U-1
	57-120	I-C-7
Balz, G.	47-15	I-U-1
Barber, C.R.	49-54	V-A-1, 2, 3, 4; V-A-2-a, b; V-A
Bardeen, J.	49-4	I-S-3; II-D-5; VI-G
Barson, F.	53-31	I-D-1; I-G-1; I-N-1; I-P-5
	56-88	I-C-7; I-D-1; I-E-2; I-G-1; I-L-1; I-N-1; I-P-5; I-Y-1
	57-13	I-C-4; I-D-1; I-E-2; I-G-1; I-L-1; I-N-1; I-P-5; I-T-3; I-Y-1
Bartenev, G.M.	40-8	II-A-1, 2, 3, 4, 5, 6, 7
Barton, J.E.	56-142	VIII-D
Barton, R.J.	57-74	I-T-5
Barzelay, M.E.	54-94	XI-B-2, 4; XI-D-4; XI-E
Basmajian, J.A.	57-82	VII-B-6-e
Bates, J.C.	53-122	I-U-1
Bates, L.F.	40-18	II-D-5
Battelle Memorial Institute	45-13	I-T-4; I-U-1; VI-F; IX-D-2
Bauer, A.A.	57-158	IV-L
Beals, R.J.	57-20	VII-A-1-a; VII-A-2-a; VII-A-3-a; VII-A-5-a; VII-A-1, 3, 5, 15; VII-B-7-a, m; VII-B-8
Beard, A.P.	57-76	IV-J-1; IV-J
Beamer, W.H.	49-39	I-P-4
Becker, J.H.	54-130	IX-F-1
Beckman, G.	56-144	IX-B-2; IX-C
Bednar, J.	57-85	IX-F-2
Beetle, R.	48-4	VII-B-6-c; VII-B-7-c
Begley, R.T.	57-151	I-N-4
Beinlich Jr., A.W.	46-14	VII-A-5-a; VII-A-5; VII-A-13; VII-B
Beksay, Z.	55-149	VII-C-1
Bell, I.P.	53-123	I-N-3
	54-103	I-M-4; I-N-3; I-T-1, 6; I-U-1; VII-A-10
Bell, W.C.	53-105	VII-C-1-b; VII-C-5

Belle, J.	56-156	VII-A-9-b; VII-A-10
	57-86	VII-A-10
	57-190	VII-A-1
Belyaevskaya, L. V.	56-151	VII-D-6
Bender, D.	49-18	I-T-4
Bendt, W.	40-15	I-A-4, 5
Benford, F.	48-35	VII-A-5-a
Bennett, D. G.	53-42	VII-E-9; VII-E
	56-97	I-J-2; II-D-2
	55-118	IV-A-5-a; IV-B-1; VIII-C
Bennett, D. G.	56-97	I-J-2; II-D-2
	52-36	II-D-7
Bens, F. P.	46-3	IV-F-2; IV-F
Bentle, G. G.	58-3	I-T-4
Berberich, L. J.	44-6	VII-C-6; VII-E-3-k; VII-E-4
Berkowitz, J.	56-44	VII-A-8, 15
	57-65	VII-A-8
	ND-2	I-Z-1; VII-A-9-b
	ND-3	VII-A-14
Berman, R.	51-14	VII-A-1-a; VII-A-1, 6; VII-C-5, 6
	53-80	I-C-3-m
	53-90	I-C-3-m
Bernard, D.	53-135	IX-C
Bertolet Jr., E. C.	54-92	X-G
Best, G.	49-34	I-A-2; I-C-7
Betz, H. T.	56-66	I-C-3-a, d; I-C-7; I-M-4; I-N-3; I-T-1; III-E; IX-C
	57-8	I-A-2; I-C-3-a, d; I-C-5, 7; I-J-2; I-M-4; I-N-3; I-P-1, 2; I-R-3; I-T-1; II-D-1, 3; II-D-3-a; III-E; IV-A-2; IV-A-5-a; V-C-1; V-C; VII-A-2-a; VII-A-5; XI-B-5; XI-C
Bibring, H.	54-29	I-C-6
Bidwell, C. C.	47-6	I-A-2; I-C-3-a
Bielanski, A.	55-150	VII-B
Binder, I.	55-76	IV-A-2, 5; IV-F-1; VIII-C; IX-C-2, 3; IX-H; IX-J-1
Bing, G.	51-64	I-Z-1; IV-J-1, 3, 7; IV-J
	51-65	I-J-2; II-A-1; II-D-2, 3; IV-A-1, 5; V-A-1, 4; V-A-5-a; V-P-4; VII-C-1-b; VII-C-5
	52-33	VII-A-1-a; VII-C-1-b; VII-C-5, 6
Birchenall, C. E.	52-69	I-S-4
	53-131	VI-A-B
Bischoff, F.	55-26	VII-C-2, 5
Bishop, S. M.	52-122	V-C-1, 2, 5
Bitsianes, G.	45-17	IX-B-2
Bizette, H.	54-58	VII-A-13
Bizzard, R.	57-92	VIII; IX-G, H
	57-166	VIII
Blackburn, A. R.	51-28	VIII-B-1
Blackburn, P. E.	50-6	I-C-5
	50-40	I-T-1
	51-40	I-T-1
	51-68	I-V-1
	52-50	I-M-4
Blalock, G. C.	53-130	II-D-2; IV-A-5
Blanter, M. E.	47-13	II-A-3, 4, 5, 6, 7; II-C-6; II-D-1
Blocher, J.	49-22	I-T-6
Blomeke, J. O.	51-29	VII-A-4-g, j, k
Bloom, D. S.	52-64	I-C-5
Bloom, F. K.	53-88	I-A-2; I-C-7; I-J-2; I-N-3; I-S-4; II-D-1, 2; III-A, R; IV-A-1
Blumenthal, B.	55-55	I-U-1
Blumenthal, H.	49-59	IX-C-2, 3; IX-C
	54-128	VIII-A-2
	54-129	VIII-A-2
Blunt, R. F.	54-130	IX-F-1
	55-136	IX-G-3
Bobone, R.	54-124	IV-A
Bochirol, L.	51-32	VII-B-8-m, n, p
	51-49	VII-B-8-a, m, n, p; VII-B-8

Bockstahler, L. I.	51-2	I-T-6; V-C-5
Bodor, G.	57-102	X-H
Boegli, J. S.	55-54	VII-A-10
Boelter, L. M. K.	44-10	I-A-2; II-D-2; IV-A-5-a; XI-B-5; XI-D
Boettcher, A.	50-28	I-A-2; I-M-1; I-S-4; V-A-3, 6; V-B-2; VI-B-1
Bollenrath, F.	43-7	III-E
	47-8	II-D-6-a; II-D-3, 4, 6, 9; IV-A-3-a; IV-A-3
	48-1	V-A-1; V-A-2-a; V-A-2
Boltaks, B. I.	49-37	VI; IX-F; IX-G-3
	55-92	IX-F-2
Bolz, L. H.	53-28	I-T-7
	54-16	IX-A-2; IX-A
	54-19	I-S-3; VII-A-8
	54-37	I-S-3; VII-A-9-b
	54-51	VII-A-8; IX-B-1
	55-58	I-S-3; I-T-7; VII-A-5-a; VII-A-5, 7, 8, 9; IX-A-1, 2, 4, 5; IX-A; IX-B-1; IX-B; IX-F-1
Bolz, L. H.	55-102	I-C-3-m; I-S-4
	55-108	I-C-3-j
	56-8	VII-A-8; VII-A-9-b; VII-B-6-n; VII-B-6; VIII-B
	57-62	I-C-3-m; I-P-2; I-S-3; VII-A-1-a; VII-A-1, 8; VII-B-6-n; IX-A-6; IX-B-1; IX-B; IX-C-3
Bommer, H.	43-16	IX-H-1: IX-H
Bonnickson, K. R.	54-62	VII-B-8-a, d
Boody, F. P.	50-42	I-H-1; I-Z-1
Boosz, H. J.	57-2	I-A-2; I-C-6, 7; I-M-4; I-T-7; VIII-A-1
Borie Jr., B. S.	50-59	IX-G-1
Bostrom, W. A.	55-111	I-U-1; VI-F-2; VI-F; IX-B-2
	56-132	VI-F-2
	57-42	VI-F-2; VI-F
	57-100	I-T-6; I-Z-1; IV-C-7; IV-J-1; IV-J
Boucher, R. R.	55-131	IX-B
Bourke, R.	56-136	X-E, F; X
Bowles, P. J.	50-56	VI-F
Boyd, C. L.	53-115	I-U-1
Boyko, E. R.	57-196	VII-B-7-d, k
Boyle, R. F.	56-119	VI-F-2
Brace, P. H.	42-3	IV-A-3-a
Bradford, A. P.	57-136	I-T-6
Bradley, J. F.	52-97	I-U-1
Brady, J. G.	54-133	VII-E-9
	56-155	VII-E-9
Brackbill, C. E.	51-22	VII-C-1-a
Brand, H.	54-150	VII-C-1-b
Brandes, E. A.	52-81	I-C-3; I-N-3; I-P-2; II-D-2; IV-A-5-a; VII-A-1-a; VII-A-4-a; VII-A-5-a; VII-A-9-b; VII-A-6, 7
	53-36	I-C-5
Brauer, G.	50-29	IX-G-3; IX-G
Brewer, L.	48-9	I-C-3
	48-10	I-C-3
	48-31	VII-D-6
	49-44	I-J-2
	49-56	VI
Brewer, L.	49-65	VII-A-11; VII-D-5-a; VII-D-5
	50-27	VII-D-6
	50-30	IX-B-1; IX-b: IX-J-4, 7, 9
	51-10	I-A-2; VII-A-1-a; VII-A-1
	51-60	I-J-2
Bridge, J. R.	56-104	I-U-1
Bridgman, P. W.	55-30	I-R-2; I-S-5; I-Y-2
Brink, C.	55-119	IV-D
Brizgys, P.	50-5	I-A-2; I-B-1; I-C-1; I-M-1
Brocklehurst, R. E.	57-118	I-P-4
Bromberg, R.	44-10	I-A-2; II-D-2; IV-A-5-a; XI-B-5; XI-D
Bromley, L.	48-31	VII-D-6
	49-65	VII-D-5-a; VII-D-5; VII-A-11
Bron, V. A.	53-145	VII-B-6-d
Brookhaven National Laboratory	50-54	II-D-5

Broom, T.	52-4	I-A-2; I-C-7; I-N-3
Brown, A.R.G.	53-125	I-C-3
	55-70	I-C-3-h; I-C-3
	57-46	I-V-1; V-C-4
Brown, D.	56-150	VII-A-14; VII-D-6
Brown Jr., F.H.	54-147	VII-A-9-b
Bruch, C.A.	56-109	I-B-4; VII-A-4-b, d, e, w; VII-A-10; VII-B-7-d, k
	56-167	VII-B
Budennaya, L.D.	56-32	IV-B-4; IV-B, D; VI-A-3; VI-D-2
Buerschaper, R.A.	44-5	I-C-3-a, b
Buessem, W.R.	52-133	VII-A-9-b; VII-B-6-d, j
	55-10	VII-A-8; VII-B-3-e; VII-E-3
Bullock, G.	56-23	I-J-2
Bungardt, W.	43-7	III-E
	47-8	II-D-3, 4, 6, 9; II-D-6-a; IV-A-3-a; IV-A-3
	51-25	I-A-2; V-A-1; V-A-2-a
Bunting, E.N.	43-14	VII-A-1-a; VII-A-1
	47-9	VII-A-8; VII-B-6-e, k
	48-3	VII-B-6-j, e
	51-86	VII-B-6
Burdick, M.D.	51-44	I-C-3-a, d
	55-144	VII-A-7, 10
Burkart, M.W.	55-111	I-U-1; VI-F-2; VI-F; IX-B-2
	57-42	VI-F-2
Burkhanov, G.S.	57-38	I-T-6
Burlakov, V.D.	57-51	I-C-5; I-J-2
Burney, J.D.	52-41	VIII-D
Busch, G.	53-93	IX-B; IX-F-1; IX-G-3
	54-34	I-A-4
	54-74	IX-F-1
Busey, R.H.	52-2	I-N-3
Bush, E.A.	55-10	VII-A-8; VII-B-3-e; VII-E-3
Buswell, R.W.A.	52-28	IV-B-1
Cadoff, I.E.	58-13	VII-D-6; IX-F-2
Caldwell, W.C.	51-59	I-C-4; I-L-1; I-N-1; I-P-5
	53-21	I-A-2; I-N-1; I-P-5
	56-83	I-A-2; I-N-1; I-P-5
Campbell, D.A.	57-110	I-C-3-p; I-C-3
Campbell, I.E.	47-22	I-Z-1
	49-22	I-T-6
Capps, W.	53-139	VII-C-2
Carlile, S.J.	49-43	I-C-5
Carlson, J.F.	51-59	I-C-4; I-L-1; I-N-1; I-P-5
Carlson, O.N.	49-49	I-C-7; I-M-2; I-U-1; III; VI-F
	50-41	I-M-4; I-T-4; I-Z-1; VI-F-3; VI-F, L
	52-105	I-H-1; I-T-4; I-Z-1
	53-120	I-T-4, 6
	54-18	I-N-4; I-V-1
Carlson, O.N.	54-101	I-V-1; IX-G-1; IX-J-10
	56-89	I-C-1
	56-129	VI
	57-115	I-U-1
Carniglia, S.C.	53-73	I-A-3; VII-D-5-a
	55-77	I-A-3; VII-D-5-a
Carpenter, J.H.	56-149	IX-J-6
Carpenter, L.G.	49-6	I-T-6
	51-58	I-T-6
Cashin, W.M.	56-109	I-B-4; VII-A-4-b, d, e, w; VII-B-7-d, k; VII-A-10
	56-167	VII-B
Castleman, L.S.	50-49	I-Z-1
Catterall, J.A.	56-85	I-P-1; VI-D
Cennamo, F.	39-3	I-N-3
Chandappa, N.	51-83	VII-C-2
Chang, P.L.	50-8	II-A-1

95

Chapin, E.J.	56-9	V-C-8
Charvat, F.R.	57-53	VII-A-1, 5, 8; VII-A-5-a; VII-D-5
Chasmar, R.P.	57-130	I-G-2; I-S-3; II-D-3; IX-F
Cherton, R.	42-7	I-C-3
Chiba, S.	55-116	II-C
Chicago Univ. Metallurgical Lab.	43-19	I-C-3-a
Chiochetti, V.R.	53-94	VII-A-1-a; VII-A-6; VII-B-4-b; VII-B-4; VII-D-1-a; VII-E-9, 10
Chiotti, P.	49-53	I-T-4; IX-A
	50-45	I-M-4; I-N-3; I-T-4
	50-61	VIII-A
	52-8	I-T-4, 6
	52-83	IX-A-7; IX-D-2; IX-D, J; IX
Chiotti, P.	53-111	I-T-1
	54-105	I-T-4
	56-99	I-J-2; I-U-1
	56-129	VI
	57-115	I-U-1
Chiswik, H.H.	56-113	I-T-6; I-Z-1; II-D-3; IV-J-1; IV-J; V-C-1
Christian, J.W.	49-43	I-C-5
Christian, S.M.	54-86	VI-G; VI
Chubb, W.	56-90	I-U-1
Chupka, W.A.	53-83	I-C-3
	53-84	I-C-3
	54-80	I-C-3
	55-62	I-C-3
	56-44	VII-A-8, 15
Chupka, W.A.	57-65	VII-A-8
	ND-2	I-Z-1; VII-A-9-b; VII-A-9
	ND-3	VII-A-14
Clark, W.B.	57-76	IV-J-1; IV-J
Cleary, H.J.	56-4	I-V-1; IV-G
Cleaves, H.E.	42-5	I-J-2
	49-29	I-U-1
	49-30	I-U-1
Cleek, G.W.	56-20	VII-C-1-k
Clegg, J.W.	53-141	VII-D-2-a; VII-D-5-a
Clements, J.F.	57-26	I-C-3-b; VII-A-5; VII-B-1; VII-D-1-a; VII-E-9, 11
Cline, C.F.	57-23	VII-B-4-a; VII-A-9-a
Clusius, K.	52-12	I-C-6
	55-32	I-J-1; I-R-3
Coble, R.L.	56-10	VII-A-1-a; VII-A-1
Coffer, L.W.	54-63	IX-G-3
Coffin, D.O.	55-120	III-C
	57-52	I-C-7
Coffin, L.B.	53-18	I-C-5; I-J-2; I-N-3; I-S-3; IV-A-2; IV-B-1; VII-A-5; VII-D-1-a; VII-D-1
Colbeck, E.W.	52-26	II-C-6
Collins, F.M.	56-49	I C-3-a; I-C-3
Colosky, B.P.	52-80	VII-C-6
Comeforo, J.E.	54-95	VII-B-9; VII-E-3-k; VII-E-4
Compton, A.H.	42-12	I-U-1
	49-20	VII-A-11
Cook, L.A.	50-49	I-Z-1
Cook, O.A.	46-6	VII-B-6-f, g, j
	48-7	VII-B-5
Cook, R.L.	57-20	VII-A-1-a; VII-A-2-a; VII-A-3-a; VII-A-5-a; VII-A-7-a, m; VII-A-1, 3, 5, 15
Coomes, E.A.	55-1	I-M-4
Cornelius, H.	43-17	II-A-1, 2, 3; II-B-1; II-C-1, 5, 6, 9; II-C; II-D-1, 3, 4, 9; II-J; II-J-4, 7; II-L-6
	47-8	II-D-6-a; II-D-3, 4, 6, 9; IV-A-3-a; IV-A-3
Corruccini, R.J.	47-1	I-U-1; VII-D-5
	47-17	VII-A-1-a
Cosgrove, L.A.	53-1	VII-A-14
Cotter, P.G.	54-126	IX-A-4
	56-140	IX-B
Coughlin, J.P.	50-2	I-Z-1; VII-A-9-b; VII-B-4-b; IX-D-3
	52-61	VII-B-6-j
	53-13	VII-B-6-e, k
	57-87	VII-B-2-c

Couling, S. L.	56-22	V-B-1, 3, 4
Covington, P. C.	54-90	XI-H-3, 5, 6
	57-97	XI-A-1, 2; XI-B-1; XI-D-1, 2, 3; XI-H-6, 7
Cowan, J. A.	57-185	VII-A-15
Cox, M.	43-1	I-T-1, 7
Cox, S. M.	51-26	VII-C-5
Craig, R. S.	54-12	I-M-1
	54-63	IX-G-3
Craighead, C. M.	52-18	I-T-6; V-B
	54-38	I-R-2
Craighead, C. M.	55-18	I-R-2
	55-59	I-R-2; VI
	56-17	I-R-2
Crandall, W. B.	51-73	VIII-A-5; VIII-B-2; IX-C-3; IX-D; IX-G-1
	52-100	VII-A-5-a; VII-A-5
Crane, W. W. T.	50-39	I-C-8
	51-56	I-C-8
Creamer, A. S.	46-4	VII-A-1
	47-9	VII-A-8; VII-B-6-e, k
	48-3	VII-B-6-j, e
	51-86	VII-B-6
Crespi, C.	58-14	X
Criscione, J. M.	53-75	I-G-2
Cubicciotti, D.	50-36	I-J-2; I-N-3; I-P-2; I-Z-1; VII-A-9-b
	51-52	I-J-2; I-N-3; I-P-2; I-Z-1
Cueilleron, J.	45-5	I-B-4
Cunningham, B. B.	50-39	I-C-8
	55-77	I-A-3; VII-D-5-a
	55-93	I-A-1; I-P-7
Currey, P. P.	51-65	I-J-2; II-A-1; II-D-2, 3; IV-A-1, 5; IV-A-5-a; V-A-1, 4; V-B-1; V-P-4; VII-C-1-b; VII-C-5, 6
Curtis, C. E.	54-45	VII-A-9-a, b; VII-B-4-a, b; VII-B-6-a
	54-46	VII-A-9-a, b; VII-B-4-a, b; VII-B-6-a
	57-22	VII-A-7
	57-24	VII-A-4-e, n
	57-84	VII-A-15
Curtis, G. C.	57-133	I-N-2; I-P-7
Custer, B. C.	58-9	I-Z-1; IX-E-1
Czanderna, A. W.	57-178	VII-A-4-a
Daane, A. H.	54-36	I-C-4; I-D-1; I-E-2; I-G-1; I-H-2; I-L-1, 2; I-N-1; I-P-3, 5; I-S-1; I-T-3, 5; I-Y-1, 2
	55-52	I-C-4; I-D-1; I-E-2, 3; I-G-1; I-H-2; I-L-1, 2; I-N-1; I-P-5; I-S-1, 2; I-T-3, 5; I-Y-1, 2
	56-86	I-C-4; I-D-1; I-E-2, 3; I-G-1; I-H-2; I-L-1, 2; I-P-5, 6; I-S-1, 2; I-T-3, 5; I-Y-1, 2
	57-74	I-T-5
	57-119	I-L-1; I-N-1; I-P-2
Dahl, A. I.	47-3	I-U-1
	47-5	I-C-4; I-N-3
	49-29	I-U-1
	49-30	I-U-1
Dale, A. E.	51-81	VII-C-2, 5
	54-140	VII-C
Damon, E. B.	55-134	IX-E-1
Danforth, W. E.	50-65	VII-A-7
	54-141	VII-A-7
	56-159	VII-A-7
Danielson, G. C.	52-106	I-T-4
	52-107	I-T-4
	52-117	IV-J, L
	54-33	I-N-3
	55-14	I-N-3; I-P-2
Danielson, G. C.	55-91	IX-G-3
	55-132	IX-B
	57-11	I-N-3; I-U-1
	57-149	I-N-3; I-P-2

Darnell, A. J.	52-73	I-C-3
Darnell, F. J.	55-89	I-G-2
Dauphinee, T. M.	47-12	I-J-2
	55-87	I-G-2
Davey, A. R.	56-78	I-C-3-m
Davey, P. O.	54-33	I-N-3
	57-11	I-N-3; I-U-1
Dayton, R. W.	55-112	I-U-1
	56-118	IV-J-1; VI-F-2
	56-139	IX-B-2; IX-G-4; IX-J-5
Dayton, R. W.	57-154	IV-J-1: VI-F-2; IX-B-2
	57-163	IV-J-1
Dean, D. J.	58-18	I-P-3
Deardorff, D. K.	56-11	I-H-1; I-T-6; I-Z-1
Deegan, G. E.	56-12	I-C-3-d
Deem, H. W.	51-31	VI-B-2
	51-46	VII-D-2
	51-65	I-J-2; II-A-1; II-D-2, 3; IV-A-1, 5; IV-A-5-a; V-A-1, 4; V-B-1; V-P-4; VII-C-1-b; VII-C-5
	52-48	I-U-1
	53-6	I-H-1
	53-46	I-Z-1; IV-J-1, 3
Deem, H. W.	54-42	VI-F-1; VI-F
	55-106	I-T-4
	56-1	I-C-3-a, d; I-C-5, 7; I-J-2; I-M-4; VII-A-1-a
	57-9	I-C-3-d
	58-5	I-C-5, 7; I-M-4; II-A-1; II-A; II-D-2, 3; IV-A-5-a; IV-A-1, 5; V-A-1, 4; V-B-1
	58-21	I-T-6; V-C-1, 2, 7
Deissler, R. G.	55-54	VII-A-10
Del Grosso, A.	57-155	VI-F-2; VI-F
Demarquay, J.	45-1	I-M-4; I-T-7
Dempsey, E.	58-17	I-P-3
Denton, E. P.	54-139	VII-C
DePue, L. A.	56-9	V-C-8
Desirant, M.	41-21	I-T-1
DeSorbo, W.	53-14	IX-A-3
	53-79	I-C-3-a
	53-81	I-C-3-m
	55-35	VI-A-4
	55-66	I-C-3-j
Deutsch, G. C.	49-23	VIII-A-2
Dever, J. L.	53-39	II-D-1, 3; IV-A-1, 5
	55-16	II-D-1, 3; IV-A-1, 5
Deverall, J. E.	52-7	I-C-7; III
DeVos, J. C.	54-112	I-T-7
DeVries, R. C.	55-72	VII-B-6-e, f
	57-82	VII-B-6-e, k
Devyatkova, E. D.	57-129	I-G-2
DeWitt, B. J.	40-9	VII-A-14
	43-3	VII-A-14
D'Eye, R. W. M.	49-40	I-T-4
Dickerson, R. F.	53-56	VI-F-1; VI-L
	54-20	I-Z-1; IV-J-1
	56-128	VI-F-2, 3
	57-158	IV-L
Dickinson, J. M.	54-18	I-N-4; I-V-1
Dickson, G.	43-6	III-A-2; III-B-1; III-A, D, E
Dies, K.	57-147	I-C-7; III-L
Dilling, E. D.	54-109	I-H-1
Ditmars, W. E.	52-129	VII-D-6; IX-A-7; IX-D-2
	54-66	IX-B-1
	57-59	VII-A-2-a; VII-A-2
Dixon, G.	45-2	VII-B-9
Doehaerd, T.	52-72	I-C-3
Dole, M.	53-97	X-G
	55-140	X-H
Domash, L.	55-38	VII-A-14
Domenicali, C. A.	53-27	I-C-7; III-F
	55-7	I-C-7; I-J-2; I-N-3; II-C-9; III-F; IV-A
	57-141	I-G-2

Doney, L.M.	54-45	VII-A-9-a,b; VII-B-4-a,b; VII-B-6-a
	54-46	VII-A-9-a,b; VII-B-4-a,b; VII-B-6-a
Doolittle, J.S.	53-99	X-F
Dorner, S.	51-41	I-G-3; I-S-4; I-T-7; VI-A, B
Dorward, J.G.	44-8	I-C-3-n, p; I-C-7; I-N-3; II-D-2; IV-A-1; XI-B-3
Douglas, E.A.	55-126	II-A-1; II-D-3; XI-E
Douglas, P.E.	54-76	I-C-1; I-P-2
Douglas, T.B.	49-52	I-B-3
	51-15	I-B-3
	53-39	II-D-1, 3; IV-A-1, 5
Douglas, T.B.	53-61	IX-B-1
	54-61	IX-B-1
	55-16	II-D-1, 3; IV-A-1, 5
	57-56	I-Z-1; II-D-3; IX-E-2
Dow Chemical Co.	54-11	I-A-2; I-M-1; V-B-1, 3, 4, 6
	54-41	V-B-1
	54-100	I-M-1
Dowell, A.M.	57-170	X-C-1; X-E, J; XI-H-3, 4, 6; XI-J
Doyama, M.	56-55	VI-A
Draghic, J.	54-102	I-T-6
Droher, J.J.	54-102	I-T-6
Drys, M.	55-74	VII-B-6-k
	57-83	VII-B-6-k
Duckworth, W.H.	57-29	IX-B-2; IX-D-2; IX-D; IX-G-1; IX
Dumes, H.E.	57-189	VII-A-4-b, d, e, n
Dumitrescu, T.	56-82	II-B-1, 8
Dunkerley, F.J.	43-3	VII-A-14
Dunmur, I.W.	57-157	VI-E-1
Durand, R.E.	57-139	I-C-3-a
Durbin, E.A.	52-31	VII-A-9-b; VII-A-1, 8, 14, 15; VII-B-3-b; VII-B-6-b; VII-C-6; VII-E-3, 4
	52-34	VII-A-14; VII-B-6-b
Duwez, P.	54-147	VII-A-9-b
	56-123	II-D-1
	56-137	IX-G-4
	57-198	VII-A-9-b
Dworkin, A.S.	54-136	VII-D-4
	56-150	VII-D-6; VII-A-14
Earhart, W.R.	52-133	VII-A-9-b; VII-B-6-d, j
Eastman, E.D.	50-27	VII-D-6
Ebert, H.	47-2	I-U-1
Eckert, R.E.	52-95	XI-H-3
Economos, G.	55-145	VII-A-13; VII-B-8
Edwards, A.R.	56-91	I-C-5
Edwards, J.W.	50-40	I-T-1
	51-11	I-C-6; I-J-2
	51-12	I-V-1
	51-13	I-Z-1
Edwards, J.W.	51-18	I-M-4; I-N-4; I-P-2- I-T-1
	51-40	I-T-1
	51-68	I-V-1
	52-50	I-M-4
	53-20	I-C-7; I-T-6
Edwards, R.K.	49-56	VI
	52-129	VII-D-6; IX-A-7; IX-D-2
Eggleston, R.R.	54-93	I-C-7
	54-107	I-G-3
	54-108	I-G-3
Ehrlich, P.	49-21	I-A-2; I-T-6; IX-A-2; IX-C, G; IX-D-1; IX
Eichelberger, R.L.	54-146	VII-A-3-a; VII-A-3; VII-B-6-f
Elder, G.E.	54-54	I-J-2; I-N-3
Eldred, V.W.	57-133	I-N-2; I-P-7
Ellerbeck, E.J.	ND-4	X-XI-C; XI-H-5
Ellinger, F.H.	54-125	IX-E
	56-40	I-P-3
	57-61	I-P-3
Elliott, R.O.	52-24	I-P-3
Elliott, R.P.	53-91	IX-J-1, 3, 4, 6, 7, 9, 11; IX-J; IX

Ellis, W.C.	48-21	I-C-6; I-J-2; II-D; IV-B-3
	48-22	I-C-6; I-J-2; II-D; IV-B-3
	48-23	I-T-6
	51-3	I-C-5
Elson, R.	51-61	I-P-7
Engel, M.	39-4	I-S-4; VI-B-2, 3; VI-B
Englander, M.	51-85	VII-A-10
Epelboin, I.	57-25	I-C-7; I-P-1, 2; I-S-4
Erfling, H.D.	40-5	I-M-2
	42-4	I-C-5; I-N-4
	42-8	I-C-1; I-N-4; I-S-3; I-T-4, 6; I-V-1; I-Z-1
Eriksen, V.O.	55-8	I-U-1
Erway, N.D.	50-22	I-A-3
	51-82	VII-A-2-a
Esaki, L.	53-100	I-G-2
Esin, O.A.	57-108	VII-A-13, 15
Esser, H.	41-17	I-A-2; I-C-7; I-G-3; I-J-2; I-M-1; I-P-2; I-S-4; II-A-1, 2, 3, 4, 5, 6; IV-F-2
Estermann, I.	47-21	I-G-2
	52-6	I-G-2
Euler, J.	52-85	I-C-3-g
	56-81	I-C-3-g; I-C-3
Eusterbrock, H.	41-17	I-A-2; I-C-7; I-G-3; I-J-2; I-M-1; I-P-2; I-S-4; II-A-1, 2, 3, 4, 5, 6; IV-F-2
Evans, E.J.	43-4	I-A-2; I-S-4; V-A-6; V-A; VI-B-1; VI-G
Evans Jr., J.E.	51-16	I-S-4; II-D-1, 2, 4; III-A-1; IV-A-3-a; IV-A-5-a; IV-B-1; V-A-1; V-A-2-a; IX-B-1
Ewing, C.T.	54-65	II-D-3; IX-B-1; VII-A-1-a
	57-45	IX-C-2
Eyring, L.	50-34	I-A-3
	50-50	I-N-2
Fabre, D.	56-60	I-T-1, 7; I-Z-1
	56-61	I-S-3
Fakidov, I.G.	49-38	IV-F
Farber, M.	52-73	I-C-3
Faris, F.E.	54-111	I-C-3-a
Farr, J.D.	53-124	I-A-1
Fellows, D.M.	49-68	VII-A-1-a; VII-E-9
	50-64	VII-E-9
Ferro, R.	52-125	VI
	53-132	VI
	56-56	IX-F-1; IX-J
Ferry, M.	57-89	II-B-1
Fieldhouse, I.B.	56-2	I-C-3-a; I-C-7; I-J-2; I-M-4; I-N-3; I-T-1
	56-6	I-C-3-a, d; I-T-1
	56-110	I-J-2; VII-A-10
	56-111	I-C-7
	57-153	I-B-3
Fieldhouse, I.B.	58-2	I-J-2; I-N-4; II-D-3; IV-A-5-a; IV-A-5; VII-A-1-a; IX-E-1
	58-4	I-B-3; II-D-1, 3; IV-A-2, 4, 5; IV-A-4-a; IV-B-1; VII-D-1-a, b
Filbert Jr., R.B.	57-77	VII-D-5-a
	57-174	VII-D-5-a
Finch, D.I.	56-114	I-C-7; III-D, H; III
Fine, M.E.	48-21	I-C-6; I-J-2; II-D; IV-B-3
	48-22	I-C-6; I-J-2; II-D; IV-B-3
	51-3	I-C-5
	53-30	I-G-2
	56-55	VI-A
Fink, F.W.	51-64	I-Z-1; IV-J-1, 3, 7; IV-J
Finkelshtein, R.N.	54-70	I-S-4; V-A-6; VI-B-1
Fischer, H.C.	55-67	VII-A-3-a
Fischer, W.A.	57-177	VII-A-13
Fisher, A.	56-148	X-C-1
Fitzsimmons, E.S.	55-20	VII-B-6-c, f
Florio, J.V.	51-71	IX-J-8
Florinskaya, V.A.	53-146	VII-A-6; VII-C-1-m
Floyd, R.W.	52-38	IX-G-1
Foerster, G.S.	56-22	V-B-1, 3, 4

Foex, M.	42-10	VII-A-2-a; VII-A-5-a
	42-14	VII-A-7
	48-5	VII-A-13, 14
	49-69	VII-A-15
	52-23	I-D-1
Foex, M.	52-43	I-G-1
	52-132	VII-A-15
Foner, A.	47-21	I-G-2
Fontana, M.G.	52-122	V-C-1, 2, 5
Forster, F.	40-6	I-C-7; III-A-3
Foster, K.W.	53-121	I-A-1
Foster Jr., E.L.	54-20	I-Z-1; IV-J-1
Fox, G.W.	51-59	I-C-4; I-L-1; I-N-1; I-P-5
Francis, R.K.	58-7	II-D-1; VII-A-1-a; VII-A-1; VII-B-2
Francl, J.	54-1	VII-A-8, 10, 14, 15; VII-A-3-a; VII-B-1, 2, 7; VII-B-4-b; VII-B-7-a; VII-E-4
	54-2	I-C-3-a; I-N-3; VII-A-1-a; VII-A-1
	54-6	VII-A-1-a; VII-A-2-a; VII-A-5-a; VII-A-1, 2, 5
Frank, L.	53-119	I-U-1
Fraser, D.B.	55-28	I-C-7; IV-A-1
Frederikse, H.P.R.	54-130	IX-F-1
	55-136	IX-G-3
Freeman, R. D.	55-11	I-G-2
Fried, S.	45-12	I-N-2
	49-46	I-N-2
	51-61	I-P-7
	58-19	I-P-2, 3; I-U-1
Friedberg, S.A.	46-12	I-C-5; I-G-2; I-H-1; I-T-6; I-Z-1; III-A-3; VII-B-8-p
	55-89	I-G-2
Freiling, J.	52-95	XI-H-3
Frink, E.P.	56-137	IX-G-4
Frost, B.R.T.	54-123	VI
Frost, D.	52-82	VII-C-6
Fulk, M.M.	57-121	I-A-2; I-C-5, 7; I-G-2; I-N-3; I-R-3; I-S-4; II-D-2; XI-B-3
Fulkerson, S.D.	56-142	VIII-D
	57-159	VI-A-2; VII-A-2-a; VII-A-9-a, b
Furukawa, G.T.	52-90	X-G
	53-59	VII-A-1-a
	56-24	VII-A-1-a
Gaines, G.B.	54-106	I-R-2
	55-24	I-R-2
	57-137	I-R-2
Gallaher, R.B.	53-63	VII-F
Gangler, J.J.	49-20	VII-A-5-a; VII-A-5; VII-A-9-b; IX-A-2, 4
	50-10	VII-A-2-a; VII-A-5-a; VII-A-9-b; VII-A-9; VII-B-4-b; VII-D-1-b; VII-D-2; IX-A-2, 4; IX-J-11; IX
	50-13	IX-A-2
	51-42	VIII-B-5
Garrett, A.B.	44-4	I-B-3
Garth, R.C.	49-47	I-A-2; I-C-3-a; V-A-1; XI-C
Gast, Th.	53-47	X
	57-101	X-F
	57-111	X-C-1
Gates, P.M.R.	57-46	I-V-1; V-C-4
Gaunt, J.	51-79	VII-A-1-a
Geach, G.A.	55-128	IX-A-2, 5, 6; IX-B-1; IX-B; IX-C-2, 3; IX-C; IX-J-6
Geballe, T.H.	52-21	I-G-3
Gebhardt, E.	51-41	I-G-3; I-S-4; I-T-7; VI-A, B
	57-70	I-T-1
Gebler, K.A.	49-19	VII-E-3
Gel'd, P.V.	52-51	I-S-3
	54-67	II-D; VI-G-1
	56-35	II-B-1, 7, 8
	56-36	II-C-9
	56-39	I-S-3; II-C-9; II-9; VI-G-1
	56-106	I-J-2; I-S-3; II-C-9; II-D; VI-G-1

Geller, R. F.	43-14	VII-A-1-a; VII-A-1
	45-4	I-P-2; VII-A-1, 9
	46-4	VII-A-1, 2, 5; VII-A-9-b; VII-B-7-a
	54-59	VIII-A-2
	55-36	VIII-A-2
Georgescu, I. I.	56-105	I-P-4
Gerard, G.	57-94	X-A, B, C, D, F; X
Gerdes, A. F.	50-62	IX-A-7
	51-50	VI-L
	52-102	VI-L
Gerritsen, A. N.	51-17	I-S-4; VI-B
Gerstein, B. C.	57-17	I-H-2
Giauque, W. F.	41-12	I-A-2; I-C-7
	52-2	I-N-3
	52-21	I-G-3
Gibson, E. D.	52-105	I-H-1; I-T-4; I-Z-1
Gideon, D. N.	53-12	I-R-2
	54-75	I-R-2
Gier, J. T.	44-10	I-A-2; II-D-2; IV-A-5-a; XI-B-5; XI-D
	54-89	I-C-7; I-G-3; I-M-4
Gilbert, N.	46-14	VII-A-5, 13; VII-A-5-a; VII-B
Gilbreath, J. R.	48-36	VII-A-2-a
Gilles, P. W.	48-9	I-C-3
	49-65	VII-A-11, VII-D-5-a; VII-D-5
	53-135	IX-C
	56-154	VII-D-2
	56-42	VII-A-10
Gillis, P. W.	56-43	VII-A-7
Ginnings, D. C.	47-1	I-U-1; VII-D-5
	47-17	VII-A-1-a
	49-52	I-B-3
	51-15	I-B-3
Ginnings, D. C.	53-59	VII-A-1-a
	54-66	IX-B-1
	57-59	VII-A-2-a; VII-A-2
Giorgi, A.	53-124	I-A-1
Glaser, F. W.	52-40	VIII-C-1
	52-84	VIII-C-1; IX-C-3; IX-J-11
Glaser, F. W.	52-127	IX-C-3
	54-82	IX-C-3; IX-C; IX-J-1, 3, 4, 7, 9, 11; IX-J
	56-122	II-D; II-C-9
Goering, H. L.	56-161	VII-A-10
Goetz, A.	42-9	I-C-3-a
Goglia, M. J.	52-7	I-C-7; III
Goldfinger, P.	52-72	I-C-3
Goldsmid, H. J.	56-76	IX-F-2
Goldstaub, S.	52-132	VII-A-15
Golubkin, V. N.	54-56	I-C-6
	55-60	I-C-6; I-J-2
Gomel'skii, K. Z.	55-71	VII-A-1-a
Goncharov, V. V.	55-148	VII-E-10
Gonser, B. W.	49-41	I-T-6
Goode, J. M.	57-118	I-P-4
Gordan, J.	52-111	I-U-1; VII-A-10
Gordan, K.	53-114	I-Z-1
Gordon, P.	48-2	I-B-3
	49-9	I-B-3
	49-58	IX-A-5
	50-52	I-U-1; VI-F; IX-G-1
Gorovitz, N. N.	56-41	VII-A-14
Gottwald, F.	40-14	X-A, B, C, D, F, J; X-C-1; X
Graeff, R. F.	43-92	X-G
Granberg, G.	57-111	X-C-1
Grand, J. A.	56-28	IX-B-1
Granovakaya, A. A.	53-76	I-S-4
Grant, N. J.	52-64	I-C-5
	54-23	IV-A-5
Grass, G.	54-113	I-C-7; I-J-2; I-S-4
Grayson-Smith, H.	50-3	I-C-5, 6; I-M-2
Grazhdankina, N. P.	49-38	IV-F
Green, A. T.	43-15	VII-B-7-a; VII-B-7
	46-8	VII-A-13; VII-B-7-a; VII-B-8-a; VII-B-7; VII-B

Green, E.C.	54-114	IV-C
Greenaway, H.T.	50-38	I-C-5
	51-34	I-C-5
Greiner, E.S.	48-23	I-T-6
	51-3	I-C-5
	52-63	I-G-2
	57-104	I-B-4
Grenell, L.H.	45-10	I-T-4
	45-16	IX-E
Grieco, A.	52-35	I-G-2
Griffel, M.	53-33	I-T-4
	53-72	I-G-1
	54-35	I-G-1
	55-33	I-E-2
Griffel, M.	56-100	I-D-1
	57-17	I-H-2
Griffiths, E.	40-1	I-J-2
Grigor'ev, A.T.	56-31	III; IV-B-4; IV-B; VI-D-2, 3
	56-32	IV-B-4; IV-B; VI-A-2, 3; VI-D-1, 2
	56-125	IV-B; VI-A-2
Grim, M.S.	49-67	VII-A-8
Grimes, D.M.	57-49	VII-B-8-p
	57-195	VII-B-8-n, p
Grinthal, R.D.	55-129	VIII-D; IX-B-1
	56-134	VIII-D; VIII; IX-B-1
Grinthal, R.D.	57-92	VIII; IX-G, H
	57-166	VIII
Grogan, J.D.	56-85	I-P-1; VI-D
Gronvold, F.	48-32	VII-A-10
	56-68	IX-J
Grootenhuis, P.	52-60	III-B-3
Groves, W.O.	55-64	VII-A-8
Gruen, D.M.	54-143	VII-A-7; VII-A-10
Gulbransen, E.A.	50-48	I-B-3; XI-E
Gunzel Jr., F.H.	52-131	VII-A-1-a; VII-A-4-g, j; VII-A-7; VII-A-9-b
	54-151	VII-A-10
Gupta, A.	52-109	I-C-7
Gurland, J.	52-37	VIII-A-1; IX-A-1
Gutowski, J.A.	57-104	I-B-4
Haas, G.G.	56-92	I-A-2
	57-123	I-A-2
Haase, G.	54-96	VII-A-5-a
	54-138	VII-A-1-a
Hagel, W.C.	54-9	I-N-3; II-A-4, 5, 6, 7; II-C-5; II-C
Hagy, H.E.	57-184	VII-C-1-b; VII-C-5
Hale, J.C.	55-126	II-A-1; II-D-3; XI-E
Halg, W.	55-8	I-U-1
Hall, A.R.	53-125	I-C-3
Hall, G.L.	45-15	XI-H
Hall, L.D.	51-37	I-G-3
Hall, T.H.	55-48	I-G-2
Hallet, A.C.H.	55-28	I-C-7; IV-A-1
Halteman, E.K.	55-111	I-U-1; VI-F-2; VI-F
	56-119	VI-F-2
	56-132	VI-F-2
	57-42	VI-F
Hamilton, E.H.	56-20	VII-C-1-k
	57-182	VII-C-1-b
Hamjian, H.J.	52-78	VII-D-2; VIII-A
Handwerk, J.H.	54-44	VII-C-1-a, b
	54-148	VII-C-5
	56-5	I-P-2; VII-A-7, 10
Hansen, M.	51-57	I-Z-1
Hardy, H.K.	55-37	V-A-1
Harman, C. G.	50-12	VII-B-6-d; VII-E
	52-31	VII-A-1, 8, 14, 15; VII-A-9-b; VII-C-6; VII-B-3-b; VII-B-6-b; VII-E-3, 4

Harman, C.G.	52-34	VII-A-14; VII-B-6-**b**
	54-47	VII-A-15
Harper, A.F.A.	57-128	I-C-5
Harris, M.A.	52-25	II-C-6; II-D-3, 4; II-D-3-a; IV-B-1
Harrison, D.E.	54-48	VII-B-5
Harrison, J.W.	57-76	IV-J-1; IV-J
Harrower, J.	48-12	I-C-6; I-J-2; IV-B-2
Hartman, H.	54-150	VII-C-1-b
Harvey, G.G.	57-144	I-T-7
Hase, **R**.	40-16	I-A-1, 2; V-A-3; V-B-2
Hashimoto, K.	56-141	IX-F-2
Hass, G.	57-136	I-T-6
Hassion, F.X.	55-50	I-G-2
Hatch, R.A.	54-95	VII-B-9; VII-E-3-k; VII-E-4
Hatcher, J.B.	50-21	VII-A-14
Hatcher, J.B.	53-58	VII-A-14
Hauck, C.A.	54-40	I-C-5; IV-F-2; VII-A-1-a, b; VIII-B-1
	55-19	I-C-5; IV-F-2; VII-A-1-a, b; VIII-B-1
Hauffe, K.	41-26	VII-A-10
Hauk, V.	48-1	V-A-1, 2; V-A-2-a
Hausner, H.H.	49-45	I-B-3
	51-36	I-Z-1
Hauth, W.E.	56-75	VII-B-2; VII-B-4-b; VII-C-6
Havekotte, W.C.	52-130	VIII-A-2
Hawkins, G.A.	52-7	I-C-7; III
Hayes, E.T.	56-11	I-H-1; I-T-6; I-Z-1
Head, E.L.	52-89	X-A-1, 8, 11; X-D, F, G, H, J; X-C-1; X; XI-H-3, 5
Hedge, J.C.	56-2	I-C-3-a; I-C-7; I-M-4; I-N-3; I-T-1
	56-6	I-C-3-a, d; I-T-1
	56-110	I-J-2; VII A-10
	56-111	I-C-7
	58-2	I-J-2; I-N-4; II-D-3; IV-A-5-a; IV-A-5; VII-A-1-a; IX-E-1
	58-4	I-B-3; I-J-2; II-D-1, 3; IV-A-2, 4, 5; IV-A-4-a;IV-B-1: VII-D-1-a, b
Heierberg, R.	40-16	I-A-1, 2; V-A-3; V-B-2
Hein, J.	57-181	VII-E-4, 9, 10, 11
Heinz, A.	57-181	VII-E-4, 9, 10, 11
Heinze, D.	56-108	I-C-7; I-G-3; I-S-4
Heldt, K.	54-138	VII-A-1-a
Hellwege, K.H.	57-101	X-F
Hemstreet, H.W.	53-26	I-C-3-d
Henry, E.C.	46-5	VII-B-4
	46-13	VII-A-4-a; VII-A-15; VII-B-5; VII-B
	51-33	I-G-2
	53-94	VII-A-1-a; VII-A-6; VII-B-4-b; VII-B-4; VII-D-1-a; VII-E-9, 10
	53-95	VII-A-5, 6, 8, 13; VII-A-1-b; VII-A-5-a; VII-B-1
Hensel, F.R.	42-1	I-C-7; I-T-7; IV-C
Hensler, J.R.	53-95	VII-A-5, 6, 8, 13; VII-A-1-b; VII-A-5-a; VII-B-1
Herasymenko, P.	55-65	VI-A-1; VI-B-2
	57-73	VI-B
Herczog, A.	57-169	IX-F-1
Herrmann, K.W.	55-52	I-C-4; I-D-1; I-E-2, 3; I-G-1; I-H-2; I-L-1, 2; I-N-1; I-P-5; I-S-1, 2; I-T-3, 5; I-Y-1, 2
	57-119	I-L-1; I-N-1; I-P-2
Hersh, H.N.	51-19	I-B-4; I-C-7
	53-19	I-C-7
Herz, W.H.	54-83	IX-G; IX
Hickman, M.J.	49-54	V-A-1, 2, 3, 4; V-A-2-a, b; V-A
Hidnert, P.	41-3	I-C-5
	41-4	I-C-5
	43-5	I-T-6
	43-6	III-A-2; III-A; III-B-1; III-D, E
Hidnert, P.	43-12	III-B-1, 3; III-C, E, F
	45-2	VII-B-9
	47-7	I-C-7; III-A, D, E, F, J
	52-70	I-A-2; V-A-1, 2; V-A-2-b; V-A, D
	55-41	IV-B-3
	57-134	I-N-3; IV-A-1, 5, 6; IV-A-5-a
Hiegel, J.M.	42-5	I-J-2
Hill, J.H.	51-38	I-M-4

Hill, R. W.	52-5	I-G-2
	53-49	I-B-3
Hirabayashi, M.	51-35	VI-A
	52-29	VI-A
	52-92	I-M-1
Hirabayashi, M.	57-162	VI-A
	57-165	VI-A
Hirakawa, K.	56-141	IX-F-2
Hirano, K.	55-29	I-A-2; I-C-7; III-A-3; III-D, H
	55-45	III-G
	58-22	VI-E-1
Hirone, T.	53-62	IX-G-3
Hoard, J. L.	51-51	I-B-4
	57-57	I-B-4
Hoch, M.	53-24	VII-A-9-b; VIII-B
	54-30	VII-A-7
Hoch, M.	54-131	VII-A-7; VIII-B-4
	54-134	VII-A-9-b
	55-61	I-C-3; IX-A-1, 5
	55-64	VII-A-8; IX-A
Hocker, C. F.	49-15	VII-B-1; VII-B-6-j
Hogan, C. L.	47-6	I-A-2; I-C-3-a
	52-75	I-N-3; II-A-1; II-D-1, 2, 3; IV-A-5-a; IV-A-5
Holden, R. J.	48-20	I-B-3
Holland, L.	55-96	I-A-2
Hollo, G.	54-94	XI-B-2, 4; XI-D-4; XI-E
Holser, A.	42-9	I-C-3, 8
Holtzberg, F.	55-146	VII-A-14
Honig, J. M.	57-178	VII-A-4-a
Honig, R. E.	54-28	I-S-3
	54-31	I-G-2
	54-81	I-C-3
Hori, K.	54-119	V-A-2-a
Horn, F. H.	51-8	I-M-1
	55-114	I-S-3
Hosler, W. R.	54-130	IX-F-1
	55-136	IX-G-3
Hove, J. E.	54-111	I-C-3-a
	57-71	I-U-1
Howe, J. T.	53-133	X-J
Huber, R. W.	49-10	I-M-2
	55-101	I-T-6; V-C
Huckler, O.	50-5	I-A-2
Hudson, D. E.	52-53	I-A-2
	53-21	I-A-2
	56-83	I-A-2; I-N-1; I-P-5
Hudson, R. G.	57-113	I-M-2; IX-A
Hugon, L.	55-13	I-N-3
Hullings, W. Q.	54-87	XI-E
Hummel, F. A.	46-5	VII-B-4
	46-13	VII-A-4-a; VII-A-15; VII-B-5; VII-B
	49-14	VII-A-6; VII-B-2-c; VII-B-3-h
	51-21	VII-B-3-e; VII-B-7-f; VII-E-6
Hummel, F. A.	51-22	VII-C-1-a
	51-23	VII-C-1-g
	51-48	VII-A-6, 8
	52-32	VII-C-1-b, m
	54-48	VII-B-5
Humphrey, G. L.	52-134	VII-D-1-a
Hunt, E. B.	50-58	IX-A
Hunter, W. R.	56-92	I-A-2
	57-123	I-A-2
Iliescu, P.	56-82	II-B-1, 8
Inghram, M. G.	53-83	I-C-3
	53-84	I-C-3
	54-80	I-C-3
	55-62	I-C-3

Inghram, M.G.	56-44	VII-A-8, 15
	57-65	VII-A-8
	ND-2	I-Z-1; VII-A-9-b; VII-A-9
	ND-3	VII-A-14
International Nickel		
Co., Inc.	49-13	IV-A-5-a; IV-A-5
Ishikawa, Y.	56-19	VII-B-6-g
Isobe, M.	51-55	I-M-2
Isserow, S.	57-167	IX-B-2
Ito, T.	40-11	I-C-7; III-A-3
Ivanick, W.	52-84	IX-C-3
	56-122	II-C-9; II-D
Ivanov, L.I.	57-63	I-J-2
Izumi, O.	55-127	III-H
Izumitani, T.	52-135	VII-C-2; VII-C
Jackson, G.B.	56-136	X-E, F; X
Jacobson, E.L.	53-89	IX-B-J
Jacobsen, E.	56-68	IX-J
Jaeger, F.M.	39-1	I-P-2
	40-2	I-C-6
	41-7	I-R-4
Jaffee, R.I.	47-22	I-Z-1
	51-86	VII-B-6
	52-18	I-T-6; V-B
	54-38	I-R-2
	54-57	I-T-6
	55-59	I-R-2; VI
Jaffray, J.	52-132	VII-A-15
	55-13	I-N-3
Jain, S.C.	54-8	I-P-2
	54-85	I-P-2
James, N.R.	52-14	I-L-1; I-N-1; I-P-5
	52-88	I-L-1; I-N-1; I-P-5
James, W.J.	56-50	I-T-4
Jamieson, C.P.	56-51	I-C-3-a; I-C-3
Janssen, S.	57-66	III-E
	57-99	III-A-3; III-B-3; VI
	57-107	III-E
Jauch, R.	50-5	I-A-2
Jenkins, F.A	48-9	I-C-3
Jenkins, I.	52-28	IV-B-1
Jennings, L.D.	56-86	I-C-4; I-D-1; I-E-2, 3; I-G-1; I-H-2; I-L-1, 2; I-P-5, 6; I-S-1, 2; I-T-3, 5; I-Y-1, 2
	57-135	I-T-3
Jette, E.R.	55-99	I-P-3
Joffe, A.F.	56-116	I-G-2; IX-F-2
Johnson, B.K.	41-20	I-A-2; I-C-5; I-P-2; I-S-3; III-B-3; VII-C-6
	41-22	I-S-4
Johnson, E.R.	54-86	VI-G; VI
Johnson, G.H.	53-104	VII-A-8
Johnson, H.A.	54-100	I-M-1; V-B-3, 4, 6
Johnson, J.R.	54-45	VII-A-9-a, b; VII-B-4-a, b; VII-B-6-a
	54-46	VII-A-9-a, b; VII-B-4-a, b; VII-B-6-a
	57-22	VII-A-7
	57-24	VII-A-4-e, n
Johnson, P.D.	50-37	I-M-4; I-T-7; VII-A-2-a; VII-A-5-a; VII-A-7; VII-A-9-b
Johnson, R.G.	52-53	I-N-1
	53-2	I-A-2; I-N-1; I-P-5
	56-83	I-A-2; I-N-1; I-P-5
Johnson, W.E.	50-49	I-Z-1
	59-49	I-Z-1
Johnston, H.L.	48-20	I-B-3
	50-6	I-C-5
	50-40	I-T-1
	51-7	I-Z-1
	51-11	I-C-6; I-J-2
	51-12	I-V-1

Johnston, H. L.	51-13	I-Z-1
	51-18	I-M-4; I-N-4; I-P-2; I-T-1
	51-19	I-B-4
	51-40	I-T-1
	51-68	I-V-1
	52-50	I-M-4
Johnston, H. L.	52-57	VII-A-13
	53-8	I-T-6
	53-20	I-C-7; I-T-6
	53-24	VII-A-9-b; VII-A-9; VIII-B
	53-25	I-Z-1
	53-114	I-Z-1
Johnston, H. L.	54-10	I-A-2; I-N-3; I-T-6; I-Z-1
	54-30	VII-A-7
	54-39	II-D-3; III-A-3
	54-131	VII-A-7; VIII-B-4
	54-134	VII-A-9-b
	55-64	VII-A-8
Johnston, H. S.	54-53	I-C-7
Johnstone, S. T. M.	50-38	I-C-5
	56-91	I-C-5
Jones, D. J.	54-114	IV-C
	56-127	II-D-5
Jones, F. O.	55-128	IX-A-2, 5, 6; IX-B-1; IX-B; IX-C-2, 3; IX-C; IX-J-6
Jones, F. W.	41-14	V-A-6
	49-55	II-D-5
Jones, L. J.	56-156	VII-A-9-b; VII-A-10
	57-190	VII-A-1
Jones, N. C.	52-9	VII-A-9-b
Jones, T. S.	54-17	I-G-3; I-J-2; I-N-3; I-P-2; I-R-3; I-T-6; I-V-1; I-Z-1
Jones, W. M.	52-111	I-U-I; VII-A-10
Joyner, B. L.	53-105	VII-C-1-b; VII-C-5
Juel, L. H.	52-114	I-C-3
Justi, E.	49-11	I-R-4
Kalish, H. S.	51-36	I-Z-1
Kallenbach, R.	51-25	I-A-2; V-A-1; V-A-2-a
Kamm, R. L.	55-95	I-C-3-a, p; I-U-1; VII-A-10; IX-A-7; IX-B-2; XI-C, E
Kanai, Y.	56-103	I-G-2
Kandare, S.	56-61	I-S-3
Karkhanavala, M. D.	52-32	VII-C-1-b, m
Kates, L. W.	52-47	I-Z-1; IV-J-1
Kato, H.	54-22	I-Z-1
Kaufmann, A. R.	49-58	IX-A-5
	50-52	I-U-1; VI-F; IX-G-1
Kaufmann, R. R.	41-11	I-Z-1
Kav, A. E.	58-18	I-P-3
Kawasaki, M.	55-127	III-H
Kay, A. E.	58-17	I-P-3
Keeler, J. H.	53-110	I-Z-1
Keesom, W. H.	41-21	I-T-1
Keller, W. H.	45-9	I-T-4
	55-51	I-C-4
Kelley, K. K.	41-2	VII-A-13; VII-D-1-a; VII-D-2
	41-15	VII-B-2-d, f; VII-B-4-b; VII-B-4
Kelley, K. K.	41-16	VII-D-3
	43-2	I-J-2
	43-8	VII-B-2-e
	43-9	IX-A
	44-1	I-T-6; IX-A-2
Kelley, K. K.	44-2	VII-A-9-b
	46-1	I-M-2; VII-C-6
	47-18	I-U-1; VII-A-10
	49-26	IX-A, D
	57-55	V-C-8

Kellogg, M. G. Co.	48-17	II-D-2
Kemp, W. R. G.	53-50	I-M-1
	55-100	I-P-1
	56-14	I-J-2; I-N-3; I-T-6; I-Z-1
	56-30	VII-B-2, 4; VI-B, D
Kemper, R. S.	53-115	I-U-1
Kempter, C. P.	57-91	IX-A, D
Kennedy, J. D.	53-48	VII-A-3
Kenney, D. J.	54-101	I-V-1; IX-G-1; IX-J-10
Kerr, E. C.	51-19	I-B-4
Khalilov, A. Yu.	55-139	IX-F-1
Khomyakov, K. G.	54-121	II-D-6
Kiessling, R.	49-60	IX-C
	49-62	IX-C
	56-144	IX-B-2; IX-C
Kikoin, A. K.	49-24	VI
	49-38	IV-F
Kikuchi, K.	53-23	I-C-4
Killelea, J. H.	50-67	VII-B-1
Kimura, K.	52-96	II-A-1; XI-B-5
Kinchin, G. H.	53-117	I-C-3-j
King, B. W.	55-17	VII-A-4-a; VII-A-15; VII-C
King, E. G.	48-7	VII-B-5
	49-27	IX-A, D.
	50-2	I-Z-1; VII-A-9-b; VII-B-4-b; IX-D-3
	55-42	VII-B-6-d, f, h, k
King, E. G.	55-44	VII-B-7-a, d
	56-165	VII-B-7; VII-B-8-m, n, p; VII-B
	57-41	VII-A-13, 14
	57-44	VII-B-2-c; VII-B-3-c
King, G. J.	52-90	X-G
Kingery, W. D.	51-75	VII-A-1-a; VII-A-2-a; VII-A-5-a; VII-B-1; VII-B-4-b
	51-76	VII-E-9
	52-65	VII-A-2-a; VII-A-5-a; VII-A-8; VII-B-4-b
	52-66	VII-A-1-a; VII A-5-a; VII-A-1, 2
	52-67	VII-A-2-a; VII-A-2, 5
Kingery, W. D.	52-68	VII-A-1-a; VII-A-1
	53-41	VII-D-1-a
	53-40	VII-D-1-a
	53-65	VII-A-1, 8, 10, 15; VII-B-4-b; VII-B-2
	53-66	VII-B-2
Kingery, W. D.	53-67	VII-A-1-a; VII-A-2-a; VII-A-5-a; VII-A-2, 5
	53-68	VII-A-10; VII-C-1-b
	53-69	VII-A-10
	54-1	VII-A-3-a; VII-A-8, 10, 14, 15; VII-B-1, 2, 4, 7; VII-B-4-b; VII-B-7-a; VII-E-2
	54-2	I-C-3-a; I-N-3; VII-A-1-a; VII-A-1
Kingery, W. D.	54-4	VII-A-1-a; VII-A-1
	54-6	VII-A-1-a; VII-A-5-a; VII-A-1, 2, 5
	54-24	VII-D-1-a; IX-A-2; IX-D-1, 3
	54-64	VII-C-1-b; VII-C-5; IX-B-1
	54-137	VII-C-6
Kingery, W. D.	54-142	VII-A-5; VII-D-1-a
	54-144	VII-A-5-a; VII-A-5, 14
	54-149	VII-C-1-b
	55-25	VII-A-5; VII-A-9-a; VII-D-1-a
	55-47	VII-A-1, 5, 8; VII-C-6
Kingery, W. D.	55-53	VII-A-4-n; VII-A-5
	55-57	VII-A-1-a; VII-A-2-a; VII-A-2; VII-C-1-b; VII-C-6
	55-75	VII-C-6
	56-10	VII-A-1-a; VII-A-1
	57-33	I-A-2; I-T-7; VII-A-5; VIII-B-2; VIII-B
	57-53	VII-A-1, 5, 8; VII-A-5-a; VII-D-5
Kirby, H. W.	52-27	II-D-3
Kirby, P. L.	51-26	VII-C-5
Kirby, R. K.	55-41	IV-B-3
Kitzes, A. S.	53-63	VII-F
	54-87	XI-E
Klasse, F.	57-181	VII-E-4, 9, 10, 11
Klauer, F.	52-82	VII-C-6
Klebanow, H. L.	54-116	IV-C; VI-A, D

Klein, D.J.	57-139	I-C-3-a
Klemens, P.G.	55-100	I-P-1
	56-30	VI-B-2, 4; VI-B, D
Knapp, W.J.	43-11	VII-A-1, 5, 6; VII-A-1-a; VII-A-5-a; VII-B-1; VII-B-3-b; VII-B-4-b; VII-C-1-b; VII-C-5, 6; VII-D-5-a
Knodler, A.	55-122	V-A-6
Knop Jr. H.W.	48-6	II-D-8; IV-B-3
	48-13	I-C-6; I-J-2; IV-B-2
Knoroz, L.I.	57-117	I-J-2; II-D-2, 6; II-D-3-a; II-D-6-a; II-D
Knudsen, F.P.	52-56	VIII-A-2
	54-59	VIII-A-2
Knudsen, F.P.	55-36	VIII-A-2
	56-18	VII-A-7
Kobaya, T.	52-121	IV-B-3
Koch, W.J.	50-12	VII-B-6-d; VII-E
Kochanovaka, A.	49-33	I-A-2; I-J-2
Koenig, C.J.	41-10	VII-B-3-c, e, f, h
Koenig, E.	45-14	X-A-1; X-F, J
Koenig, J.H.	53-3	VII-B
	53-5	VII-E-6
	53-43	IV-A-5-a; VII-A-2-a; VII-A-2; VII-B-6-e; VII-C-1-b, h, m; VII-C-5; VII-E-4, 6; VII-E
Kohlhepp, E.	57-101	X-F
Kohn, J.A.	54-126	IX-A-4
	56-140	IX-B
Kojima, T.	53-23	I-C-4
Kolechkove, A.F.	55-148	VII-E-10
Komarek, K.	58-13	VII-D-6; IX-F-2
Kondo, K.	50-26	VII-D-1-a
Kono, H.	57-165	VI-A
Konobeeyskii, S.T.	55-94	I-P-3; VI; IX-G-2; IX-J-5
Kornev, Y.V.	53-53	I-J-2; II-A
	54-56	I-C-6
	55-60	I-C-6; I-J-2
Kornilov, I.I.	46-9	II-D-4
	55-124	II-C, D
	58-12	VI-C-3; IV-D
Konorov, P.P.	55-92	IX-F-2
Kostanyan, K.A.	57-188	VII-C-1-b
Koster, W.	55-122	V-A-6
	57-160	IV-A-5
Kothen, C.W.	53-8	I-T-6
	57-34	I-M-4; I-T-6
Kover, F.	56-146	IX-F-1
Krasotkina, N.I.	56-168	VII-C-1-b
Kratz, H.R.	44-9	I-U-1
Krauss, F.	55-34	I-N-3
Krebs, K.	57-152	I-A-2; V-A-6
Krider, H.S.	47-7	I-C-7; III-A, D, E, F, J
	52-70	I-A-2; V-A-1, 2; V-A-2-b; V-A, D
Krier, C.A.	54-12	I-M-1
	54-63	IX-G-3
Krikorian, N.H.	57-91	IX-A, D
	55-138	IX-B-1
Krishnan, K.S.	46-11	I-C-3-m
	54-8	I-P-2
	54-85	I-P-2
Kross, E.	43-16	IX-H-1; IX-H
Krystyniak, C.W.	57-189	VII-A-4-b, d, e, n
Kubaschewski, O.	40-17	I-N-3
	41-24	I-J-2; VII-C-5
	43-13	VI-A-1; VI-A; VI-B; VI; VII-C-5, 6
	50-1	I-A-4; I-J-2; I-N-3
	50-5	I-A-2; I-B-1; I-C-1; I-M-1
Kuchkuda, R.W.	54-91	X-A-1, 2, 3, 5; X-C-1, 2, 3; X-E, F, G; XI-H-2, 3, 6
Kuczyniski, G.C.	56-55	VI-A
Kuprina, V.V.	56-31	IV-B-4; IV-B; VI-D-2, 3
Kuprovskii, B.B.	56-35	II-B-1, 7, 8
	56-36	II-C-9
	56-106	I-J-2; I-S-3; II-C-9; II-D; VI-G-1

Kurnakov, N.N.	49-32	I-M-2; IV-A-6; VI-E-2
Kussman, A.	50-9	II-D; VI-C
Kuwayama, N.	56-160	VII-D-1-a
Kuz'menki, P.P.	55-81	II-D-1, 4; II-L-6
Kuznetsov, A.K.	57-193	VII-A-9-b
Lagrenaudie, J.	53-101	I-B-4
	53-118	I-B-4
Laidler, D.S.	50-68	VII-D-1-a
Lal, J.	54-73	X-F
Lamar, R.S.	54-49	VII-E-3-j, k; VII-E-3
Lambertson, W.A.	52-131	VII-A-1-a; VII-A-4-g, j; VII-A-7; VII-A-9-b
	55-138	VII-A-9-b; VII-A-10
	54-151	VII-A-10
	56-5	I-P-2; VII-A-7, 10
Lampson, F.K.	51-62	I-B-3; I-J-2
	54-102	I-T-6
Lander, J.J.	51-78	VII-A-13-a; VII-A-13
Lang, J.I.	57-153	I-B-3
	58-2	I-J-2; I-N-4; II-D-3; IV-A-5-a; IV-A-5; VII-A-1-a; IX-E-1
Lang, S.M.	56-18	VII-A-7
Langeron, J.P.	55-110	I-U-1
	57-142	I-U-1
Laquer, H.L.	52-39	I-R-3; I-T-6; I-U-1; II-A-1; II-D-2; IV-A-1; IV-A-4-a; IV-A-5-a; V-B-1; VII-C-5; VIII-B; IX-E-1; X-G
	52-89	X-A-1, 8, 11; X-C-1; X-D, F, G, H, J; X; XI-H-3, 5
	52-108	I-C-1; I-U-1
Larrabee, R.D.	57-88	I-T-7
Laszlo, T.S.	51-47	VII-A-5-a; VII-A-9-b
Laurent, B.	53-144	VII-C-2
Lawrence, W.G.	51-73	VIII-A-5; VIII-B-2; IX-C-3; IX-D; IX-G-1
Lee, H.	50-8	II-A-1, 2, 3, 4, 5, 6
Leech, P.	41-14	V-A-6
Lefort, H.G.	56-97	I-J-2; II-D-2
Legvold, S.	52-14	I-L-1; I-N-1; I-P-5
	52-88	I-L-1: I-N-1: I-P-5
	53-16	I-D-1; I-G-1
	53-31	I-D-1; I-G-1; I-N-1; I-P-5
	56-86	I-C-4; I-D-1; I-E-2, 3; I-G-1; I-H-2; I-L-1, 2; I-P-5, 6; I-S-1, 2; I-T-3, 5; I-Y-2
Legvold, S.	56-88	I-C-7; I-D-1; I-E-2; I-G-1; I-L-1; I-N-1; I-P-5; I-Y-1
	57-13	I-C-4; I-D-1; I-E-2; I-G-1; I-L-1; I-N-1; I-P-5; I-T-3; I-Y-1
	57-195	VII-B-8-n, p
Lehr, P.	55-110	I-U-1
	56-72	I-J-2
	57-142	I-U-1
Leinhardt, T.E.	53-26	I-C-3-d
Lement, B.S.	52-123	II-D-5
Lemmon Jr., A.W.	57-164	IV-J-1; VII-A-9-b
Lemons, C.	51-74	XI-H-3, 5
Lengyel, B.	55-149	VII-C-1
Lenning, G.A.	52-18	I-T-6; V-B
Leontis, T.E.	52-91	I-M-1; V-B-4
LeRoux, R.	53-128	III-E
Leung, K.	46-15	VII-C-1-b
Levingston, H.L.	53-108	I-T-4; I-V-1
Levitas, A.	55-88	I-G-2; I-S-3; VI
Lewis, G.	57-23	VII-B-4-a; VII-A-9-a
Lidman, W.G.	49-23	VIII-A-2
	52-78	VII-D-2; VIII-A
Lieberman, D.S.	54-79	VI-A-1; VI-A
Lietz, J.	56-52	VII-A-8
Lillie, H.R.	44-11	VII-C-6
Linde, J.O.	51-17	I-S-4; VI-B
Lisle, H.S.	57-103	XI-H-3, 5, 6
Litton, F.B.	49-41	I-T-6

Liu, T.S.	54-124	IV-A
Llewellyn, J.P.	57-30	IX-F-2
Lloyd, G.P.	48-35	VII-A-5-a
Loasby, R.G.	58-18	I-P-3
Loewen, E.G.	56-21	I-J-2; I-T-6; II-C-5, 8; II-D-8; V-C-2, 5; VIII-A-1
Lofgren, N.L.	49-65	VII-A-11; VII-D-5-a; VII-D-5
Logan, W.M.	53-61	IX-B-1
	54-61	IX-B-1
Loh, E.	57-198	VII-A-9-b
Lones, J.	52-46	I-Z-1; II-D-3
Long, E.A.	52-111	I-U-1; VII-A-10
Long, R.A.	50-15	IX-B-1
	50-60	IX-B-1
Lonsdale, T.H.	56-27	II-A-1, 2, 3
Loomis, B.A.	52-105	I-H-1; I-T-4; I-Z-1
Lord, W.B.H.	54-110	I-P-3
Lorenson, R.E.	52-13	VII-B-6-e, k
	52-59	VII-B-6-e, k
Lorenz, G.	57-177	VII-A-13
Loriers, J.	48-8	I-C-4
Los, G.J.	57-105	I-C-7
	57-132	I-G-3; III-D; VI-A-4
Losa, C.G.	55-32	I-J-1; I-R-3
Lovell, G.H.B.	43-15	VII-B-7-a; VII-B-7
	46-8	VII-A-13; VII-B-7-a; VII-B-8-a; VII-B-7; VII-B
Lucks, C.F.	51-46	VII-D-2
	51-65	I-J-2; II-A-1; II-D-2, 3; IV-A-1; IV-A-5-a; IV-A-5; V-A-1, 4; V-B-1; V-P-4; VII-C-5, 6; VII-C-1-b
	52-33	VI-A-1; IV-A-5-a; VII-A-1-a; VII-C-1-b; VII-C-5, 6; X-F
	54-27	II-A-1, 2, 3; II-D-2, 3; IV-A-1; IV-A-5-a; V-A-1, 4; V-B-1; VII-C-1-b; VII-C-2, 5, 6; X-F
	54-42	VI-F-1
Lucks, C.F.	56-1	I-C-3-a, d; I-C-5, 7; I-J-2; I-M-4; VII-A-1-a
	57-9	I-C-3-d
	58-5	I-C-5, 7; I-M-4; II-A-1, 2, 3; II-A-1; II-A; II-D-2, 3; IV-A-1; IV-A-5; IV-A-5-a; V-A-1, 4; V-B-1
	58-21	I-T-6; V-C-1, 2, 7
Lukens, H.C.	49-10	I-M-2
Lunt, H.E.	53-120	I-T-4, 6
Lustman, B.	57-86	VII-A-10
Lyand, R.	52-132	VII-A-15
Lyon, W.	55-51	I-C-4
Lyubimov, A.P.	53-76	I-S-4
MacNair, D.	41-6	I-A-2; I-C-7; I-G-3; I-J-2; I-N-3
	42-2	I-M-4; I-P-1, 2; I-S-4; I-T-1, 7
Maeda, S.	53-62	IX-G-3
Mah, A.D.	57-55	V-C-8
Mair, W.N.	51-58	I-T-6
Maisner, H.	51-74	XI-H-3, 5
Makin, S.M.	54-103	I-N-3; I-T-1, 6; I-U-1
Maksimova, M.V.	56-125	IV-B; VI-A-2
Male, D.	53-92	I-G-3
Mallett, M.W.	50-62	IX-A-7
	51-50	VI-L
	52-102	VI-L
Malm, J.G.	48-36	VII-A-2-a
Maniwa, H.	55-29	I-A-2; I-C-7; III-A-3; III-D, H
Manowitz, R.	55-137	VII-A-5-a; IX-D; X-F
Mansfield, R.	53-102	VII-A-5-a
Marcus, H.	57-171	X-G
Mardon, P.G.	53-112	I-P-3
	57-192	VII-A-11
Mark, M.	57-7	XI-A-2
Markovskii, L. Ya.	55-79	IX-C, G
Marple, D.T.F.	56-62	I-R-2
Marples, J.A.C.	57-16	I-P-3; I-T-4; VI
	57-75	I-T-4; IV-L; VI

111

Marshall, A.L.	50-23	I-C-3
Marshall, T.A.	53-98	X-F, G, J; X
Martens, H.	56-123	II-D-1
Martin, J.	52-112	I-N-3; II-D-5; IV-A-4
Marx, P.	53-97	X-G
	55-140	X-H
Maskrey, J.T.	54-123	VI
Mason, G.L.	57-156	II-D-2, 6; IV-A-5-a; IV-A-5; VII-A-2-a; VII-D-1-a;
		IX-A-2
Massachusetts Inst.		
of Technology	50-43	I-B-3; I-Z-1
	52-104	I-J-2; I-T-4; I-Z-1
	53-126	VI-F-1; VI-F
Massengale, C.B.	52-79	II-B-1; VIII-A-1, 2; VIII-B-1; VIII-C-1
Mastick, D.F.	49-44	I-J-2
	51-60	I-J-2
Masumoto, H.	51-70	II-D-7; II-L
	52-77	III-A-3
	52-121	IV-B-3
Masumoto, H.	53-129	II-D-1, 4; IV-F
	54-60	I-N-3; III-E; IV-A-5
	54-118	II-D; IV-B-3
	54-120	IV-B-3
	55-121	III-E
	55-123	IV-B-3
Matolich, J.	54-27	II-A-1, 2, 3; II-D-2, 3; IV-A-1; IV-A-5-a; V-A-1, 4;
		V-B-1; VII-C-1-b; VII-C-2, 5, 6
Matsukura, T.	52-93	II-D-1, 4
Matsumoto, K.	51-24	VII-B-3-a
Matsumoto, N.	57-64	VII-A-13
Matthews, S.	56-155	VII-E-9
Matuyama, E.	55-109	I-C-3-n
Matveev, O.A.	55-92	IX-F-2
Matveeva, M.P.	57-63	I-J-2
Mauer, F.A.	53-28	I-T-7
	54-16	IX-A-2; IX-A
	54-19	I-S-3; VII-A-8
	54-37	I-S-3; VII-A-9-b
	54-51	VII-A-8; IX-B-1
Mauer, F.A.	55-58	I-S-3; I-T-7; VII-A-5-a; VII-A-5, 7, 8, 9; IX-A-1, 2, 4;
		IX-A-5; IX-A; IX-B-1; IX-B; IX-F-1
	55-102	I-C-3-m; I-S-4
	55-108	I-C-3-j
	56-8	VII-A-6, 8; VII-A-9-b; VII-B-6-n; VIII-B
	57-62	I-C-3-m; I-P-2; I-S-3; VII-A-1-2; VII-A-1, 8; VII-B-6-n;
		IX-A-4, 6; IX-B-1; IX-B; IX-C-3
Maulawer, L.	57-96	VI-A, B
Maxwell, C.R.	49-39	I-P-4
Maxwell, L.H.	53-140	VII-A-1-a
Maxwell, W.A.	49-36	IX-B-1; IX-J-4
	49-63	IX-B-1
	52-94	IX-B-1
Maybury, P.C.	55-134	IX-E-1
Maykuth, D.J.	54-57	I-T-6; IV-H; V-C-2; V-C; VI-E
McCabe, C.L.	52-69	I-S-4
	53-131	VI-A, B
	57-113	I-M-2; IX-A
McCarthy, K.A.	55-3	I-G-2
McClelland, J.D.	57-5	I-C-3-a, d; I-M-4; I-T-1
McCoskey, R.E.	52-90	X-G
McCreight, L.R.	52-119	IV-J-3; VI-F; VII-A-10; VIII-B-3
	57-148	I-M-1; I-Z-1; IV-J-3; VI-F; VII-A-2, 5, 10; VII-B-9;
		VII-D-2; VII-E-4; VIII-B-3
McDonald, H.J.	39-2	IX-A
	40-9	VII-A-14
McDonald, J.J.	53-123	I-N-3
McDonald, R.A.	45-18	IX-E
	55-31	I-M-1; II-D-1
McElroy, D.L.	54-54	I-J-2; I-N-3
McGlone, W.R.	57-170	X-C-1; X-E, J; XI-H-3, 4, 6; XI-J
McGuire, J.C.	57-91	IX-A, D

McKee, J. H.	50-11	VII-B-4-b
McKeown, J. J.	58-6	I-C-4; I-N-1; I-P-5; I-S-1
McKinney, V. L.	54-88	XI-E
McKinstry, H. A.	48-4	VII-B-6-c; VII-B-7-c
	49-15	VII-B-1; VII-B-6-j
McKinstry, H. A.	51-22	VII-C-1-a
	54-48	VII-B-5
McMahon, H.	51-80	VII-C-1-b, m; VII-C-5, 6
McMillan, P. W.	56-79	VII-C-6
	56-158	VII-C-2
	56-170	VII-C-2
McNamara, E. P.	58-7	II-D-1; VII-A-1-a; VII-B-2
McNees Jr., R. A.	53-75	I-G-2
	53-77	IX-B
McPherson, D. J.	51-57	I-Z-1
	53-91	IX-J-1, 3, 4, 6, 7, 9, 11; IX-J; IX
McPherson, L.	40-13	III-E
McQuarrie, M.	54-3	VII-A-1, 2, 5; VII-A-1-a; VII-A-2-a; VII-A-5-a
McQuillan, M. K.	50-38	I-C-5
McQuillan, A. D.	54-25	I-N-4; I-T-6; IV-E; V-C
	56-15	I-T-6; V-C-1, 8; V-C
	56-95	I-T-6; V-C; IX-E
McQuillan, M. K.	50-38	I-C-5
McVay, T. N.	54-44	VII-C-1-a, b
	54-148	VII-C-5
Meads, P. F.	41-12	I-A-2; I-C-7
Meechan, C. J.	54-93	I-C-7
	54-107	I-G-3
	54-108	I-G-3
Mehl, R. F.	54-9	I-N-3; II-A-4, 5, 6, 7; II-C-5; II-C
Messer, C. E.	55-134	IX-E-1
Michels, W. C.	49-5	I-T-6
	49-8	I-T-6
Middleton, A. E.	57-169	IX-F-1
Mikleev, V. S.	46-9	II-D-1, 4
	55-124	II-C, D
	58-8	IV-C
Mikol, E. P.	52-10	I-M-4
Mikryukov, V. E.	44-3	I-C-7
	53-103	II-C
	54-50	II-C, D
	56-71	I-C-7; III-D, E, K, L
	57-50	I-T-6; I-Z-1; IV-C-7; IV-J
Miller, E.	58-13	VII-D-6; IX-F-2
Miller, P. H.	41-27	VII-A-15
Miller, R. R.	56-28	IX-B-1
	57-45	IX-C-2
Milne, T. A.	57-145	I-T-4; VII-A-2-a; VII-A-4-g; VII-D-3-a; VII-D-5-a; IX-A-4
	57-146	I-T-4
	57-194	VII-D-5-a
Millner, T.	56-126	VII-D-5, 6
Mitchell, D. W.	49-28	IX-D
Mitchell, K. W.	53-36	I-C-5
Miyazaki, Y.	56-65	I-C-3-a
Mizushima, S.	50-51	I-C-3-b
Mochizuki, T.	56-38	I-G-3; I-S-4
Mohr, W. C.	47-11	VII-E-4
Mokhov, V. M.	55-56	I-M-2; IV-A-6; VI-E-1, 2; VI-E
Montgomery, H. C.	52-35	I-G-2
Moody, J. W.	56-161	VII-A-10
Moore, D. G.	53-136	VII-B-9; XI-D, E
	56-69	VII-C-1-m; VII-C-6
Moore, G. E.	42-11	I-U-1; VII-A-10
	43-9	IX-A
	47-18	I-U-1; VII-A-10
	50-24	VII-A-15
Moore, H.	56-79	VII-A-6; VII-C-6
	56-158	VII-C-2
	56-170	VII-C-2

Mooser, E.	55-87	I-G-2
Moreland, E.R.	51-44	I-C-3-d
	54-59	VIII-A-2
	55-36	VIII-A-2
Morgan, P.H.	50-65	VII-A-7
Mori, S.	56-143	IX-F-2
Morris, J.C.	58-1	I-C-3-a, d; I-C-5; I-J-2; II-D-3; IV-A-2; IV-A-5-a; V-C-1; V-C; VII-A-1; VII-A-5-a; XI-C, E; XI-H-3, 5, 6, 7
	59-1	VII-A-1-a; VII-A-2-a; VII-A-5-a; VII-A-9-b; VII-C-1-b; VII-C-1, 5, 6; VII-D-1-a; XI-C, E
Moser, H.	41-13	I-N-3; I-S-4; III-A-1; VII-A-6; VII-C-6
Moskowitz, D.	54-82	IX-C-3; IX-C; IX-J-1, 3, 4, 7; IX-J
	55-76	IV-A-2, 5; IV-F-1; VIII-C; IX-C; IX-C-2, 3; IX-H; IX-J-1
Moskowitz, M.	52-47	I-Z-1; IV-J-1
Moss, M.	55-6	I-N-3; I-Z-1; IV-J-1
Mrozowski, S.	56-51	I-C-3; I-C-3-a
Mueller, M.H.	53-138	VII-A-9-b; VII-A-10
Muldawer, L.	57-96	III-A-3; VI-B-2; VI-B
Munster, A.	56-112	I-T-6; V-C-1
	56-131	V-A-4
	56-145	IX-A-2; IX-D-1
Murchara, M.	54-119	V-A-2-a
Murphy, G.	52-106	I-T-4
	52-107	I-T-4
Murphy, W.K.	54-21	VII-A-1-a; VII-A-3
Murr, W.E.	56-128	VI-F-2, 3
Murray, J.R.	52-116	I-T-4
Murray, P.	ND-1	VII-A-10
Muto, Y.	57-162	VI-A
Myers, C.E.	53-71	I-B-4
	57-58	I-B-4
Myers, R.T.	50-47	I-T-1
Nadler, M.R.	53-37	VII-B-6-f
	55-20	VII-B-6-f
Nagasaki, S.	57-165	VI-A
Nakata, M.	53-24	VII-A-9-b; VII-A-9
	54-134	VII-A-9-b
Nakazawa, Y.	56-64	VII-A-9
Nakhodnova, A.P.	56-73	VII-A-2-a; VII-A-3-a; VII-A-5-a; VII-A-13, 15
Napolitano, A.	56-169	VII-C-5
Nasledov, D.N.	55-139	IX-F-1
National Bureau of Standards	53-96	VII-A-6; VII-C-1-m; VII-C-6
	53-142	VII-C-1-m
	53-143	VII-C-1-m
	54-127	IX-B-1
	54-132	VII-A-1, 7; VII-A-1-a; VII-A-2-a; VII-A-9-a
National Bureau of Standards	54-145	VII-C-1-m
	55-147	VII-A-7
	56-37	IX-E-2
	57-179	VII-C-5
Nauman, V.O.	56-59	I-J-2
Navias, L.	41-9	VII-A-8
Naylor, B.F.	45-3	VII-A-1-a
	46-1	I-M-2; VII-C-6
	46-2	IX-A-2; IX-D-1; IX-D; IX
	46-6	VII-B-6-f, g, j
Neely, J.J.	48-16	VII-D-3-a
	48-33	VII-D-3-a
	48-34	VII-D-3-a
	50-19	VII-D-3-a
Neimark, B.E.	55-68	II-C-6, 7; II-D-1, 3, 9; II-L-6, 7
Nelson, H.R.	45-10	I-T-4
	45-16	IX-E
	51-31	VI-B-2

Nelson, H.R.	51-50	VI-L
	52-48	I-U-1
	52-102	VI-L
	57-176	VII-A-2-a
	57-191	VII-A-2-a
Nelson, R.G.	54-22	I-Z-1
Neshpor, V.S.	57-28	IX-A-1, 2, 4, 6; IX-C-2, 3; IX-D-1
Nemilov, V.A.	48-14	I-P-2
Nesbitt, L.B.	53-38	II-D-3; V-B-2
Neubert, T.J.	47-19	I-C-3-a, c
	56-115	I-C-3-a
New Jersey Ceramic Research Station	53-3	VII-A-5, 7; VII-A-5-a; VII-A-15; VII-C-6
	53-4	VII-A-5-a; VII-A-5, 15
	53-5	VII-A-2, 5, 15; VII-A-2-a; VII-E-6; VIII-B-5
New Jersey Ceramic Research Station	53-44	VII-E-6
	53-45	VII-E-3-j
	54-69	VII-B-1, 7; VII-B-6-e, f, k; VII-B-7-a; VII-E-3, 4
	55-22	VII-B-2-a; VII-E-3-j; VII-E
Newkirk, J.B.	52-120	III-A-3
Nicolaid, M.	56-82	II-B-1, 8
Nii, R.	56-103	I-G-2
Nivert Jr., J.M.	56-169	VII-C-5
	57-182	VII-C-1-b
Niwa, K.	57-64	VII-A-13
Nix, F.C.	41-6	I-A-2; I-C-7; I-G-3; I-J-2; I-N-3
	42-2	I-M-4; I-P-1, 2; I-S-4; I-T-1, 7
Noeron, J.T.	49-59	IX-C-2, 3; IX-C
Noguchi, T.	56-65	I-C-3-a
Nomura, S.	51-20	VII-B-6-e
Nopco Chemical Co.	55-85	X-A-10
Nordberg, M.E.	44-11	VII-C-6
Nordheim, R.	54-23	IV-A-5
North, J.M.	52-45	I-U-1
Norton, F.H.	49-68	VII-A-1-a; VII-E-9
	50-64	VII-A-1-a; VII-E-9
	50-66	VII-A-1-a; VII-A-5-a
	51-75	VII-A-1-a; VII-A-2-a; VII-A-5-a; VII-B-1; VII-B-4-b
	51-76	VII-A-5-a; VII-A-9-b; VII-E-9
	51-77	VII-A-1-a; VII-A-5-a; VII-A-9-b; VII-E-9
Norton, F.H.	52-65	VII-A-2-a; VII-A-5-a; VII-A-8; VII-B-4-b
	52-66	VII-A-1-a; VII-A-1; VII-A-2; VII-A-5-a
	52-67	VII-A-2-a; VII-A-2; VII-A-5
	52-68	VII-A-1-a; VII-A-1
	53-40	VII-D-1-a
	53-65	VII-A-1, 8, 10, 15; VII-B-2; VII-B-4-b
Norton, F.H.	53-66	VII-B-2
	53-67	VII-A-1-a; VII-A-2-a; VII-A-2; VII-A-5-a; VII-A-5
	53-68	VII-A-10; VII-C-1-b
	53-69	VII-A-10
	54-64	VII-C-1-b; VII-C-5; IX-B-1
	54-137	VII-C-6
Norton, F.H.	54-142	VII-A-5; VII-D-1-a
	54-144	VII-A-5-a; VII-A-5; VII-A-14
	54-149	VII-C-1-b
	55-25	VII-A-5; VII-A-9-a; VII-D-1-a
	55-47	VII-A-1, 5, 8; VII-C-6
Norton, F.H.	55-53	VII-A-3, 5; VII-A-4-n
	55-57	VII-A-1-a; VII-A-2-a; VII-A-2; VII-C-1-b; VII-C-6
Norton, F.J.	50-23	I-C-3
Norton, J.T.	52-37	VIII-A-1; IX-A-1
Nottorf, R.	48-26	IX-E
Novikova, S.I.	57-81	I-A-2; I-C-7

Oak Ridge National Laboratory	57-150	I-S-1; VII-A-1-a; VII-A-2-a; VII-A-6, 8; VII-B-2-e; VII-B-2; VII-B-4-b; VII-B-7-a; VII-B-9; VII-C-1-b; VII-C-6; VII-E-3, 4; X-A-9; X-J
O'Brien, C.J.	57-87	VII-B-2-c
O'Brien, F.R.	54-90	XI-H-3, 5, 6
	55-83	X-A-10; XI-A-1, 2; XI-H-3, 5, 6
	55-84	XI-H-3, 5
O'Connor, W.F.	51-47	VII-A-5-a; VII-A-9-b
Oelsen, O.	55-2	I-A-2; I-J-2; I-N-3
Oelsen, O.	55-103	I-A-2, 4; I-T-4
	55-125	I-A-2; I-J-2; I-N-3; II-A-5
Oelsen, W.	55-2	I-A-2; I-J-2; I-N-3; II-A-5
	55-103	I-A-2, 4; I-T-4
	57-131	I-S-4; II-A-1, 2, 3
Oetjen, R.A.	56-147	IX-F-1
Ogden, H.R.	54-57	I-T-6; IV-H; V-C-2; V-C; VI-E
Oglesby Jr. S.	55-83	X-A-10; XI-A-1, 2; XI-H-3, 5, 6
	55-84	XI-H-3, 5, 6
	57-97	XI-A-1, 2; XI-B-1; XI-D-1, 2, 3; XI-H-6, 7
Oishi, J.	56-38	I-G-3; I-S-4
Olette, M.	57-40	I-S-3
Oliver, D.A.	52-25	II-C-6; II-D-3-a; II-D-3, 4; IV-B-1
	53-34	I-R-2
Olson, O.H.	56-66	I-C-3-a, d; I-C-7; I-M-4; I-N-3; I-T-1; III-E; XI-C
	57-8	I-A-2; I-C-3-a, d; I-C-5, 7; I-J-2; I-M-4; I-N-3; I-P-1, 2; I-R-3; I-T-1; II-D-1; II-D-3-a; II-D-3; III-E; IV-A-2; IV-A-5-a; V-C-1; V-C; VII-A-2-a; VII-A-5-a; XI-B-5; XI-C, E; XI-E-3, 5, 6, 7
	58-1	I-C-3-a, d; I-C-5; I-J-2; II-D-3; IV-A-2; IV-A-5-a; V-C-1; V-C; XI-C, E; XI-H-3, 5, 6, 7
	59-1	VII-A-1-a; VII-A-2-a; VII-A-5-a; VII-A-9-b; VII-C-1-b; VII-C-1, 5, 6; VII-D-1-a
Onstott, E.I.	56-113	I-S-1
Oriani, R.A.	51-84	VII-A-1-a
	54-17	I-G-3; I-J-2; I-N-3; I-P-2; I-R-3; I-T-6; I-V-1; I-Z-1
	54-21	VII-A-1-a; VII-A-3
Orlowski, H.J.	41-10	VII-B-3-c, e, f, k
Ormont, B.F.	56-133	IX-A-5
Orr, R.L.	52-61	VII-B-6-j
	53-13	VII-B-6-e, k
	53-57	VII-A-14, 15
	53-87	VII-B-2-d, e
	54-135	VII-A-14, 15
Osborn, R.H.	41-1	I-M-4; I-T-7
Osborne, D.W.	50-21	VII-A-14
	53-55	VII-A-7
	53-58	VII-A-14
Otter, F.A.	55-7	I-N-3; II-C-9; IV-A
	56-46	I-C-7; I-G-3; I-S-4; III-H; III-VI-A-3, 5; VI-A; V-B-4; VI-B, E
Owens Illinois Glass Co. Research Labs.	48-38	VII-C-1-b
Pallister, P.R.	49-2	I-J-2
	54-15	I-J-2
	57-6	II-A-1, 2, 3;
Panteleimonov, L.A.	56-31	IV-B-4; IV-B; VI-D-2, 3
Parikh, N.M.	55-143	VII-C-1-b; VII-C
Parke, R.M.	46-3	IV-F-2; IV-F
Parker, H.S.	55-144	VII-A-7, 10
Parkinson, D.H.	51-1	I-C-4; I-L-1; I-N-1; I-P-5
	52-5	I-G-2
Pattison, J.R.	55-86	VII-A-1-a; VII-B-1; VII-E-10, 11
	56-27	II-A-1, 2, 3
Pawlek, F.	56-13	I-C-7
Pawlowski, S.	57-183	VII-E-11
Payson, P.	56-80	II C-4; II-C; II-D-6, 9

Pearson, G. J.	56-11	I-N-3; I-U-1
	57-149	I-N-3; I-P-2
Pearson, G. L.	49-4	I-S-3; II-D-5; VI-G
Pecijare, O.	57-66	III-E
	57-99	III-A-3; III-B-3; VI
	57-107	III-E
Pegg, E. F.	51-81	VII-C-2, 5
	54-140	VII-C
Peguignot, J. R.	52-118	V-C-4; IV-G
Pell, E. M.	57-47	I-S-3
Pellini, W. S.	51-5	I-M-4; I-T-7; II-D-3; II-D-6-a;IV-A-4-a; IV-A-5-a; IV-B-1, 3
Pelzel, E.	57-80	I-C-7; I-T-7; III-B, C; VI
Penn. State	48-37	VII-B-2-b; VII-B-7-b; VII-B-7
Perova, V. I.	57-117	I-J-2; II-D-2; II-D-3-a; II-D-6-a; II-D-6; II-D
Perrot, S.	44-7	I-C-5; XI-C
Perry, S.	45-6	I-A-2; I-C-7; II-C-6, 7; II-D-1, 3, 4; III-A-2, 3; III-B-3; III-D, E, G; IV-A-1; V-A-1, 3, 4; V-A-2-b; V-B-1; VII-C-6
Persoz, B.	40-4	I-C-7; I-N-3; I-P-2; III-D; IV-A-1
Petersen, D.	55-51	I-C-4
Petersen, V. C.	55-101	I-T-6; V-C
Peterson, D.	52-106	I-T-4
Petrash, E. V.	55-135	IX-C-2; IX-D-1
Pevtsov, D. M.	58-8	IV-C
Phipps, T. E.	50-63	VII-A-11
Pierrey, J.	46-10	I-C-3
	49-17	I-C-3-n; VII-A-9-b
Pietrokowsky, P.	56-137	IX-G-4
Pijanowski, S. W.	57-199	VII-A-10
Pinto, N. P.	49-45	I-B-3
Pitkin, W. R.	52-28	IV-B-1
	54-114	IV-C
Plankenhorn, W. J.	53-42	VII-E-9; VII-E
Pleasance, R. J.	56-85	I-P-1; VI-D
Ploetz, G. L.	57-189	VII-A-4-b, d, e, n
Pochapsky, T. E.	53-7	I-A-2
Podnogin, A. K.	53-145	VII-B-6-d
Pole, G. R.	46-14	VII-A-5-a; VII-A-5; VII-A-13; VII-B
Pollock, B. D.	53-135	IX-C
Pollock, D. D.	56-114	I-C-7; III-D, H; III
Polmear, I. J.	55-37	V-A-1
Polyakova, R. S.	57-19	I-R-4
	58-12	IV-C-3; IV-D
Poole, D. M.	57-16	I-P-3; I-T-4; VI
	57-75	I-T-4; IV-L; VI
Post, B.	52-127	IX-C-3
	54-82	IX-C-3; IX-C; IX-J-1, 3, 4, 7, 9, 11; IX-J
Potter, E. V.	49-10	I-M-2
Potter, R. A.	56-140	IX-B
Poulter, J.	53-80	I-C-3-m
Pound, G. M.	54-9	I-N-3; II-A-4, 5, 6, 7; II-C-5; II-C
Powell, H.	43-4	I-A-2; I-S-4; V-A-6; V-A, G; VI-B-1
Powell, L. S.	55-97	I-P-4
Powell, R. L.	55-120	III-C
	57-37	I-C-7; III-A-1; III-F, J; III
	57-52	I-C-7
Powell, R. W.	45-11	I-C-3-a, j; I-U-1
	49-54	V-A-1, 2, 3, 4; V-A-2-a, b; V-A
	52-60	III-B-3
	53-29	I-B-3
	54-7	VII-A-2-a; VII-A-2; VII-B
Powell, R. W.	55-104	I-J-1; I-R-3
	56-121	II-C-1, 6
	56-124	II-C-2, 6
	57-10	I-C-5
Powers, W. D.	53-130	II-D-2; IV-A-5
Powers, R. M.	52-17	I-N-3; I-T-6; I-V-1; IV-C-5; IV-G; V-B-4; V-C-4
Pozdnyak, N. Z.	53-103	II-C
	54-50	II-C, D

Prettyman, I. B.	45-15	XI-H
Prod'homme, M.	55-43	VII-C-1-k, m; VII-C-2, 5
Prosenkova, T. E.	56-41	VII-A-14
Pugh, E. M.	56-26	IV-A-1
Pumphrey, W. I.	49-55	II-D-5
Pupke, G.	57-12	I-C-7; I-J-2; I-N-3; II-D-5
Putley, E. H.	49-48	I-G-2
Putman, J. W.	52-64	I-C-5
Quirk, J.	54-47	VII-A-15
Rabotnov, S. N.	44-3	I-C-7
Raeth, C. H.	44-9	I-U-1
Raeuchle, R. F.	48-26	IX-E
	55-130	IX-G-2
	58-23	IX-G-2
Raezer, S. D.	54-14	II-A-1
Rait, J. R.	52-26	II-C-6
Randall, J. A.	47-21	I-G-2
Randolph, B. W.	53-116	I-M-4
Rase, D. E.	55-73	VII-B-6-e
Rasor, N. S.	54-32	I-C-3-a, b, d, g, j
	55-12	I-C-2-a, b, d, g, j
	56-57	I-C-3-d, n
	56-58	I-C-3-d, n
	57-5	I-C-3-d; I-M-4; I-T-1
	60-1	I-C-3-a; I-M-4; I-T-1
Raub, E.	39-4	I-S-4; VI-B-2, 3; VI-B
	49-12	VI-B-3; VI-B
	50-57	VI-A
Rauch, W. G.	54-68	VII-A-10; VIII-B-3
Rauh, E. G.	54-71	I-U-1
	54-72	I-U-1
	56-102	I-U-1
Ravdel, M. P.	57-31	IX-J-5
Rawson, H.	54-139	VII-C
Rayner, J. M.	52-118	IV-G; V-C-4
Raytheon Mfg. Co.	55-90	I-S-3
Rea, J. A.	56-3	I-T-6
Reactor Handbook	55-152	VII-A-2-a
Reavell, F. R.	49-6	I-T-6
Redfield, T. A.	51-38	I-M-4
Redmond, R. F.	52-46	I-Z-1; II-D-3
Reed, D.	44-8	I-C-3-n, p; I-C-7; I-N-3; II-D-2; XI-B-3
Rehner Jr., J.	47-20	X-J; X
Reichel, K.	56-13	I-C-7
Reid, H. W.	51-23	VII-C-1-q
Reinartz, K.	50-5	I-A-2
Reisman, A.	55-146	VII-A-14
Rentschler, R. R.	57-3	I-Z-1; IX-E-2
Repko, A. J.	49-23	VIII-A-2
Resnick, R.	52-76	I-Z-1; IV-J-1
	53-119	I-U-1
Reynolds, J. M.	53-26	I-C-3-d
Reynolds, M. M.	57-121	I-A-2; I-C-5; I-G-3; I-N-3; I-R-3; I-S-4; II-D-2; XI-B-3
Reysen, W. H.	57-25	X-G
Rhines, F. N.	52-120	III-A-3
Rhodes, R. G.	51-88	VII-B-6-a, e
Richards, J. W.	41-19	I-A-2; I-C-7
	41-23	I-A-2; I-C-7
Richards, L. E.	53-136	VII-B-9; XI-D, E
Richmond, J. C.	57-186	VII-D-1-a
Ricker, R. W.	51-48	VII-A-6, 8
Rieder, Z.	56-135	VIII-C; IX-C-2, 3; IX-C

Rieskamp, K. H.	55-2	I-A-2; I-J-2; I-N-3; II-A-5
	55-125	II-A-5
Rigby, G. R.	43-15	VII-B-7-a; VII-B-7
	46-8	VII-A-13; VII-B-7; VII-B-7-a; VII-B-8-a; VII-B
Rigney, C. J.	51-2	I-T-6; V-C-5
Riley, W. C.	56-101	I-C-3-a, j
Rinck, E.	52-22	I-S-5
Ritland, H. N.	57-184	VII-C-1-b; VII-C-5
Rittberg, G. G.	50-9	II-D; VI-C
Robards, C. F.	49-20	VII-A-5; VII-A-5-a; VII-A-9-b; IX-A-2, 4
	51-42	VIII-B-5
Robertson, W. D.	48-28	IX-G-3
Robertson, J. A. L.	53-112	I-P-3
	54-98	I-P-3
Robson, H. E.	56-154	VII-D-2
Rocholl, P.	57-160	IV-A-5
Rockwell, III, T.	54-88	XI-E
Roder, H. M.	57-37	I-C-7; III-A-1-III-F, J; III
Rodignia, E. N.	55-71	VII-A-1-a
Rogener, H.	40-20	VII-A-1-a; VII-A-2-a; VII-A-9-b; VII-B-7-a
	52-86	IX-D
Rogers, B. A.	52-106	I-T-4
	53-108	I-T-4: I-V-1
	54-104	I-N-4; I-Z-1
	55-105	I-N-4; I-Z-1
Rogers, W. M.	57-37	I-C-7; III-A-1; III-F, J; III
	57-52	I-C-7
Roinet, C.	56-53	V-A-4
Rolla, L.	43-10	I-C-4; I-L-1; I-P-5; IX-G-3; IX-H
Romand, J.	56-60	I-T-1, 7; I-Z-1
Rose, E. E.	54-73	X-F
Rosenberg, H. M.	55-107	I-A-2; I-B-3; I-C-6, 7; I-G-3; I-J-2; I-M-4; I-P-2; I-R-7; I-S-4; I-T-1, 6; I-Z-1
Rosenbohm, E.	39-1	I-P-2
	40-2	I-C-6
	41-7	I-R-4
Rosenfield, A. R.	55-15	II-A-1; II-D-6
Rosenholtz, J. L.	41-8	VII-A-6
Rostoker, W.	53-91	IX-J-1, 3, 4, 6, 7, 9, 11, IX-J
Rouard, P.	53-92	I-G-3
Rough, F. A.	53-56	VI-F-1; VI-L
	53-109	I-Z-1; IV-J; VI-F-3
	55-23	I-U-1; VI-F-1, 3
Rough, F. A.	56-90	I-U-1
	57-158	IV-L
Rowe, G. H.	54-102	I-T-6
Roy, R.	55-72	VII-B-6-e, f
	55-73	VII-B-6-e
Royal, J.	47-19	I-C-3-a, c
	56-115	I-C-3-a
Rubin, T.	54-10	I-A-2; I-N-3; I-T-6; I-Z-1
	54-39	II-D-3; III-A-3
	54-53	I-C-7
Rudner, M. A.	54-92	X-G
Rudnitsky, A. A.	48-14	I-P-2
Rudnitskii, A. A.	56-70	III; VI-C
	57-19	I-R-4
Rudorff, W.	53-85	VII-A-4-a; VII-A-10
Rume-Rothery, W.	49-43	I-C-5
Rundle, R. E.	45-18	IX-E
	48-19	I-U-1
	48-26	IX-E
	48-29	IX-A-7
Rundle, R. E.	48-30	IX-D-2
	49-42	I-U-1
	49-57	VI
	50-58	IX-A
	51-72	IX-J-8

Runnalls, O. J. C.	55-131	IX-B
Russell, H. W.	45-10	I-T-4
	45-16	IX-E
Russell Jr., R.	44-6	VII-C-6; VII-E-3-k; VII-E-4
	47-11	VII-E-4
Russell, R. B.	51-54	I-H-1; I-Z-1
	54-55	I-Z-1
	54-97	I-Z-1
Saba, W. G.	57-1	I-M-1
	57-35	I-M-1
Sagai, Y.	54-120	IV-B-3
	55-123	IV-B-3
Sagel, K.	56-96	I-T-6; V-C-1
Sagel, K.	56-112	I-T-6; V-C-1
	56-131	V-A-4
	56-145	IX-A-2; IX-D-1
Sailer, V. L.	49-47	I-A-2; I-C-3-a; V-A-1; XI-C
Saito, H.	51-70	II-L; II-M-7
	52-77	III-A-3
	52-121	IV-B-3
	53-129	II-D-1, 4; IV-F
	54-60	I-N-4; III-E; IV-A-5
Saito, H.	54-118	II-D; IV-B-3
	54-120	IV-B-3
	55-121	III-E
	55-123	IV-B-3
Saito, T.	52-96	II-A-1; XI-B-5
Salkovitz, E. I.	56-16	I-N-3; I-P-1; IV-A; VI-D
	57-18	I-N-3; I-P-1; IV-A; VI-D
	57-27	IV-A
Saller, H. A.	53-56	VI-F-1; VI-F, L
	53-109	I-Z-1; IV-J-3; VI-F-3
Saller, H. A.	54-20	I-Z-1; IV-J-1
	53-127	II-D-2; II-D-6-a; IV-A-4-a; IV-A-5-a; IV-A-5
	54-116	IV-C; VI-A, D
	55-23	I-U-1; VI-F-1, 3
	56-90	I-U-1
	56-128	VI-F-2, 3
Samsonov, G. V.	55-135	IX-C-2; IX-D-1
	56-87	I-C-5; I-H-1; I-M-4; I-N-4; I-T-1, 6, 7; I-V-1; I-Z-1; IX-A-1, 2, 3, 4, 5, 6; IX-A; IX-C-2, 3; IX-C; IX-D-1; IX-D
	56-153	VII-D-2
	57-28	IX-A-1, 2, 4, 6; IX-C-2, 3; IX-D-1
Sands, D. E.	57-57	I-B-4
Sasaki, W.	52-98	VII-D-1-a
Sasmor, D. J.	54-136	VII-D-4
	56-150	VII-A-14; VII-D-6
Sato, S.	40-19	IX-D
Satterhwaite, C. B.	57-172	IX-F-2
Savage, W. R.	56-83	I-A-2; I-N-1; I-P-5
Savitskii, E. M.	57-38	I-T-6
Savitskaya, Ya. S.	53-64	VII-C-1-b
Sawada, S.	51-20	VII-B-6-e
	56-19	VII-B-6-g
Sawyer, R. B.	52-75	I-N-3; II-A-1; II-D-1, 2, 3; IV-A-5-a; IV-A-5
	55-5	II-A-1
	55-115	II-A-1
Schachinger, L.	52-12	I-C-6
Schadel Jr., H. M.	53-131	VI-A, B
Schelton, S. M.	54-109	I-H-1
Schindler, A. I.	56-16	I-N-3; I-P-1; IV-A; VI-D
	57-18	I-N-3; I-P-1; IV-A; VI-D
	57-27	IV-A
Schmidt, D. L.	57-95	X-F
Schneider, A.	41-18	I-M-1
	54-74	IX-F-1
Schoefer, E. A.	53-35	II-D-2, 3

Schofield, T.H.	53-10	I-J-2; I-N-3; I-P-2; I-T-6
	56-98	I-J-2; I-T-6
	57-4	I-N-4
Scholes, W.A.	50-4	VII-A-2-a; VII-A-2
Schrag, G.	40-17	I-N-3
Schramm, C.H.	49-58	IX-A-5
Schuch, A.F.	52-108	I-C-7; I-U-1
Schulte, H.A.	57-110	I-C-3-p; I-C-3
Schultz, A.W.	58-15	X-G; XI-H-1
Schulz, L.G.	45-7	I-C-7; I-G-3; I-S-4
	45-8	I-S-4
Schulze, A.	47-2	I-U-1
Schuman, R.	44-4	I-B-3
Schwartz, B.	52-11	VII-A-1-a; VII-A-1, 5, 9
	52-30	VII-A-2-a
Schwartz, C.M.	56-104	I-U-1
Schwartz, H.S.	57-103	XI-H-3, 5, 6
Schwartz, S.	48-35	VII-A-5-a
Scott, G.D.	50-46	I-A-2; I-C-5; I-G-3; I-N-3; I-P-1; I-S-4
Scott, J.L.	57-43	I-T-6; I-Z-1; IV-J-2; IV-J
Searcy, A.W.	50-30	IX-B-1; IX-B; IX-J-4, 7, 9
	51-10	I-A-2; VII-A-1-a; VII-A-1
	51-33	I-G-2
	51-63	I-B-4
	52-62	I-G-2
Searcy, A.W.	52-101	IX-B-1; IX-B; IX-J-4, 7
	53-71	I-B-4
	53-75	I-G-2
	53-77	IX-B
	53-89	IX-B, J
Searcy, A.W.	55-11	I-G-2
	56-149	IX-J-6
	57-58	I-B-4
Sebilleau, F.	54-29	I-C-6
Sedlacek, R.	57-187	VII-C-1-b, m; VII-C-3
	57-197	VII-C-1-m
Seghezzi, H.D.	57-70	I-T-1
Seibel, R.D.	57-156	II-D-2, 3; IV-A-5-a; IV-A-5; VII-A-2-a; VII-D-1-a
Seifert, R.L.	48-15	VII-A-2-a
	51-82	VII-A-2-a
	52-1	VII-A-1-a; VII-A-1; VII-C-6
Seifert, R.L.	52-49	I-U-1; VII-D-1-a; VII-D-1
	53-17	I-A-2; I-C-3-a; I-J-2; I-N-3; I-U-1; VII-A-1, 2, 6, 10; VII-A-2-a; VII-B-7-a; VII-B-7; VII-D-1-a
Selisskii, Ya. P.	57-31	IX-J-5
Sellers, P.	51-61	I-P-7
Seltz, H.	39-2	IX-A
	40-9	VII-A-14
	43-3	VII-A-14
Sennet, R.S.	50-46	I-A-2; I-C-5; I-G-3; I-N-3; I-P-1; I-S-4
Sense, K.A.	53-141	VII-D-5-a
	57-77	VII-D-5-a
	57-174	VII-D-5-a
Serebrennikov, N.N.	52-51	I-S-3
	54-67	II-D; VI-G-1
Serebrennikov, N.N.	56-36	II-C-9
	56-39	I-S-3; II-C-9; II-D; VI-G-1
Seybold, A.U.	43-18	I-G-3; VI-A-4, 5; VI-A
Shaler, A.J.	52-128	VIII-A-2
Shapiro, E.	52-16	VII-A-7
Shartsis, L.	53-139	VII-C-2
Sheehy, J.P.	50-67	VII-B-1
Shelton, G.R.	47-9	VII-A-8; VII-B-6-e, k
	48-3	VII-B-6-e, j
	51-86	VII-B-6
Shermer, H.F.	56-157	VII-C-1-a, b; VII-C-2
	56-166	VII-C-1-a, c; VII-C-6
Sherwood, E.M.	55-113	I-R-2

Shevlin, T. S.	51-28	VIII-B-1
	52-42	VIII-B-1
	54-40	I-C-5; IV-F-2; VII-A-1-a, b; VII-B-1
	54-52	VIII-B-1
	55-19	I-C-5; IV-F-2; VII-A-1-a, b
	58-24	VIII-B-1
Shigetomi, S.	56-143	IX-F-2
Shilts, J. L.	55-1	I-M-4
Shimazaki, E.	57-64	VII-A-13
Shinozaki, M.	54-118	II-D; IV-B-3
Shirane, G.	51-87	VII-B-6-e
Shoemaker, D. P.	55-119	IV-D
Shomate, C. H.	45-3	VII-A-1-a
	46-1	I-M-2; VII-C-6
	47-16	VII-A-8
	49-26	IX-A, D
Silver, I.	56-148	X-C-1
Silverman, L.	53-2	I-J-2; I-N-3; I-T-6; II-D-1, 2, 5, 6; III-D; IV-A-1, 3, 4, 5; IV-A-4-a; IV-A-5-a; IV-A
Simmons, R. O.	57-120	I-C-7
Simon, F. E.	51-1	I-C-4; I-L-1; I-N-1; I-P-5
	53-90	I-C-3-m
Simpson, H. E.	51-83	VII-C-2
	55-143	VII-C-1-b; VII-C
Simpson, O. C.	49-31	I-C-3
	50-22	I-A-3
	52-99	I-C-3-a; I-C-3
Simpson, O. C.	53-106	I-C-3-a; I-C-3
	53-107	I-C-3-a; I-C-3
Sims, C. T.	53-12	I-R-2
	53-74	I-R-2
	54-38	I-R-2
	54-75	I-R-2
Sims, C. T.	54-106	I-R-2
	55-18	I-R-2
	55-24	I-R-2
	55-59	I-R-2; VI
	56-17	I-R-2
	57-137	I-R-2
Sindeband, S. J.	49-59	IX-C-2, 3; IX-C
Sinel'nikov, N. N.	53-60	VII-A-6
Sinnott, M. J.	53-86	II-B-7, 8
Skinner, B.	53-114	I-Z-1
Skinner, B. J.	57-21	I-C-3-m; VII-A-5-a; VII-A-5, 7
Skinner, G. B.	51-7	I-Z-1
	51-13	I-Z-1
	53-25	I-Z-1
Skochdopole, R. E.	53-33	I-T-4
	54-35	I-G-1
Skochdopole, R. E.	55-33	I-E-2
	56-100	I-D-1
Skogen, H. S.	55-39	VII-A-6; VII-C; VII-D-1-a
Smirnov, I. A.	57-129	I-G-2
Smirnova, V. I.	56-133	IX-A-5
Smirous, K.	57-85	IX-F-2
Smith, A. R.	51-65	I-J-2; II-A-1; II-D-2, 3; IV-A-5-a; IV-A-5; V-A-1, 4; V-B-1; V-P-4; VII-C-1-b; VII-C-5, 6
Smith, A. W.	54-32	I-C-3-a, b, d, g, j
	56-67	I-C-3-d, n
	56-58	I-C-3-d, n
Smith, C. W.	55-140	X-H
Smith, D. F.	56-150	VII-A-14; VII-D-6
Smith, D. T.	41-8	VII-A-6
Smith, J. F.	56-89	I-C-1
Smith, J. H.	57-106	VI-A-5
	57-157	VI-E-1
Smith, K. F.	56-113	I-T-6; I-Z-1; II-D-3; IV-J-1; IV-J; V-C-1
	57-36	I-V-1; IV-G
Smith, P. L.	53-49	I-B-3

122

Smith, R.J.	56-16	I-N-3; I-P-1; IV-A; VI-D
	57-18	I-N-3; I-P-1; IV-A; VI-D
	57-27	IV-A
Smith, T.	57-30	IX-F-2
Smith Jr. W.T.	53-34	I-R-2
Smoke, E.J.	49-3	VII-A-1-a; VII-A-1
	54-43	VII-C-1-a; VII-E-2, 6
Snow, A.I.	51-72	IX-J-8
Snyder, M.J.	53-141	VII-D-5-a
	57-29	IX-B-2; IX-D-2; IX-G-1; IX
Snyder, N.H.	53-3	VII-B
Snyder, P.E.	53-1	VII-A-14
Snyder, T.M.	55-95	I-C-3-a, p; I-U-1; VII-A-10; IX-A-7; IX-B-2; XI-C, E
Sochtig, H.	40-3	I-C-5
Sogabe, T.	40-19	IX-D
Sokolovskaya, E.M.	56-32	IV-B-4; IV-B; VI-A-2, 3; VI-D-1, 2
	56-125	IV-B; VI-A-2
Somiya, S.	57-93	VII-A-7; VII-A-9-b
Southard, J.C.	41-25	VII-C-2
Spedding, F.H.	49-64	IX-E
	51-1	I-C-4; I-L-4; I-N-1; I-P-5
	52-14	I-L-1; I-N-1; I-P-5
	52-53	I-A-2
	52-88	I-L-1; I-N-1; I-P-5
Spedding, F.H.	53-16	I-D-1; I-E-2; I-G-1
	53-21	I-A-2
	53-31	I-D-1; I-G-1; I-N-1; I-P-5
	54-36	I-C-4; I-D-1; I-E-2; I-G-1; I-H-2; I-L-1, 2; I-N-1; I-P-5; I-S-1; I-T-3, 5; I-Y-1, 2
	55-33	I-E-2
Spedding, F.H.	55-52	I-C-4; I-D-1; I-E-2, 3; I-G-1; I-H-2; I-L-1, 2; I-N-1; I-P-5; I-S-1, 2; I-T-3, 5; I-Y-1, 2
	56-83	I-A-2; I-N-1; I-P-5
	56-86	I-C-4; I-D-1; I-E-2, 3; I-G-1; I-H-2; I-L-1, 2; I-P-5, 6; I-S-1, 2; I-T-3, 5; I-Y-1, 2
	56-88	I-C-7; I-D-1; I-E-2; I-G-1; I-L-1; I-N-1; I-P-5; I-Y-1
	56-100	I-D-1
Spedding, F.H.	57-13	I-C-4; I-D-1; I-E-2; I-G-1; I-L-1; I-N-1; I-P-5; I-T-3 I-Y-1
	57-74	I-T-5
	57-119	I-L-1; I-N-1; I-P-2
	57-135	I-T-3
Speiser, R.	48-20	I-B-3
	50-6	I-C-5
	51-18	I-M-4; I-N-4; I-P-2; I-T-1
Spindler, W.E.	57-32	IX-D-3
Spinner, S.	53-139	VII-C-2
Spretnak, J.W.	52-122	V-C-1, 2, 5
Spriggs, R.M.	56-97	I-J-2; II-D-2
Squire, C.F.	41-11	I-Z-1
Sreedhar, A.K.	53-50	I-M-1
	55-100	I-P-1
St. Pierre, P.D.S.	52-74	VII-A-8
Stacy, J.T.	54-116	IV-C; VI-A, D
Stalinski, B.	57-173	IX-E
Stansbury, E.E.	54-54	I-J-2; I-N-3
Stanworth, J.E.	51-81	VII-C-2, 5
	54-139	VII-C
	54-140	VII-C
Statton, W.O.	51-45	VII-A-8
Steierman, B.L.	46-4	VII-A-1
Steinitz, R.	57-92	VIII; IX-G, H
	57-166	VIII
Stewart, J.E.	57-186	VII-D-1-a
Stirling, J.F.	51-26	VII-C-5
Stockdale, D.	40-12	I-S-4; VI-B
Stoll, E.K.	41-18	I-M-1
Stone, R.W.	57-77	VII-D-5
	57-174	VII-D-5-a
Stourac, L.	57-85	IX-F-2
Stradley, J.G.	58-24	VIII-B-1

Straumanis, M. E.	52-20	I-G-2; I-S-3
	56-50	I-T-4
Strauss, S. W.	53-136	VII-B-9; XI-D, E
	56-69	VII-A-6; VII-C-1-m; VII-C-6
	56-163	VII-C-1-a, b
Street, R.	57-106	VI-A-5
	57-157	VI-E-1
Strelkov, P. G.	57-81	I-A-2; I-C-7
Strittmater, R. C.	55-14	I-N-3; I-P-2
	57-149	I-N-3; I-P-2
Struthers, J. D.	50-24	VII-A-15
Stubblefield, C. T.	55-151	VII-A-4-k
Stuckes, A. D.	57-130	I-G-2; I-S-3; II-D-3; IX-F
Stull, D. R.	55-31	I-M-1; II-D-1
Sturm, W. J.	57-78	VI-A-1
Suber, L. L.	55-17	VII-A-4-a; VII-A-15; VII-C
Sugai, Y.	54-120	IV-B-3
	55-123	IV-B-3
Sugihara, M.	52-77	III-A-3
	53-129	II-D-1, 4; IV-F
Suhrmann, R.	40-15	I-A-4, 5
Sukharev, P. M.	56-39	I-S-3; II-C-9; II-D; VI-G-1
Sully, A. H.	52-81	I-C-3; I-N-3; I-P-2; II-D-2; IV-A-5-a; VII-A-1-a; VII-B-4-a; VII-A-5-a; VII-A-9-b; VII-A-6, 7
	53-36	I-C-5
Suzuki, H.	56-160	VII-D-1-a
	57-93	VII-A-7; VII-A-9-b
Suzuki, T.	49-25	V-A-1
	49-51	I-C-7
Suzuoka, T.	57-168	IX-F-1
Sweeny, W. O.	47-14	II-D-3-n; II-D-3; IV-A-2; IV-A-3-a; IV-B-1
	50-14	II-D-3-a; II-D-3; IV-A-2, 3; IV-A-3-a; IV-B-1
Swica, J. J.	58-25	VII-A-1-a; XI-J
Swift, R. M.	56-29	IX-C-1
	57-48	IX-C-1
Sykes, C.	52-27	II-D-3
Takagi, Y.	55-29	I-A-2; I-C-7; III-A-3; III-D, H
Takahashi, M.	54-60	I-N-3; III-E; IV-A-5
	55-121	III-E
Takeda, A.	51-87	VII-B-6-e
Tarasov, V. V.	53-64	VII-C-1-b
Tate, R. E.	52-24	I-P-3
Taylor, A.	50-68	VII-D-1-a
	52-38	IX-G-1
Taylor, K. M.	55-69	VII-D-4
Taylor, J. R.	56-136	X-E, F; X
Teeter, C. E.	48-16	VII-A-3-a
	48-33	VII-D-3-a
	48-34	VII-D-3-a
	50-19	VII-D-3-a
Teitel, R. J.	52-124	VI
	56-130	VI-F; VI
	57-161	VI-F
Templeton, D. H.	49-56	VI
	49-61	IX-C
Terai, R.	52-135	VII-C-2; VII-C
Thackray, R. W.	ND-1	VII-A-10
Thewlis, J.	52-19	I-U-1; VII-A-10
	56-78	I-C-3-m
Thiel, D.	55-103	I-A-2, 4; I-T-4
Thielke, N. R.	51-33	I-G-2
Thomas, H.	50-31	II-C-6; II-C; II-D-4, 7
	51-43	I-N-3; IV-A-5
Thomas, V.	56-127	II-D-5
Thompson, H. B.	51-64	I-Z-1; IV-J-1, 3, 7; IV-J
	51-65	I-J-2; IV-A-5-a; IV-A-5; VII-C-5, 6

Thompson, N.	40-10	IX-J-5
Thorn, R.J.	49-31	I-C-3
	52-99	I-C-3-a; I-C-3
	53-106	I-C-3-a; I-C-3
	53-107	I-C-3-a; I-C-3
Thorn, R.J.	54-71	I-U-1
	54-72	I-U-1
	56-42	VII-A-10
	56-43	VII-A-7
	57-138	I-C-3-a; I-C-3
Thurmond, C.D.	55-50	I-G-2
Tiesler, J.	50-29	IX-G-3; IX-G
Timper, A.J.	52-76	I-Z-1; IV-J-1
Tinklepaugh, J.R.	53-18	I-C-5; I-J-2; I-N-3; I-S-3; IV-A-2; IV-B-1; VII-D-1-a; VII-D-1; VIII-A-5
	58-7	II-D-1; VII-A-1-a; VII-B-2
	58-25	VII-A-1-a; XI-J
Tipton Jr., C.R.	55-112	I-U-1
	56-118	IV-J-1; VI-F-2
	56-139	IX-B-2; IX-G-4; IX-J-5
	57-154	IV-J-1; VI-F-2; IX-B-2
	57-163	IV-J-1
Todd, S.S.	50-18	VII-B-1
	51-30	VII-B-2-c,j
	52-13	VII-B-6-e,k
	52-59	VII-B-6-e,k
Tokuda, T.	55-141	VII-A-6
Tomlin, D.H.	54-77	I-C-1; I-P-2
Tomlinson, J.R.	55-38	VII-A-14
Tong, K.N.	54-94	XI-B-2, 4; XI-D-4; XI-E
Topchiashvili, L.I.	55-56	I-M-2; IV-A-6; VI-E-1, 2
Torgeson, D.R.	48-7	VII-B-5
Tottle, C.R.	57-126	I-N-4
Tousey, R.	56-92	I-A-2
	57-123	I-A-2
Tramposch, H.	57-94	X-A, B, C, D, F; X
Treco, R.M.	50-44	I-B-3
Trice, J.B.	48-16	VII-D-3-a
	48-33	VII-D-3-a
	48-34	VII-D-3-a
	50-19	VII-D-3-a
Trombe, F.	49-16	VII-A-1-a; VII-A-2-a; VII-A-3-a; VII-A-4-a; VII-A-5-a; VII-A-9-a, b; VII-A-7, 15
	52-23	I-D-1
	52-43	I-G-1
	53-70	I-D-1; I-E-3; I-G-1; I-S-1, 2; I-Y-2
Trompette, J.	53-92	I-G-3
	56-77	I-S-4
Troneva, M.Ya.	49-32	I-M-2; IV-A-6; VI-E-2
Troshkina, V.A.	54-121	II-D-6
Trostel Jr., L.J.	55-78	II-D-3; VIII-B-1; VIII-B
Truesdale, R.S.	58-25	VII-A-1-a; XI-J
Trumbore, F.A.	55-50	I-G-2
Trzebiatowski, W.	55-74	VII-B-6-k
	57-83	VII-B-6-k
Tschentke, G.	40-6	I-C-7; III-A-3
Tsubokawa, I.	53-62	IX-G-3
Tsuya, N.	53-62	IX-G-3
	56-93	I-M-4
Tucker Jr., C.W.	49-50	I-U-1
	50-53	I-U-1
	51-66	I-U-1
Twidle, G.G.	57-122	I-A-2
Tye, R.P.	52-60	III-B-3
	55-104	I-J-1; I-R-3
	56-121	II-C-1, 6
	57-10	I-C-5

Tyler, W. W.	52-44	I-U-1
	52-55	II-D-3; V-C-2
	52-71	I-C-3-j
	52-113	I-U-1
	52-115	I-C-3-j
Tyler, W. W.	53-9	I-U-1
	53-38	II-D-3; V-C-2
	53-78	I-C-3-a, g, j
	53-79	I-C-3-a
Uei, I.	56-64	VII-A-9-b
Uetsuki, T.	56-64	VII-A-9-b; VII-A-9
Uhlig, H. H.	48-28	IX-G-3
University of Chicago	43-19	I-C-3-a; V-A-1
Ure Jr., R. W.	57-172	IX-F-2
Uyeno, K.	41-5	VII-A-13, 14, 15
Valet, G.	53-85	VII-A-4-a; VII-A-10
Van Artsdalen, E. R.	54-136	VII-D-4
	56-150	VII-A-14, VII-D-6
Van Dusen, M. S.	47-3	I-U-1
	47-5	I-C-6; I-N-3
Van Dyken, A. R.	47-19	I-C-3-a, c
	56-115	I-C-3-a
Vanstrum, P. R.	47-25	X-G
Van Thyne, R. J.	57-36	I-V-1; IV-G
Van Valzor, J. A.	54-27	II-A-1, 2, 3; II-D-2, 3; IV-A-1; IV-A-5-a; V-A-1, 4; V-B-1; VII-C-1-b; VII-C-2, 5, 6; X-F
Vapaille, A.	57-25	I-C-7; I-P-1, 2; I-S-4
Vargin, V. V.	56-168	VII-C-1-b
Vasenin, F. I.	55-80	IX-F-2
Vasil'ev, E. L.	55-27	VII-E-6
	56-162	VII-B-8-n, p
Vasilos, T.	53-41	VII-D-1-a
	54-24	VII-D-1-a; IX-A-2' IX-D-1, 3
Vassamillet, L. F.	57-118	I-P-4
Vaughan, D. A.	50-62	IX-A-7
	57-104	I-U-1
Vero, J. A.	51-69	V-A-1
Vest, R. W.	56-89	I-C-1
Vianney, L. R.	51-27	I-Z-1; II-D-3
Vickery, R. C.	57-187	VII-C-1-b, m; VII-C-3
	57-197	VII-C-1-m
Victor, A. C.	57-56	I-Z-1; II-D-3; IX-E-2
Vieweg, R.	40-14	X-A, B, C, D, F, J; X-C-1; X
Vintaikin, E. Z.	57-39	I-J-2; II-A-3, 5; II-A
Viting, L. M.	57-68	II-D; IV-B-3
	57-69	II-D-5; IV-A-4
Vogt, O.	54-34	I-A-4
Volger, J.	52-54	VII-A-13
	52-58	VII-B-6-e
Von Batchelder, F. W.	55-130	IX-G-2
	58-23	IX-G-2
Vyse, J.	57-26	I-C-3-b; VII-A-5; VII-B-1; VII-D-1-a; VII-E-9, 11
Wachtman, J. B.	53-140	VII-A-1-a
Wade, W. R.	58-20	I-A-2; I-C-7; I-M-4; I-T-1, 6; II-A-1; II-D-3; V-C-2
Wagner, H. E.	52-34	VII-A-14; VII-B-6-b
Wahlin, H. B.	48-12	I-C-6; I-J-2; IV-B-2
	48-13	I-C-6; I-J-2; IV-B-2
	52-112	I-N-3; II-D-5; IV-A-4
Waldron, M. B.	57-116	I-P-3
	57-192	VII-A-11

Waldhauser, I.	55-117	III; VI-B-3
Walkenhorst, W.	40-16	I-A-1, 2; V-A-3; V-B-2
Walker, B.E.	56-28	IX-B-1
	57-45	IX-C-2
Wallace, W.E.	54-63	IX-G-3
	57-35	I-M-1
Wallman, J.C.	50-39	I-C-8
Walter, P.	50-57	VI-A
Wang, C.C.	55-49	I-G-2; VI-G; VI
Ward, L.	56-107	I-C-6; I-J-2; I-N-3
	57-109	I-N-3
Warncke, H.	55-34	I-N-3
Warner, N.F.	54-49	VII-E-3-j, k; VII-E-3
Wartenberg, H.V.	52-15	VII-A-1-a
Waterhouse, R.B.	52-81	I-C-3; I-N-3; I-P-2; II-D-2; IV-A-5-a; VII-A-1-a; VII-A-4-a; VII-A-5-a; VII-A-9-b; VII-A-6, 7
Waterman, T.E.	56-6	I-C-3-a, d; I-T-1
Watt, W.	53-125	I-C-3
Waxler, R.	56-169	VII-C-5
	57-182	VII-C-1-b
Wechsler, M.S.	57-78	VI-A-1
Weeks, J.L.	51-39	VII-A-1-a; VII-A-1; VII-C-6
	52-1	VII-A-1-a; VII-A-1; VII-C-6
	52-49	I-U-1; VII-D-1-a; VII-D-1
	53-17	I-A-2; I-C-3-a; I-J-2; I-N-3; I-U-1; VII-A-1, 2, 6, 10; VII-A-2-a; VII-B-7-a; VII-B-7; VII-D-1-a
	55-9	I-U-1
Weertman, J.R.	52-6	I-G-2
Weiner, L.	52-8	I-J-2; I-T-4, 6
Weise, E.K.	56-152	VII-B-6-e, f, j, k
Weigelt, W.	54-96	VII-A-5-a
Welesz, R.	56-126	II-D-5, 6
Wells, C.	39-2	IX-A
Wessel, E.T.	56-94	I-H-1
Wessel, G.	51-67	I-J-2
West, E.D.	54-66	IX-B-1
Weston, J.C.	40-18	II-D-5
Westrum Jr., E.F.	50-21	VII-A-14
	50-34	I-A-3
	50-50	I-N-2
	53-55	VII-A-7
	53-58	VII-A-14
Westrum Jr. E.F.	57-49	VII-B-8-p
	57-195	VII-B-8-n, p
	58-19	I-P-2, 3; I-U-1
Westwater, J.W.	52-95	XI-H-3
Wey, R.	52-132	VII-A-15
White, D.	56-29	IX-C-1
	56-45	IX-C-1
	56-167	VII-B
	57-48	IX-C-1
White, D.W.	56-167	VII-B
White, G.K.	53-32	I-S-4
	53-51	I-G-3
	53-52	I-C-7
	55-4	I-B-3; I-C-7; I-G-2; III
	55-100	I-P-1
White, G.K.	56-34	I-G-2; I-S-3
	57-14	I-M-2
	57-15	I-J-1; I-P-2; I-R-3
	57-125	I-H-1; I-N-4; I-V-1
	57-127	I-C-6; I-R-2; I-T-7
	57-140	I-M-2
Whitsett, C.R.	55-91	IX-G-3
	55-132	IX-B
Whittemore Jr. O.J.	49-1	VII-A-1-a; VII-A-5-a; VII-A-7; VII-A-9-b
	51-4	VII-A-9-b; VII-A-9
	56-7	VII-A-1, 3, 5, 7, 8; VII-A-3-a; VII-A-9-b; VII-B-3-e; VII-B-4-b; VII-B-6-d; VII-B-7-a; VII-B-7; VII-C-6; VII-D-1-a; VII-D-2; VII-D-5-a

Wicklein, H. W.	57-170	X-C-1; X-E, J; XI-H-3, 4, 6; XI-J
Wiesner, J. B.	57-144	I-T-7
Wilford, S.	49-5	I-T-6
	49-8	I-T-6
Wilhelm, H. A.	49-49	I-C-7; I-M-2; I-U-1; III; VI-F
	49-53	I-T-4; IX-A
	52-8	I-J-2; I-T-4, 6
	52-17	I-N-3; I-T-6; I-V-1; IV-C-5; IV-G; V-B-4; V-C-4
	53-120	I-T-4, 6
Wilhelm, H. A.	54-18	I-N-4; I-V-1
	54-101	I-V-1; IX-G-1; IX-J-10
Wilkes, G. B.	54-122	II-D-2, 3; IV-A-1; IV-A-5-a; V-A-1, 4; V-B-2; XI-D
Willardson, R. K.	56-161	VII-A-10
Williams, B. J.	55-96	I-A-2
Williamson, G. K.	57-16	I-P-3; I-T-4; VI
	57-75	I-T-4; IV-L; VI
Wilkinson, D.	57-32	IX-D-3
Wilmore, T. A.	55-118	IV-A-5-a; IV-B-1; VIII-C
Wilson Jr., A. C.	52-44	I-U-1
	52-55	II-D-3; V-C-2
	52-71	I-C-3-j
	52-113	I-U-1
	52-115	I-C-3-j
Wilson Jr., A. C.	53-9	I-U-1
	53-38	II-D-3; V-C-2
	53-78	I-C-3-a, g, j
Wilson, A. J. C.	42-6	I-A-2
Wilson, A. S.	45-18	IX-E
	48-19	I-U-1
	48-26	IX-E
	48-29	IX-A-7
	49-42	I-U-1
	49-57	VI
Winkler, R.	57-152	I-A-2; V-A-6
Winkler, U.	53-93	IX-B; IX-F-1; IX-G-3
	55-133	IX-B; IX-G-3
Winn, R. A.	54-42	VI-F-1
	55-106	I-T-4
Winslow, G. H.	49-31	I-C-3
	57-138	I-C-3-a; I-C-3
Wisely, H. R.	49-19	VII-E-3
	57-98	VII-E-3, 6; VII-E-3-k
Wisnyi, L. G.	57-196	VII-B-7-d, k
	57-199	VII-A-10
Wittig, F. E.	41-24	I-J-2; VII-C-5
	52-52	I-A-2; I-G-2
Wolff, K.	49-12	III; VI-B-3; VI-B
Wolga, G. J.	52-44	I-U-1
	52-113	I-U-1
	53-9	I-U-1
Wong, A. K.	58-15	X-G; XI-H-1
Wood, J. E., ed.	54-11	V-B-6
	55-40	I-A-2; I-M-1; V-B-1, 3, 4, 6
Wood, W. D.	57-164	IV-J-1; VII-A-9-b
	58-21	I-T-6; V-C-1, 2, 7
Woodruff, E. M.	56-101	I-C-3-a, j
Woods, S. B.	55-4	I-B-3; I-C-7; I-G-2; III
	56-34	I-G-2; I-S-3
	57-14	I-M-2
	57-15	I-J-1; I-P-2; I-R-3
Woods, S. B.	57-125	I-H-1; I-N-4; I-V-1
	57-127	I-C-6; I-R-2; I-T-7
	57-140	I-M-2
Worner, H. W.	49-7	I-T-6
	56-138	IX-G-4
Worthington, A. E.	55-140	X-H
Wucher, J.	52-132	VII-A-15
Wyatt, J. L.	53-15	I-T-6
Wyler, E. N.	53-74	I-R-2
Wyman, L. L.	52-97	I-U-1

Yamaji, K.	55-127	III-H
Yamamoto, M.	50-35	I-C-6; I-N-3; IV-A-3; IV-B-2
Yamauchi, T.	56-160	VII-D-1-a
	57-93	VII-A-7; VII-A-9-b
Yamshchikova, A.I.	54-70	I-S-4; V-A-6; VI-B-1
Yavorsky, P.J.	45-4	I-P-2; VII-A-1-a; VII-A-1
	46-4	VII-A-9-b; VII-B-7-a
Yoshida, S.	56-93	I-M-4
Yoshiki, B.	51-24	VII-B-3-a
Yoshinaga, H.	55-98	I-G-2; VII-D-5,6; IX-F-1
	56-147	IX-F-1
Yosim, S.J.	57-145	I-T-4; VII-A-2-a; VII-A-4-g; VII-D-3-a; VII-D-5-a; IX-A-4
	57-146	I-T-4
	57-194	VII-D-5-a
Zachariasen, W.H.	48-27	IX-B-2
	49-66	VII-D-5
	51-53	I-P-7; VII-A-14
	51-61	I-P-7
	51-71	IX-A
Zachariasen, W.H.	52-110	I-N-2
	52-126	IX-A
	57-61	I-P-3
Zaleski, F.V.	57-171	X-G
Zalkin, A.	49-61	IX-C
Zelikman, A.N.	56-41	VII-A-14
	56-151	VII-D-6
Zenter, R.	52-112	I-N-3; II-D-5; IV-A-4
Zhdanov, G.S.	56-67	VI; IX
Zhuralev, N.N.	56-67	VI; IX
	56-153	VII-D-2
Ziegler, W.T.	51-29	VII-A-4-g,j,k
Zimmerman, F.J.	55-82	I-F; I-S-4
Zimmerman, H.J.	57-144	I-T-7
Zimmerman, W.F.	53-42	VII-E-9; VII-E
	56-164	VII-A-5-a; VII-B-7-a
Zuithoff, A.J.	40-2	I-C-6
	40-7	II-C-1; II-D-5; IV-A-4
Zweig, B.	51-44	I-C-3-a,d
Zwetsch, A.	55-21	VII-B-9
Zwicker, U.	56-112	I-T-6; V-C-1
Zyazev, V.L.	57-108	VII-A-13,15
Z.G.	57-79	I-U-1
	57-90	I-N-2

EXPANDED LISTING OF MATERIALS INDEX

This is an expanded list of ALL materials for which at least one property is reported herein. It also lists some of the more common trade names to show their location in the material index, even if NO DATA are reported for them. See also alphabetic listing of materials.

I. ## PURE ELEMENTS

I-A-1   Actinium Ac

I-A-2   Aluminum Al

        99. 996 Al
        99. 0 + Al
        24ST Aluminum Alloy
        Alclad 2024
        Aluminum Alloy 25
        AP Aluminum
        Commercially Pure Aluminum

I-A-3   Americium Am

I-A-4   Antimony Sb

I-A-5   Arsenic As

I-A-6   Astatine At

I-B-1   Barium Ba

I-B-2   Berkelium Bk

I-B-3   Beryllium Be

        Flake Beryllium
        Process Q Beryllium
        QM-V Beryllium
        Yb-9052 Beryllium
        Yb-9053 Beryllium
        Yb-9054 Beryllium

I-B-4   Boron B

I-C-1   Calcium Ca

I-C-2   Californium Cf

I-C-3   Carbon C

I-C-3-a   Extruded Acheson Graphite, Multicrystalline

        Artificial Graphite
        Grade A, Artificial Extruded Acheson Graphite
        Grade B, Artificial Extruded Acheson Graphite
        Grade CS Extruded Acheson Graphite
        Type 3474D Extruded Acheson Graphite
        Type AG-1 Extruded Acheson Graphite
        Type 7087 Extruded Acheson Graphite, Multicrystalline
        Type AGHT Extruded Acheson Graphite, Multicrystalline
        Type AGKT Artificial Pitch Bonded Petroleum Coke
        Type AGOT Extruded Acheson Graphite
        Type AGOT-C Extruded Acheson Graphite
        Type AGOT-CSF Extruded Acheson Graphite
        Type AGOT-KC Extruded Acheson Graphite
        Type AGOT-W Extruded Acheson Graphite
        Type GBE Extruded Acheson Graphite

I-C-3-b	Extruded Acheson Amorphous Carbon

Acheson Amorphous Carbon
Carbon Black
Carbon Electrodes
Gas Baked Coke
Index Rod Extruded Acheson Amorphous Carbon

I-C-3-c	Extruded Acheson Graphite, Carbon Impregnated

I-C-3-d	Molded Acheson Graphite, Multicrystalline

Grade C Artificial Molded Graphite
Type AWG(EPB) Molded Acheson Graphite
Type GBH Molded Acheson Graphite

I-C-3-e	Molded Acheson Amorphous Carbon

I-C-3-f	Molded Acheson Graphite, Carbon Impregnated

I-C-3-g	Lampblack-Base Carbon or Graphite

Molded Lampblack Base Graphite
Type SA-25 Lampblack Base Graphite

I-C-3-h	Pyrolytic Graphite

EYX4 Pyrolytic Carbon
Pyrolytic Carbon

I-C-3-j	Natural Graphite-Base Graphite

Hilger H.S. Graphite
Natural Ceylon Block Graphite
Natural Cumberland Graphite
Natural Graphite
Type KC Graphite

I-C-3-k	Natural Graphite-Base Carbon

I-C-3-m	Diamond

Bort Diamond
Commercial Diamond Powder
Gem Quality Diamond
Industrial Diamond

I-C-3-n	Single Crystal Graphite

Flake Graphite

I-C-3-p	Lampblack and Powder

Acetylene Soot
Carbon Black
Lampblack Powder
Soot

I-C-3	Other Carbons and Graphites

Acheson Graphite
Amorphous Carbon
Canadian Natural Graphite Flake
Carbon
Coke
Electrode Carbon
Graphite
Kendall Coke
Kendall Graphite
RKS Type Ringsdorff Carbon Electrode
Spectrochemical Carbon Electrode

I-C-4	<u>Cerium Ce</u>
I-C-5	<u>Chromium Cr</u>

Chrome Metal
Ductile Chromium
Electrolytic Flake Chromium
Hydride Process Chromium
Pure Chromium

I-C-6	<u>Cobalt Co</u>
I-C-7	<u>Copper Cu</u>

Bus Bar Copper
Coalesced Copper
Deoxidized Copper
Electrolytic Tough Pitch Copper
Fed. Spec. QQC-502 Tough Pitch Copper
Fed. Spec. QQC-576 Electrolytic Tough Pitch Copper
High Conductivity Copper
OFHC Copper
Oxygen Free High Conductivity Copper
Phosphorized Copper
Pure Copper
Touch Pitch Copper

I-C-8	<u>Curium Cm</u>
I-D-1	<u>Dysprosium Dy</u>
I-E-1	<u>Einsteinium E</u>
I-E-2	<u>Erbium Er</u>
I-E-3	<u>Europium Eu</u>
I-F-1	<u>Fermium Fm</u>
I-F-2	<u>Francium Fr</u>
I-G-1	<u>Gadolinium Gd</u>
I-G-2	<u>Germanium Ge</u>
I-G-3	<u>Gold Au</u>
I-H-1	<u>Hafnium Hf</u>
I-H-2	<u>Holmium Ho</u>
I-J-1	<u>Iridium Ir</u>
I-J-2	<u>Iron Fe</u>

Armco Ingot Iron
Bureau of Standards Iron
Carbonyl Iron
Electrolytic Iron
Hydrogen-Purified Iron
Ingot Iron
Kahlbaum Iron
Pure Iron
Svea Iron
Technical Iron

I-L-1	<u>Lanthanum La</u>
I-L-2	<u>Lutetium Lu</u>

I-M-1	<u>Magnesium Mg</u>
	Mazlo AM25 Magnesium
I-M-2	<u>Manganese Mn</u>
	Flake Manganese
I-M-3	<u>Mendelevium Mv</u>
I-M-4	<u>Molybdenum Mo</u>
I-N-1	<u>Neodymium Nd</u>
I-N-2	<u>Neptunium Np</u>
I-N-3	<u>Nickel Ni</u>
	99.95 Ni + Co
	99.4 Ni + Co
	"A" Nickel
	Carbonyl Nickel
	Electrolytic Nickel
	Electronickel
	Grade A Nickel
	"L" Nickel
	Nivac
I-N-4	<u>Niobium Nb</u>
	Columbium Nb
I-N-5	<u>Nobelium No</u>
I-O-1	<u>Osmium Os</u>
I-P-1	<u>Palladium Pd</u>
I-P-2	<u>Platinum Pt</u>
	Thermocouple Grade Platinum
I-P-3	<u>Plutonium Pu</u>
I-P-4	<u>Polonium Po</u>
I-P-5	<u>Praseodymium Pr</u>
I-P-6	<u>Promethium Pm</u>
I-P-7	<u>Protactinium Pa</u>
I-R-1	<u>Radium Ra</u>
I-R-2	<u>Rhenium Re</u>
I-R-3	<u>Rhodium Rh</u>
I-R-4	<u>Ruthenium Ru</u>
I-S-1	<u>Samarium Sm</u>
I-S-2	<u>Scandium Sc</u>
I-S-3	<u>Silicon Si</u>
	Doped Silicon
I-S-4	<u>Silver Ag</u>
	Inquartation Silver
	Mint Proof Silver
	Sterling Silver
	Silver Lume
I-S-5	<u>Strontium Sr</u>

I-T-1	<u>Tantalum Ta</u>
I-T-2	<u>Technetium Tc</u>
I-T-3	<u>Terbium Tb</u>
I-T-4	<u>Thorium Th</u>
I-T-5	<u>Thulium Tm</u>
I-T-6	<u>Titanium</u>

A-55 Alloy
Crystal Bar Titanium
Iodide Process Titanium
RC-55 Alloy
Ti-75A Titanium

I-T-7	<u>Tungsten W</u>
I-U-1	<u>Uranium U</u>

Tuballoy Metal X

I-V-1	<u>Vanadium V</u>
I-Y-1	<u>Ytterbium Yb</u>
I-Y-2	<u>Yttrium Y</u>
I-Z-1	<u>Zirconium Zr</u>

Iodide Process Zirconium
Sponge Zirconium
WAPD Grade 1 Crystal Bar Zirconium

II.   IRON-BASE ALLOYS

        (Iron greatest weight fraction with one or more other elements.)

II-A   Plain Carbon Steels (Mn < 2.5%; Si < 0.36%; P, S < 0.051% each)

II-A-1   0.02 < C < 0.20%

        AISI-C1010
        AISI-C1020
        AISI-C-1005 to C-1019
        AISI-1321
        Mild Steel

II-A-2   Plain Carbon Steels 0.20 < C < 0.40%

        AISI-C-1020 to 1038
        AISI-1320
        AISI-1321
        AISI-1330

II-A-3   Plain Carbon Steels 0.40 < C < 0.60%

        Austenite
        AISI-C-1039 to C-1057
        AISI-1340
        A-1345
        Die Iron Tool Steel
        National Emergency Steel NE-1350
        NE-1350 Steel

II-A-4   Plain Carbon Steels 0.60 < C < 0.80%

        AISI-C-1058 to C-1078

II-A-5   Plain Carbon Steels 0.80 < C < 1.00%

        AISI-C-1080 to C-1095
        Austenite
        Carbon Tool Steel

II-A-6   Plain Carbon Steels 1.00 < C < 1.20%

        Carbon Tool Steel

II-A-7   Plain Carbon Steels 1.20 < C < 1.50%

        Carbon Tool Steel

II-A-8   Plain Carbon Steels 1.50 < C < 2.00% C

        Carbon Tool Steel

II-A   Plain Carbon Steel

II-B   Cast Irons

II-B-1   Gray, Unalloyed and Low Alloy (Less than 2% total alloying elements exclusive
            of C, Mn < 1%, Si, P, S)

        Gray Cast Iron - Ferritic, Pearlitic
        Gray Cast Iron, Low Alloy

II-B-2   Gray, Alloyed (More than 2% total alloying elements exclusive of C, Mn < 1%, Si, P, S)

        Gray Cast Iron, Alloyed

II-B-3   White, Unalloyed and Low Alloy (Less than 2% total alloying elements exclusive of
            C, Mn < 1%, Si, P, S)

        White Cast Iron, Low Alloy

II-B-4   White, Alloyed (More than 2% total alloying elements exclusive of C, Mn < 1%, Si, P, S)

        White Cast Iron, Alloyed

II-B-5	Malleable Cast Iron, Ferritic
	Ferritic Malleable Cast Iron
II-B-6	Malleable Cast Iron, Pearlitic
	Pearlitic Malleable Cast Iron
II-B-7	Nodular Cast Iron, Ferritic
	Ferritic Nodular Cast Iron
II-B-8	Nodular Cast Iron, Pearlitic
	Pearlitic Nodular Cast Iron
	Fe + Si + X

II-C	Low Alloy Steels (Less than 10% of any single alloying element, exclusive of C; $Mn < 2.5\%$; $Si < 0.36\%$; P, S $< 0.051\%$ each. Alloying elements listed in decreasing order of their weight fractions. X may be none, one, or more elements; $X = X_1 + X_2 + \ldots$)

II-C-1	Low Alloy Steels Fe + Ni
	AISI-2300 Series
	AISI-2515 Low Alloy Steel
	AISI-E-2512 Low Alloy Steel
	AISI-E-2517 Low Alloy Steel
	EN-8 (British)
	Magnetic Alloy Steel

II-C-2	Low Alloy Steels Fe + Ni + Cr + X
	AISI-3100 Series Low Alloy Steels
	AISI-4300 Series Low Alloy Steels
	AISI-8600 Series Low Alloy Steels
	AISI-8700 Series Low Alloy Steels
	AISI-9840 to 9850
	AISI-E-9310
	AISI-E-9315
	AISI-E-9317
	AISI-E-9437 to 9445
	High-Chromium, Nickel Tool Steel
	Low-Chromium, Nickel Tool Steel
	National Emergency Steel NE-8613
	Nickel-Chromium-Molybdenum Tool Steel
	Nickel Chromium Tool Steel
	Nitralloy N

II-C-3	Low Alloy Steels Fe + Ni + Mo + X
	AISI-4600 Series Low Alloy Steels
	AISI-4800 Series Low Alloy Steels
	AISI-9747 Low Alloy Steel
	AISI-9763 Low Alloy Steel

II-C-4	Low Alloy Steels Fe + Ni + X ($X_1 \neq$ Mo, Cr)
	Magnetic Alloy Steel

II-C-5	Low Alloy Steels Fe + Mo + X
	AISI-4000 Series Steels
	Fe + Mo
	Fe + Mo + Cr + X
	High Speed Steel M-1
	High Speed Steel M-10
	High Speed Tool Steel
	Molybdenum High Speed Tool Steel
	Molybdenum Hot Worked Tool Steel
	Molybdenum - Low Tungsten, Vanadium High Speed Tool Steel
	Molybdenum - Vanadium High Speed Tool Steel

II-C-6   Low Alloy Steels Fe + Cr + X $(X_1 \neq Mo)$

AISI-501 Steel
AISI-E-50100 Steel
AISI-502 Steel
AISI-5045 Steel
AISI-5046 Steel
AISI-5100 Series Steels
AISI-E-51100 Steel
AISI-E-52100 Steel
AISI-6100 Series Steels
AISI-7 Cr Type Steel
AISI-8653 Steel
Carbon-Chromium Tool Steel
Chromium-Manganese Tool Steel
Chromium Tool Steel
Chromium-Tungsten Hot Worked Tool Steel
Chromium-Vanadium Shock Resisting Tool Steel
EN-19 (British)
EN-31 (British)
Enduro 18-8B Steel
HGT-3 Steel (British)
Hot Worked Tool Steel
Jessop H-40 Steel (British)
National Emergency Steel NE-52100C
Nitralloy EZ
Oil Hardening, High Alloy, High Chromium Tool Steel
Oil Hardening, Low Alloy, Low Manganese Tool Steel
Shock Resisting Tool Steel
Water Hardening Tool Steel

II-C-7   Low Alloy Steels Fe + Cr + Mo + X

AISI-4100 Series Steel
AISI-4130 Steel
AISI Type 9 Cr Steel
Air Hardening High Alloy, High Chromium Tool Steel
Air Hardening Low Alloy, High Manganese Tool Steel
Chromium Hot Worked Tool Steel
Chromium-Molybdenum, Hot Worked Tool Steel
Chromium-Molybdenum-Manganese Tool Steel
Manganese Tool Steel
Oil Hardening Low Alloy High Manganese Tool Steel

II-C-8   Low Alloy Steels Fe + W + X

Chromium-Tungsten Hot Worked Tool Steel
Finishing Tool Steel
High Speed Steel M-2
Oil Hardening, Low Alloy, Low Manganese Tool Steel
Oil Hardening, Low Alloy, Tungsten Tool Steel
Molybdenum, High Tungsten, High Speed Tool Steel
Tungsten Hot Worked Tool Steel
Tungsten-Silicon Shock Resisting Tool Steel
Tungsten Shock Resisting Tool Steel

II-C-9   Low Alloy Steels Fe + Si + X

AISI 9200 Series
High Silicon, Manganese Shock Resisting Tool Steels
Low Silicon, Manganese Shock Resisting Tool Steels
Magnetic Alloys

II-C   Other Low Alloy Steels in Alphabetic Order by Major Alloying Element

Anti-Friction Alloys
Carbon-Vanadium Tool Steels
Fe + Al
Fe + Al + Cr
Fe + Al + X
Fe + Co + X
Fe + Mn + X
Fe + Te + X
Fe + V + X
    Carbon-Vanadium Tool Steels
    Ferrovanadium
Iron + Graphite Antifriction Alloys
Nitralloys 125 (Type H)
Nitralloys 135 (G)
Nitralloys 135 (Modified)
Nitralloys 230 (Alamo)
Porous Iron + Graphite Anti-Friction Alloys
Spiegeleisen

II-D   High Alloy Steels (More than 10% of any single alloying element exclusive of C; Mn 2.5%; Si 1.00%; P, S < 0.051% each. Alloying elements listed in decreasing order of their weight fractions. X may be none, one or more elements; $X = X_1 + X_2 + \ldots$)

II-D-1   Fe + Cr

AISI-403 Stainless Steel
AISI-410 Stainless Steel
AISI-420X Stainless Steel
AISI-430 Stainless Steel
AISI-442 Stainless Steel
AISI-446 Stainless Steel
High Chromium Tool Steel
Stainless Iron
Stainless Steel

II-D-2   Fe + Cr + Ni

ACI Types CB-30
ACI Types CC-50
AISI-301 Stainless Steel
AISI-302 Stainless Steel
AISI-304 Weldable Stainless Steel
AISI-308 Stainless Steel
AISI-309 Stainless Steel
AISI-309S Stainless Steel
AISI-310 Stainless Steel
AISI-414 Stainless Steel
AISI-431 Stainless Steel
HF Grade Alloy
Iron-Chromium Corrosion Resistant Castings
Wrought Chromium-Nickel Heat Resistant Steel
Stainless Steel 18-8 Type

II-D-3   Fe + Cr + Ni + X (X≠ 0)

II-D-3-a   Fe + Cr + Ni + Co + X

AMS-5532 b
AMS-5376 a
Cobalt Alloy N-155
Jessop G - Steel (British)
S - 590 (AMS - 5333) Alleghany Steel
DVL - 46 (German)
DVL - 47 (German)
DVL - 48 (German)
DVL - 49 (German)
DVL - 50 (German)
Multimet Alloy NR-21
NR - 21

II-D-3   Other Fe + Cr + Ni + X

17-7 P.H.
18-8 Stainless Steel
19-9 W-Mo
234-A-5
N-153
ACI Types CA-15
ACI Types CA-40
ACI Types CE-30
ACI Types CF-8
ACI Types CF-16F
ACI Types CF-20
ACI Types CG
ACI Types CH-10
ACI Types CH-20
ACI Types CK-20
ACI Types HB
ACI Types HC
ACI Types HD
ACI Types HE
ACI Types HF
ACI Types HH
ACI Types HI
ACI Types HK
ACI Types HL
AISI-302B High Temperature Scale Resistant Stainless Steel
AISI-303 Free Cutting Stainless Steel
AISI-304 Weldable Stainless Steel
AISI-310 Stainless Steel
AISI-316 Chemical Corrosion Resistant Stainless Steel
AISI-317 Chemical Corrosion Resistant Stainless Steel
AISI-321 Stabilized Stainless Steel
AISI-347 Stabilized Stainless Steel
Allegheny Metal 18-8M
AM-350 Alleghany Metal Stainless Steel
A.T.S. (German)
DVL-30 (German), Contains W
DVL-51 (German), Contains B
DVL-52 (German), Contains W
EME

```
            Fe + Cr + Ni + Al + X
            Fe + Cr + Hi + B + X
            Fe + Cr + Ni + Mn + X
            Fe + Cr + Ni + Mo + X
            Fe + Cr + Ni + Nb + X
            Fe + Cr + Ni + Si + X
            Fe + Cr + Ni + Ti + X
            Fe + Cr + Ni + W + X
            Iron-Chromium-Nickel Corrosion Resistant Casting
            Jessop G-21 (British), Contains W
            Jessop R-20 (British), Contains Nb
            MIL-S-5059A
            MIL-S-6721A
            P.H. 15-7 Mo Armco Steel, Contains Mo
            SAS-8 (German)
            V-444D (German)
            WF-100D (German) Krupp, Contains W
            Wrought Chromium-Nickel Heat Resistant Steels

II-D-4      Fe + Cr + X (X₁ ≠ O, Ni)

            AISI-405
            AISI-406
            AISI-416
            AISI-420F
            AISI-430F
            AISI-440A
            AISI-440B
            AISI-440C
            AISI-443
            B-759 (German)
            Electric Resistance Alloys, Furnace Elements
            Fe + Cr + Al + X
            Fe + Cr + Co + X
            Fe + Cr + V + X
            High Chromium High-Carbon Cold Work Tool Steels
            Jessop No. 46 Steel (British)
            Kanthal
            N-155 (Low C)

II-D-5      Fe + Ni

            FENI-36 (German)
            Invar
            Low Expansion Alloys
            Magnetically Soft Alloys

II-D-6      Fe + Ni + X (X ≠ O)

II-D-6-a    Fe + Ni + Cr + X

            ACI CN-7
            ACI HN
            P-193 (German)
            S-495 Alleghany Steel
            Timken 16-25-6
```

II-D-6	Other Fe + Ni + X
	ACI CM-25
	ACI CT-7
	ACI HP
	ACI HS
	ACI HT
	ACI HU
	AISI-330
	DVL-31 (German)
	DVL-4/V869 (German)
	Electric Resistance Alloys
	Fe + Ni + Al + X
	Fe + Ni + Co + X
	Fe + Ni + Cr + X
	Fe + Ni + Mn + X
	Kovar
	Permanent Magnet Materials (Alnico Series)
	S-590 Alleghany Steel
II-D-7	Fe + Al + X
	Heat Resisting Alloys
II-D-8	Fe + W + X
	Fe + W
	Fe + W + Cr
	High Speed Steel (Ti)
	Tungsten-Cobalt High Speed Tool Steels
	Tungsten High Speed Tool Steels
	Tungsten Hot Work Tool Steels
II-D-9	Fe + Mn + X
	Fe + Mn + Cr + Si
	Fe + Mn + Cr + X
	Fe + Mn + Ni + X
	815 (German)
	ASTM A-128-33
	FCM (German)
	Hadfields Chromium-Manganese Steel
	Hadfields Manganese Steel
II-D	Other High Alloy Steels, in Alphabetic Order by Major Alloying Element
	Anti-Friction Alloys
	Fe + Co + Cr + Ni
	Fe + Co + X
	S-497 Alleghany Fe-Co Steel
	Fe + Cu + X
	Porous Iron + Copper + Graphite Anti-Friction Alloys
	Graphite Anti Friction Alloys
	Fe + Mo + X
	Comol, Remalloy
	Fe + Pt + X
	Fe + Si + X
	Fe + V + X

III. COPPER-BASE ALLOYS

(Copper greatest weight fraction with one or more other elements. Alloying elements listed in decreasing order of their weight fractions. X may be none, one, or more elements.)

III-A   **Copper + Zinc + X**

III-A-1   **Cu + Zn + Pb + X**

Brass, α Phase
Free Cutting Leaded Brass
Brass

III-A-2   **Cu + Zn + Sn + X**

Manganese Bronze No. 937
Naval Brass SAE-73
Red Brass

III-A-3   **Cu + Zn**

Brass
Brass, α Phase, also β Phase
Yellow Brass

III-A   **Other Copper + Zinc + X**

Aluminum Brass
Cu + Zn + Ni
Nickel Silver
Tellurium Nickel Brass

III-B   **Copper + Tin + X**

III-B-1   **Cu + Sn + Pb + X**

Bronze
Leaded Bronze

III-B-2   **Cu + Sn + Zn + X**

Sn - Zn Bronze

III-B-3   **Cu + Sn**

Bronze
Phosphor Bronze
Porosint
Porous Copper + Tin
Speculum

III-C   **Copper + Lead + X**

Leaded Bronze

III-D   **Copper + Nickel + X**

Admiralty Nickel
Advance, Contains Mn
Cu + Ni + Be + X
Lohm
Nickel Silver No. 719
Phosnic Bronze
Supernickel No. 701
Tempaloy 836

III-E   **Copper + Aluminum + X**

Aluminum Bronze
Fed. Spec. QQ-B-667 Composition 3
Fed. Spec. QQ-B-667 Composition 5
Te-Al Bronze
Tempaloy 841

III-F   **Copper + Silicon + X**

Silicon Bronze

III-G   **Copper + Beryllium + X**

Beryllium Copper No. 175

III-H	Copper + Manganese + X
III-J	Copper + Tellurium + X
	Tellurium Copper
III-K	Copper + Chromium + X
III-L	Copper + Zirconium + X
III	Other Copper Base Alloys, in Alphabetic Order by Major Alloying Element

Copper + Silver + X

Copper + Cobalt + Palladium + X

Copper + Iron + X

Copper + Germanium + X

Copper + Phosphorous + X

  Phosphorized Deoxidized Copper

Copper + Palladium + X

Copper + Platinum + X

Copper + Titanium + X

Copper + Uranium + X

IV.   NICKEL-BASE, COBALT-BASE, AND REFRACTORY METAL-BASE ALLOYS

(Major element greatest weight fraction with one or more other elements. Alloying
elements listed in decreasing order of their weight fractions. X may be none, one,
or more elements.)

IV-A   Nickel-Base Alloys

IV-A-1   Ni + Cu + X

1040 Alloy

Cast Monel

K-Monel, Contains Al

Monel

Ni + Cu

Ni + Cu + Al + X

Ni + Cu + Fe + X

R-Monel, Free Cutting

S-Monel, Contains Si

IV-A-2   Ni + Mo + X

AMS-5530

GE-B-129

Hastelloy A

Hastelloy B

Hastelloy C

Hastelloy W

INOR-8

Kinsalloy

Ni + Mo

Ni + Mo + Cr + X

Ni + Mo + Cr + Fe + X

Ni + Mo + Cu + Fe + X

Ni + Mo + Fe + X

IV-A-3   Ni + Co + X

IV-A-3-a   Ni + Co + Cr + X

AMS-5378

DVL-32 (German)

DVL-321a (German)

DVL-321i (German)

DVL-321a (German)

Ni + Co + Cr

Ni + Co + Cr + Fe + X

Ni + Co + Cr + Mo + Ta

Nimonic 90

Nimonic 100

NR-60

Refractaloy 26

Stellite No. 27

IV-A-3   Other Ni + Co + X

100 NT-2

Hastelloy C

K-42-B (Type 5)

Konel

NRDC-60

RCA-N 91

RCA-N 97

IV-A-4   Ni + Fe + X

IV-A-4-a	Ni + Fe + Cr + X
	ACI-HU Alloy
	ACI-HW Alloy
	ASTM-B-83-46
	Contracid
	Nichrome

IV-A-4	Other Ni + Fe + X
	100NT-2
	Chromel C
	Hyperm
	Hipernik
	Megaperm 6510
	Midvale BTG
	Mumetal, Contains Cu
	Nicaloi
	Ni + Fe + Mo + X
	Permafy
	Permalloy
	Supermalloy
	Tophet C
	Zorite

IV-A-5	Ni + Cr + X

IV-A-5-a	Ni + Cr + Fe + X
	Hastelloy R
	Hastelloy R-235
	Hastelloy X
	Inconel
	Inconel B
	Inconel X
	Nimonic 75 (British)

IV-A-5	Other Ni + Cr + X
	80 Ni-20 Cr
	100 NT 2
	Chromel A
	Evanohm
	Firearmor
	GEH-62-V
	Hastelloy-C
	F-342
	G-157
	Illium G
	Illium R
	J-8100 Brazing Alloy
	M-600
	Multi-alloy
	Nickel-Chromium-Iron
	Nichrome IV
	Nichrome V
	Ni + Cr + Mo + X
	Nimonic 80 (British), Contains Ti
	Rene 41
	Thetalloy
	Tophet A
	Udimet 500, Contains Co
	Udimet 600, Contains Co
	Waspaloy
	Waspaloy (Modified)

IV-A-6	Ni + Mn + X

Haskins Alloy 667
Manganese Nickel
Ni + Mn + Fe + X
Ni + Mn + Si + X

IV-A	Other Nickel-Base Alloys

Cast Nickel
D-Nickel, Contains Mn
Hastelloy D, Contains Si
Ni + Al + X
   Grade Z Duranickel
   Z Nickel
Ni + **P**d + Cr + X
Ni + Pd + X
Ni + Si + X
Palau

IV-B	Cobalt Base Alloys

IV-B-1	Co + Cr + X

73 J
111 VT 2-2
6059
AMS-5375
AMS-5380
AMS-5382
AMS-5385
CF-43
Co + Cr + Mo + Ni + Fe
Co + Cr + Mo + X
Co + Cr + Ni + V + X
Co + Cr + Ni + X
Co + Cr + W + Ni + X
F-484
He-1049
I-336
Illium D
Illium X
Jessop G 32 Alloy (British), Contains Ni
Jessop G 34 Alloy (British), Contains Fe
ML-1700
L-251
L-605
NDRC No. NR-10
NDRC No. NR-12
NDRC No. NR-61
NDRC No. NR-70
Refractaloy 70
S-816
S-816 + B
S-844
Stellite No. 1
Stellite No. 6, Contains W
Stellite No. 12
Stellite No. 21

```
               Stellite No. 23  (G1)
               Stellite "2400"
               Stellite No. 25, Contains W
               Stellite No. 30 (422-19)
               Stellite No. 31 (X-40), Contains W
               Stellite No. 36, Contains Ni
               Stellite Star J-Metal
               V-36
               Vitallium
               WI-52
               X-40, Stellite No. 31
               X-50
               X-63

IV-B-2         Co + Ni + X
               25 Ni
               25 Ni + V
               J-1570
               M-203
               M-204
               S- 816
               Stellite 27  (6059)

IV-B-3         Co + Fe + X
               Co + Fe + Cr + X
               Co + Fe + Cr + Ni
               M-205

IV-B           Other Cobalt Alloys
               Co + Au + Pd + X
               Co + Cu + Pd + X
               Co + Pd + Au + X
               Co + Pd + Cu + X

IV-C           Tungsten-Base Alloys
               Ferrotungsten
               Heavy Alloy
               W + Cu + X
               W + Fe + X
               W + Mo + X
               W + Nb + X
               W + Ni + Cu
               W + Ni +  Fe

IV-D           Molybdenum-Base Alloys
               Ferromolybdenum
               Mo + Fe + X
               Mo + Nb + Ti + X
               Mo + Ti + X
               Mo + Ti + Nb + X
               Mo + Zr + X

IV-E           Niobium-Base Alloys
               Nb + Mo + Ti + X
               Nb + Ti + X
               Nb + Ti + Mo + X

IV-F           Chromium-Base Alloys

IV-F-1         Cr + Ni + X

IV-F-2         Cr + Mo + X
               Cr + Mo + Fe + X

IV-F           Other Chromium-Base Alloys
               Chronin
               Cm -469
```

```
                    Cr + Fe + Mo + X
                    Cr + Te + X
                    Cr + W + X
                    Cr + W + Fe + X

IV-G        Vanadium-Base Alloys
            Ferrovanadium
            V + Al + X
            V + Cr + X
            V + Cu + X
            V + Fe + X
            V + Mn + X
            V + Ni + X
            V + Pd + X
            V + Sb + X
            V + Sn + X
            V + Ti + X
            V + Zr + X

IV-H        Tantalum-Base Alloys
            Ta + Ti + X

IV-J        Zirconium-Base Alloys
IV-J-1      Zr + Sn + X
            Zircaloy 2
            Zircaloy B

IV-J-2      Zr + Nb + X

IV-J-3      Zr + U + X

IV-J        Other Zirconium-Base Alloys
            Sponge Zirconium
            Zr + Al + X
            Zr + Ag + X
            Zr + B + X
            Zr + In + X
            Zr + Fe + X
            Zr + O$_2$ + X
            Zr + Ta + X
            Zr + Th + X
            Zr + Ti + X

IV-K        Hafnium-Base Alloys

IV-L        Thorium-Base Alloys
            Th + Pu + X
            Th + Ti + X
            Th + U  + X
            Th + U + Zr + X
            Th + Zr + X
            Th + Zr + U + X
```

V.   LIGHT METAL ALLOYS, INCLUDING TITANIUM ALLOYS

(Major element greatest weight fraction with one or more other elements.
Alloying elements listed in decreasing order of their weight fractions.
X may be none, one, or more elements; $X = X_1 + X_2 + \ldots$)

V-A   Aluminum -Base Alloys

V-A-1   Al + Cu + X

11S

14S (R 301), Contains Mn

17S

18S

24S

25S

108

112

113

138

142, Contains Ni

Alloy 2014

Alloy 195

Alloy 2024-5

Alloy C-46, Contains Si

Al + Cu + Mg + X

Al + Cu + Ni + X

Al + Cu + Si + X

B 195

C 113

Duralite

Duralumin (British)

R-317

RR-59 (British)

Thermafond C3-INA (Italian)

Y-alloy (British)

V-A-2   Al + Si + X

V-A-2-a   Al + Si + Cu + X

Allcast 60

Lo-ex (British)

RAE-SA-1 (British)

RAE-SA-44 (British)

RedX-8

RR -50 (British)

RR-53 (British)

V-A-2-b   Al + Si + Mg + X

Alloy 356

Alpax Gamma (British)

V-A-2   Other Al + Si + X

13

32S

43

51S

85

319

355

356

360

380

	A-108
	A-132
	Al + Si
	Al + Si + Fe + X
	Al + Si + Ni + X
	Red X-13
V-A-3	Al + Mg + X
	50S
	52S
	53S
	56S
	61S
	63S
	214
	218
	220
	406
	A214
	Alloy 220
	Al + Mg + Mn + X
	B214
	Hydronalium 5 (German)
	Hydronalium 7 (German)
	Hydronalium 51 (German)
	Recidal (Italian)
	RR-131-D (British)
V-A-4	Al + Zn + X
	40E
	Alloy 7075
	Alloy 75ST
	Al + Zn + Mg + Cu + X
	L'A-Z5G (French)
	RR-77 (British)
V-A-5	Al + Ni + X
	3S
	4S
V-A-6	Al + Ag + X
V-A	Other Aluminum Alloys
	Al + Be + X
	Al + Ni + X
	RAE-40 (British)
	RAE-47 (British)
	RAE-55 (British)
	RA E-470 (British)
V-B	Magnesium-Base Alloys
V-B-1	Mg + Al + Zn + X
	AN-M-29
	ASTM-AZ-31A
	ASTM-AZ-31B
	ASTM-AZ-31X
	ASTM-AZ-61X

	ASTM-AZ-63
	ASTM-AZ-80X
	ASTM-AZ-81
	ASTM-AZ-91
	ASTM-AZ-91C
	ASTM-AZ-92A
	Dowmetal C
	Dowmetal FS-1
	MAZLO-AM-C52S
V-B-2	$\underline{Mg + Al + X}$ $(X_1 \neq Zn)$
	ASTM A8
	ASTM A10
	ASTM AM11
	ASTM AM-100A
	ASTM AZ-51X
	Eclipsaloy 130
	Hydronalium 71 (German)
	Mg + Al + Mn
V-B-3	$\underline{Mg + Rare Earth + X}$
	ASTM-EK-30
	ASTM-EK-30A
	ASTM-EK-32A
	ASTM-EK-33A
	ASTM-EK-41
	ASTM-EK-41A
	ASTM-EZ-33A
	ASTM-HM-31XA
	Mg + Rare Earth + Zn + X
V-B-4	$\underline{Mg + Th + X}$
	ASTM-HK-31
	ASTM-HK-31A
	ASTM-HK-31XA
	ASTM-HM-21XA
	ASTM-HZ-32XA
V-B-5	$\underline{Mg + Li + X}$
V-B-6	$\underline{Mg + Zn + X}$
	ASTM-ZK-60A
V-B	<u>Other Magnesium Base Alloys</u>
	ASTM M1, Contains Mn
	Dowmetal M, Contains Mn
	MAZLO AM 3S, Contains Mn
	MAZLO AM 403, Contains Mn
V-C	<u>Titanium-Base Alloys</u>
V-C-1	$\underline{Ti + Al + X}$
	A-110-AT
	C-130-AM
	RC-130-B
	Ti-150-A
	Ti-155-A
	Ti + Al
	Ti + Al + Cr + X
	Ti + Al + Fe + X
	Ti + Al + Mn + X
	Ti + Al + Mo + X
	Ti + Al + Nb + X
	Ti + Al + Sn + X
	Ti + Al + V + X

151

V-C-2	Ti + Mn + X
	RC-130-13
	RS-120
	Ti-150-A
	Ti + Mn + Al + X
V-C-3	Ti + Mo + X
V-C-4	Ti + V + X
	Ti + V + Al
V-C-5	Ti + Cr + X
	Ti + Cr + Al + X
	Ti + Cr + Fe + X
V-C-6	Ti + Fe + X $(X_1 \neq Cr)$
	Ti + Fe + V + X
V-C-7	Ti + Fe + Cr + X
	Ti + Fe + Cr + Mo + X
	Ti-140A
V-C-8	Ti + O + X
V-C	Other Titanium Base Alloys
	Ti + Cu + X
	Ti + Ge
	Ti + H_2
	Ti + Nb + X
	Ti + Ta + X
	Ti + Sn + X
	Ti + W + X
	Ti + Zr + X
V-D	Beryllium-Base Alloys
	Be + Al + X

VI.	OTHER METAL ALLOYS (Melting temperature above 1000°F. Major element greatest weight fraction with one or more other elements.)
VI-A	Gold-Base Alloys
VI-A-1	Au + Cd + X
VI-A-2	Au + Co + X
	Au + Co + Pd + X
VI-A-3	Au + Pd + X
	Au + Pd + Co + X
VI-A-4	Au + Ni + X
	Au + Ni + Cu + Zn + X
VI-A-5	Au + Mn + X
	Au_2 Mn
VI-A	Other Gold-Base Alloys
	Au + Ag + X
	Au + Ag + Cu + Ni + Zn + X
	Au + Ag + Pt + X
	Au + Cu
	Au + Cu + Ag + X
	Au + Cu + Pd + X
	Au + Cu + X
	Au + Cu + Zn + X
	Au + Fe
	Au + Pt
	Au + U
	Au + Zn + X
	$CuAu_3$
VI-B	Silver-Base Alloys
VI-B-1	Ag + Al + X
VI-B-2	Ag + Cd + X
VI-B-3	Ag + Cu + X
	Ag + Cu + Cd + X
	Ag + Cu + Sn + X
	Ag + Cu + Zn + X
VI-B-4	Ag + Pd + X
VI-B	Other Silver-Base Alloys
	Ag + Au + X
	Ag + Pb + X
	Ag + Pt + X
	Ag + Mg + X
	Ag + Mn + X
	Ag + Mo + X
	Ag + Ni + X
	Ag + W + X
	Ag + Zn
	Ag + Zn + Au
	Ag + Zn + Be

VI-C	Platinum-Base Alloys
	GE-76 Brazing Alloy
	Pt + Cu + X
	Pt + Ir + X
	Pt + Fe + X
	Pt + Ni + X
	Pt + Pd + Ru + X
	Pt + Rh + X
	Pt + Ru + X
	Pt + W + X
VI-D	Palladium-Base Alloys
VI-D-1	Pd + Au + X
	Pd + Au + Ag + X
	Pd + Au + Co + X
VI-D-2	Pd + Co + X
	Pd + Co + Au + X
	Pd + Co + Cu + X
VI-D-3	Pd + Cu + X
	Pd + Cu + Co + X
VI-D	Other Palladium-Base Alloys
	Pd + Ag + X
	Pd + Ag + Cu + X
	Pd + Ni + X
	Pd + Pt + X
	Pd + Pt + Ag + X
	Pd + Rh + X
	Pd + Ru + X
	Pd + Ru + Rh + X
	Pd + U + X
VI-E	Manganese-Base Alloys
VI-E-1	Mn + Cu + X
	Mn + Cu + Ni + X
VI-E-2	Mn + Ni + X
	Mn + Ni + Cu + X
VI-E	Other Manganese-Base Alloys
	Mn + Fe + X
	Mn + Fe + C + X
	Mn + Ti + X
VI-F	Uranium-Base Alloys
VI-F-1	U + Cr + X
VI-F-2	U + Mo + X
	Fissium Alloy
	U + Mo + Ru + X
VI-F-3	U + Zr + X

VI-F	Other Uranium-Base Alloys
	U + Bi + X
	U + Co + X
	U + Fe + X
	U + Mg + X
	U + Mn + X
	U + Nb + X
	U + Ni + X
	U + Pb + X
	U + Pu + X
	U + Th + X
VI-G	Silicon-Base Alloys
VI-G-1	Si + Fe + X
	Lebolite
VI-B	Other Silicon-Base Alloys
	Si + B + X
	Si + Ge + X
	Si + P + X
VI	Other Metal Alloys

Bismuth-Base Alloys
   Bi + U + X
Cadmium-Base Alloys
   Cd + Ag + X
Cerium-Base Alloys
   Ce + Fe + X
   Ce + Zn + Fe + X
Germanium-Base Alloys
   Ge + Si + X
Lead-Base Alloys
   Pb + Cu + X
   Pb + Pu + X
   Pb + U + X
Osmium-Base Alloys
   Os + Pt + X
Plutonium-Base Alloys
   Pu + Al + X
   Pu + Fe + X
   Pu + Mn + X
   Pu + Os + X
Rhenium-Base Alloys
   Re + W + X
Tellurium-Base Alloys
   Te + Cr + X
Tin-Base Alloys
   Sn + Mg + X
   Sn + U + X
Zinc-Base Alloys
   Zn + Ag + X
   Zn + Cu + X
   Zn + Zr + X

155

VII.	CERAMICS

VII-A   <u>Oxide Ceramics</u> (Nominal oxide; or nominal oxide greatest weight fraction with one or more other oxides.) X may be none, one or more oxides. Also see VII-B and VII-E.

VII-A-1   <u>Aluminum Oxide + X</u>

VII-A-1-a   <u>Aluminum Oxide</u> (Alumina, Corundum, Sapphire)

Activated Alumina
Alundum
Emery
Fused Alumina
Norton LA-603
Norton RA-4213
Rokide
Rokide A
Synthetic Sapphire

VII-A-1-b   <u>Alumina + Chromium Oxide + X</u>

VII-A-1   <u>Other Alumina + X</u>

Alumina + Magnesia + Beryllia + X
Alumina + Niobium Oxide + X
Alumina + Thoria + Beryllia + X
Alumina + Uranium Oxide + X
Alumina + Zirconia + X

VII-A-2   <u>Beryllium Oxide + X</u>

VII-A-2-a   <u>Beryllium Oxide</u> (Beryllia, Bromellite)

VII-A-2   <u>Other Beryllia + X</u>

Beryllia + Alumina + Thoria + Magnesia + X
Beryllia + Alumina + Magnesia + X
Beryllia + Alumina + Thoria + X
Beryllia + Uranium Oxide + X

VII-A-3   <u>Calcium Oxide + X</u>

VII-A-3-a   <u>Calcium Oxide</u> (Calcia, Lime)

VII-A-3   <u>Other Calcia + X</u>

Calcia + Titania

VII-A-4   <u>Rare Earth Oxides</u> (Atomic Numbers 57-71 in Alphabetic Order)

VII-A-4-a   <u>Cerium Oxide + X</u> (Ceria)

$2 CeO_2 \cdot V_2O_4$
Ceria + Uranium Oxide

VII-A-4-b   <u>Dysprosium Oxide + X</u> (Dysprosia)

VII-A-4-c   <u>Erbium Oxide + X</u> (Erbia)

VII-A-4-d   <u>Europium Oxide + X</u> (Europia)

VII-A-4-e   <u>Gadolinium Oxide + X</u> (Gadolinia)

VII-A-4-f   <u>Holmium Oxide + X</u>

VII-A-4-g   <u>Lanthanum Oxide + X</u> (Lanthan a)

VII-A-4-h   <u>Lutetium Oxide + X</u>

VII-A-4-j   <u>Neodymium Oxide + X</u> (Neodymia)

VII-A-4-k   <u>Praseodymium Oxide + X</u> (Praseodymia)

VII-A-4-m   <u>Promethium Oxide + X</u>

VII-A-4-n	Samarium Oxide + X (Samaria)
	Samaria + Gadolinia
	Samaria + Gadolinia + X
VII-A-4-p	Terbium Oxide + X (Terbia)
VII-A-4-q	Thulium Oxide + X (Thulia)
VII-A-4-r	Ytterbium Oxide + X (Ytterbia)
VII-A-5	Magnesium Oxide + X
VII-A-5-a	Magnesium Oxide
	Calcined Magnesite
	Magnesia
	Magnesite A, B or C
	Periclase
VII-A-5	Other Magnesia + X
	Magnesia + Alumina + Beryllia + X
	Magnesia + Beryllia + X
	Magnesia + Niobium Oxide + X
	Magnesia + Silica + X
	Magnesia + Tin Oxide + X
	Magnesia + Uranium Oxide + X
	Magnesia + Zinc Oxide + X
VII-A-6	Silicon Oxide + X
	Crystobalite
	Lechatelierite
	Opal, Quartz
	Silicon Dioxide
	Silica
	Silica + Titania
	Super Duty Silica
	Tridymite
VII-A-7	Thorium Oxide + X
	Thoria
	Thoria + Alumina + X
	Thoria + Uranium Oxide + X
	Thorianite
	Thorium Dioxide
VII-A-8	Titanium Oxide + X
	Anatase
	Brookite
	Rutile
	Titania
	Titania + Niobium Oxide
	Titania + Silica + X
	Titanium Dioxide
	Titanium Monoxide
	Titanium Sesquioxide
	Titan ox

VII-A-9	Hafnium Oxide + X; Zirconium Oxide + X
VII-A-9-a	Hafnium Oxide
	Hafnia
	Hafnia + Tantalum Oxide + X
	Hafnium Dioxide
	Hafnium Oxide - Stabilized
	Hafnium Oxide - Unstabilized
VII-A-9-b	Zirconium Oxide
	Baddeleyite
	Zirconia
	Zirconia + Beryllia + Alumina + X
	Zirconia + Beryllia + Magnesia + X
	Zirconia + Calcia + X
	Zirconia + Ceria + X
	Zirconia + Magnesia + X
	Zirconia + Niobium Oxide + X
	Zirconia - Nonstabilized
	Zirconia + Silica + X
	Zirconia Stabilized
	Zirconia + Thoria + X
	Zirconia + Titania + X
	Zirconia + Uranium Oxide + X
	Zirconium Dioxide
VII-A-10	Uranium Oxide + X
	Uranium Dioxide
	Uranium Octoxide
	Uranium Oxide + Alumina
	Uranium Oxide + Beryllia
	Uranium Oxide + Calcium Fluoride
	Uranium Oxide + Magnesia
	Uranium Oxide + Manganese Oxide
	Uranium Oxide + Thoria
	Uranium Oxide + Titania
	Uranium Oxide + Zirconia
	Uranium Oxide + Zirconium Hydride
VII-A-11	Plutonium Oxide + X
VII-A-13	Other Oxide Ceramics, in Alphabetic Order: A - L
	Antimony Oxide
	Barium Oxide
	Bismuth Oxide
	Boron Oxide
	Boric Oxide
	Cadmium Oxide
	Chromium Oxide
	Chromium Oxide + Alumina
	Cobalt Oxide
	CoO - Ni_2O Inverse Spinel
	Copper Oxides, Paramelaconite, Tenorite; Cuprite
	CH. D. A. Brand (Russian)
	Gallium Oxide
	Germanium Monoxide
	Germanium Dioxide
	Iron Oxide, Magnetite

VII-A-14	Other Oxide Ceramics, in Alphabetic Order: J-R

Lead Oxide
Manganese Oxide, Manganosite
Molybdenum Pentoxide
Molybdenum Trioxide, Molybdite
Neptunium Oxide
Neptunium Dioxide
Nickel Oxide, Bunsenite
Nickel Oxide + Magnesia
Niobium Oxide
Niobium Dioxide
Niobium Monoxide
Niobium Pentoxide
Niobium Sesquioxide
Niobium Oxide + Alumina + X
Niobium Oxide + Beryllia + X
Niobium Oxide + Magnesia + X
Niobium Oxide + Titania + X
Niobium Oxide + Zirconia + X
Protactinium Oxide

VII-A-15	Other Oxide Ceramics, in Alphabetic Order: S-Z

Scandium Oxide, Scandia
Strontium Oxide
Strontium Peroxide
Tantalum Oxide
Tantalum Pentoxide
Tellurium Oxide
Tellurium Monoxide
Tellurium Dioxide, Tellurite
Tellurium Trioxide
Tin Oxide
Tin Dioxide, Cassiterite
Tin Oxide + Magnesia + X
Vanadium Oxide
Vanadium Monoxide
Vanadium Sesquioxide
Vanadium Dioxide
Yttrium Oxide
Zinc Oxide, Zincite

VII-B	Mineral Ceramics (Also see VII-A and VII-E)
VII-B-1	Aluminosilicates, Non-Hydrous (Mullite, Kyanite)

Amohibole
Andalusite
Bentonite
Cordierite
Illite
Kaolin
Kyanite
Montmorillonite
Sillimanite
Sillimanite Brick
Syenite
Zeolite
$3\ Al_2O_3 \cdot 2\ SiO_2$

VII-B-2	<u>Silicates of Ba, Be, Ca, Fe, Mg, Mn, Ni, Sr, and Zn</u>
VII-B-2-a	<u>Barium Silicate</u>
	Barium Magnesium Silicate
	Barium Calcium Silicate
VII-B-2-b	<u>Beryllium Silicate</u>
	$2 BeO \cdot SiO_2$
	Phenacite
VII-B-2-c	<u>Calcium Silicate</u>
	Alite
	Bellite
	Calcium Ortho-silicate, $Ca_2 SiO_4$
	$CaMg (SiO_4)_2$
	Calcium Magnesium Silicate
	$Na_2 CaSiO_4$
	Sodium Calcium Silicate
	Tricalcium Disilicate
	Tricalcium Silicate
VII-B-2-d	<u>Iron Silicate</u>
	$Fe_2 SiO_4$
VII-B-2-e	<u>Magnesium Silicate</u>
	$Mg_2 SiO_4$
	Forsterite
	Steatite
VII-B-2-f	<u>Manganese Silicate</u>
	Manganous Silicate
VII-B-2-g	<u>Nickel Silicate</u>
VII-B-2-h	<u>Strontium Silicate</u>
VII-B-2-j	<u>Zinc Silicate</u>
	Zinc Orthosilicate
	Willemite
	$Zn_2 SiO_4$
VII-B-3	<u>Alkali and Alkaline-Earth Aluminosilicates</u> (Feldspars)
VII-B-3-a	<u>Barium Modified Feldspar</u>
VII-B-3-b	<u>Beryllium Modified Feldspar</u>
	Beryl
	Beryllium Aluminosilicate
	Euclase
VII-B-3-c	<u>Calcium Modified Feldspar</u>
	Andesine
	Anorthite
	Calcium Aluminosilicate
VII-B-3-d	<u>Cesium Modified Feldspar</u>
	Cesium Aluminosilicate
VII-B-3-e	<u>Lithium Modified Feldspar</u>
	Crystalline Lithium Aluminosilicate
	Eucryptite
	$LiO \cdot Al_2 O_3 \cdot 4 SiO_2$
	Lithium-Potassium Feldspar
	Lithium Aluminosilicate
	For Magnesium Aluminosilicate (see VII-E-3 Cordierite)

VII-B-3-f	Potassium Modified Feldspar

Anorthoclase
Orthoclase
Muscovite
Microcline
Potassium Aluminosilicate
Potassium Feldspar, Anisotropic
Potassium Feldspar, Crystalline
Potassium Feldspar, Glassy
Potassium Feldspar, Isotropic

VII-B-3-g	Rubidium Modified Feldspar

Rubi dium Aluminosilicate

VII-B-3-h	Sodium Modified Feldspar

Albite
Labradorite
Sodium Aluminosilicate
Na Al SiO$_4$

VII-B-3-j	Strontium Modified Feldspar

Strontium Aluminosilicate

VII-B-4	Hafnium Silicate: Zirconium Silicate
VII-B-4-a	Hafnium Silicate

Hafnon

VII-B-4-b	Zirconium Silicate

Superpax Zircon
Zircon

VII-B-5	Borates (Borax, Colemanite); Phosphates

Boron Phosphate
Calcium Borate
Calcium Silico-Phosphate
CaO · B$_2$O$_3$
2 CaO · B$_2$O$_3$
2 CaO · B$_2$O$_3$
Gerstly Borate
Zirconium Phosphate

VII-B-6	Hafnates; Niobates; Titanates; Zirconates
VII-B-6-a	Hafnates

Calcium Hafnate, CaHfO$_3$

VII-B-6-b	Niobates

Magnesium Niobate

VII-B-6-c	Zirconates

Barium Zirconate
Calcium Zirconate

VII-B-6-d	Aluminum Titanate

Al$_2$O$_3$ · TiO$_2$

VII-B-6-e	Barium Titanate

Barium-Beryllium Titanate
Barium-Lead Titanate
Barium Magnesium Titanate
Barium-Strontium Titanate
BaO · TiO$_2$
BaTiO$_4$

VII-B-6-f	Calcium Titanate
	Calcium Metatitanate
	$CaO \cdot TiO_2$
	Tricalcium Dititanate
	$Ca_3 Ti_2 O_7$
	Perovskite
VII-B-6-g	Iron Titanate
	$FeTiO_3$
	Ilmenite
	Menaccanite
	Titanic Iron Ore
VII-B-6-h	Lithium Titanate
	Lithium Metatitanate
	$Li_2 TiO_3$
VII-B-6-j	Magnesium Titanate
	$Mg_2 TiO_4$
	$MgTi_2 O_5$
	$MgTiO_3$
VII-B-6-k	Strontium Titanate
	$SrTiO_3$
	Strontium Metatitanate
	Strontium Orthotitanate
	$Sr_2 TiO_4$
	Strontium Barium Titanate
VII-B-6-m	Zinc Titanate
	Zinc Orthotitanate
	$Zn_2 TiO_4$
VII-B-6-n	Zirconium Titanate
	$ZrTiO_4$
VII-B-6	Other Titanates
	Beryllium Titanate
	Nickel Titanate
VII-B-7	Aluminates
VII-B-7-a	Magnesium Aluminate
	Spinel
VII-B-7-b	Barium Aluminate
	$BaO \cdot Al_2 O_3$
VII-B-7-c	Beryllium Aluminate
	$BeO \cdot Al_2 O_3$
	Chrysoberyl
VII-B-7-d	Calcium Aluminate
	$CaO \cdot 2 Al_2 O_3$
	$CaO \cdot Al_2 O_3$
	$3 CaO \cdot Al_2 O_3$
	$12 CaO \cdot 7 Al_2 O_3$

VII-B-7-e	Cesium Aluminate	
VII-B-7-f	Lithium Aluminate	
VII-B-7-g	Potassium Aluminate	
VII-B-7-h	RubidiumAluminate	
VII-B-7-j	Sodium Aluminate	
VII-B-7-k	Strontium Aluminate	

$$SrO \cdot 2 Al_2O_3$$

VII-B-7-m	Zinc Aluminate	
VII-B-7	Other Aluminates	

Cobalt Aluminate
Iron Aluminate

VII-B-8	Ferrites	
VII-B-8-a	Magnesium Ferrite	

Magnesioferrite
$MgO \cdot Fe_2O_3$

VII-B-8-b	Barium Ferrite	
VII-B-8-c	Beryllium Ferrite	
VII-B-8-d	Calcium Ferrite	

$Ca_2 Fe_2 O_5$
$CaO \cdot Fe_2 O_3$

VII-B-8-e	Cesium Ferrite	
VII-B-8-f	Lithium Ferrite	
VII-B-8-g	Potassium Ferrite	
VII-B-8-h	Rubidium Ferrite	
VII-B-8-j	Sodium Ferrite	
VII-B-8-k	Strontium Ferrite	
VII-B-8-m	Cobalt Ferrite	

$CoO \cdot Fe_2 O_3$

VII-B-8-n	Nickel Ferrite	

$NiO \cdot Fe_2 O_3$
Ferramic - E Nickel-Zinc Ferrite

VII-B-8-p	Zinc Ferrite	

$ZnO \cdot Fe_2 O_3$

VII-B-8	Other Ferrites	

Copper Ferrite
Manganese Ferrite

VII-B-9	Micas (Illites)	

Barium Mica
Biotite
Black Mica
Cericite
Magnesium Mica
Muscovite
Phlogopite
Potassium Mica
Ripidolite
White Mica
Zinn Waldite

VII-B-10	<u>Asbestos Minerals</u>
VII-B	<u>Other Mineral Ceramics</u>

Aragonite, $CaCo_3$
Bismuth Stannate, $Bi_2 Sn_3 O_9$
Calcium Stannate
Chromite
Colomite, $CaCO_3 \cdot MgCO_3$
Iron Cobaltite
Limestone
Magnesite, $MgCO_3$
Magnesium Stannate
Marble

VII-C	<u>Vitreous Structures</u>
VII-C-1	<u>Silicate Glasses</u>
VII-C-1-a	<u>Lithium Silicate Glass</u>

Lithium Aluminosilicate Glass
Lithium Aluminum Silicate Glass
Lithium Calcium (Lime) Silicate Glass
Lithium Sodium Silicate Glass
Lithium Magnesium Barium Silicate Glass

VII-C-1-b	<u>Sodium Silicate Glass</u>

Corning 0080
Flint Glass
Soda Lime Aluminosilicate Glass
Soda Lime Silica Glass
Soda Strontia Silicate Glass
Soda Lime Window Glass
Sodium Barium Silicate Glass
Sodium Barium Aluminosilicate Glass
Sodium Calcium (Lime) Silicate Glass
Sodium Strontium Aluminosilicate Glass
Sodium Lead Silicate Glass
Sodium Magnesium Copper Silicate Glass
Sodium Silicate Glass
Solex 2808X Plate Glass
Solex "S" Glass
White Plate Glass

VII-C-1-c	<u>Potassium Silicate Glass</u>
VII-C-1-d	<u>Rubidium Silicate Glass</u>
VII-C-1-e	<u>Cesium Silicate Glass</u>
VII-C-1-f	<u>Beryllium Silicate Glass</u>
VII-C-1-g	<u>Magnesium Silicate Glass</u>

Magnesium Aluminum Silicate Glass

VII-C-1-h	<u>Calcium Silicate Glass</u>

Lime Window Glass

VII-C-1-j	<u>Strontium Silicate Glass</u>

Strontium Lead Silicate Glass

VII-C-1-k	<u>Barium Silicate Glass</u>

Barium Crown Glass
Barium Titanium Silicate Glass
Crown Glass

VII-C-1-m   Lead Silicate Glass

Barium Lead Silicate Glass
Cadmium Lead Silicate Glass
Calcium Lead Silicate Glass
Cobalt Lead Silicate Glass
Corning 0120
Dense Flint Glass
Iron Lead Silicate Glass
Lithium Lead Silicate Glass
Magnesium Lead Silicate Glass
Nickel Lead Silicate Glass
Optical Flint Glass
Potassium Lead Silicate Glass
Sodium Lead Silicate Glass
Strontium Lead Silicate Glass
Television Tube Glass
Zinc Lead Silicate Glass

VII-C-1   Other Silicate Glasses

Container Glass
Flint Glass
Optical Glass
Corning 1723

VII-C-2   Borate Glasses

Barium Borate Glass
Barium Fluoborate Glass
Borax Glass
Calcium Borate Glass
Fluoborate Glass
Lead Borate Glass
Lithium Aluminum Borate Glass
Lithium Beryllium Borate Glass
Lithium Borate Glass
Potassium Borate Glass
Sodium Beryllium Borate Glass
Sodium Boroaluminate Glass
Sodium Magnesium Borate Glass

VII-C-3   Phosphate Glasses

VII-C-4   Arsenic Oxide Glasses

VII-C-5   Borosilicate Glasses

Borosilicate Crown Glass
Corning 7740
Lead Borosilicate Glass
Lithium Borosilicate Glass
Phoenix Glass
Pittsburgh No. 3235
Pyrex
Pyrex 774
Sodium-Potassium Borosilicate Glass
Sodium-Zinc Borosilicate Glass
Supremax (German)
Zinc-Magnesium Aluminum Borosilicate Glass

VII-C-6   Silica Glasses

 Corning 7940
 Fused Quartz
 Refrasil
 Fused Silica, SiO_2
 Multiform 790
 Vitreous Silica, SiO_2
 Vitrosil
 Vycor

VII-C   Other Glasses

 Barium Uranate Glass
 Barium Vanadate Glass
 Calcium Uranate Glass
 Gels
 Lead Vanadate Glass
 Lithium Uranate Glass
 Magnesium Uranate Glass
 Phosphorus Uranate Glass
 Potassium Uranate Glass
 Sodium Uranate Glass
 Strontium Uranate Glass
 Strontium Vanadate Glass
 Tellurium Oxide Glass
 Tellurium Vanadate Glass
 TeO_2 - MoO_3 Glass
 TeO_2 - WO_3 Glass

VII-D   Covalent Ceramic Structures (Also see Section IX)

VII-D-1   Silicon Carbide + X

VII-D-1-a   Silicon Carbide

 Carbofrax
 Carborundum
 Exolon Type SiC
 Globar
 SiC

VII-D-1-b   Silicon Carbide + Boron Carbide + X

VII-D-2   Boron Carbide

 B_4C
 D-11, 776-2 Boron Carbide
 D-11, 798-1 Boron Carbide

VII-D-3   Alkali and Alkaline Earth Carbides

VII-D-3-a   Beryllium Carbide

 Be_2C

VII-D-3   Other Alkali and Alkaline Earth Carbides

 Barium Carbide, BaC_2
 Calcium Carbide, CaC_2
 Sodium Carbide, Na_2C_2
 Strontium Carbide, SrC_2

VII-D-4   Boron Nitride

 BN

VII-D-5   Halides and Oxhalides

VII-D-5-a   <u>Fluorides</u>

Americium Trifluoride, AmF_3

Beryllium Difluoride, BeF_2

Calcium Fluoride, CaF_5

Fluorite

Lithium Fluoride, LiF

Plutonium Trifluoride, PuF_3

Rubidium Fluoride, RbF

Thorium Fluoride, ThF_4

Zirconium Fluoride, ZrF_4

Zirconium Fluoride + Lithium Fluoride

Zirconium Fluoride + Rubidium Fluoride

Zirconium Fluoride + Sodium Fluoride

VII-D-5   <u>Other Halides</u>

Cerium Bromide, $CeBr_3$

Cerium Chloride, $CeCl_3$

Lanthanum Bromide, $LaBr_3$

Lanthanum Chloride, $LaCl_3$

Neodymium Chloride, $NdCl_3$

Neptunium Bromide, $NpBr_3$

Neptunium Chloride, $NpCl_3$, $NpCl_4$

Plutonium Bromide, $PuBr_3$

Plutonium Chloride, $PuCl_3$

Plutonium Iodide, PuI_3

Praseodymium Bromide, $PrBr_3$

Praseodymium Chloride, $PrCl_3$

Thallium Chloride, $TlCl$

Thorium Chloride, $ThCl_4$

Uranium Bromide, UBr_3

Uranium Chloride, UCl_3, UCl_4

VII-D-6   <u>Sulfides; Selenides</u>

Barium Selenide, $BaSe$

Beryllium Sulfide, BeS

Cadmium Sulfide

Cerium Sulfide, CeS, Ce_2S_3, Ce_3S_4

Lead Selenide, $PbSe$

Lead Sulfide, PbS

Molybdenite, MoS_2

Thorium Sulfide, ThS_2, ThS, Th_7S_{12}, Th_4S_7, Th_2S_3

Uranium Sulfide, US, US_2

Zinc Sulfide, ZnS

VII-E   <u>Vitreous Bonded Crystalline Ceramics</u>

Conventional Ceramics; also see VII-A and VII-B

VII-E-1   <u>Alkaline Earth Silicate Glass Bond</u>

VII-E-2   <u>Alkali Silicate Glass Bond</u>

Lithium Silicate - Quartz Body

Sierra Talc, Unfired

Yellowstone Talc, Unfired

VII -E-3   <u>Magnesium Aluminosilicate Glass Bond</u>   (Cordierite, Steatite Talc Body)

VII-E-3-a	Lithium Modified Magnesium Aluminosilicate
VII-E-3-b	Sodium Modified Magnesium Aluminosilicate
VII-E-3-c	Potassium Modified Magnesium Aluminosilicate
	Fired Steatite
VII-E-3-d	Rubidium Modified Magnesium Aluminosilicate
VII-E-3-e	Cesium Modified Magnesium Aluminosilicate
VII-E-3-f	Beryllium Modified Magnesium Aluminosilicate
VII-E-3-g	Calcium Modified Magnesium Aluminosilicate
	Ball Clay
	Edgar Plastic Kaolin (EPK)
	Kaolin
	North Carolina Kaolin
VII-E-3-h	Strontium Modified Magnesium Aluminosilicate
VII-E-3-j	Barium Modified Magnesium Aluminosilicate
	Barium Lead Cordierite
VII-E-3-k	Lead Modified Magnesium Aluminosilicate
	Lead Cordierite
VII-E-3	Other Magnesium Aluminosilicate Glass-Bond
	Cordierite 202
	Fired Magnesium Aluminosilicate
	Ordinary High Alumina Magnesium Aluminosilicate
	Selfglazed Fired Steatite
	Sierralite, Fired
	Sierra Talc, Fired
	Ultra-Steatite
	Yellowstone Talc, Fired
VII-E-4	Calcium Aluminosilicate Glass Bond (Porcelain)
	Beryllia Porcelain
	Brick
	China
	Earthenware
	Electrical Porcelain
	High Tension Electrical Porcelain
	Magnesium Titanate Porcelain
	Porcelain 576
	Terra Cotta
	Tile
	Type 4811 Commercial Porcelain
	Wet Process Porcelain No. 7A2
	Whiteware
	Zircon Porcelain
VII-E-5	Other Alkaline Earth Aluminosilicate Glass Bond
VII-E-6	Alkali Aluminosilicate Glass Bond
	Clay
	Eucryptite
	Feldspar Porcelain
	K-3 Body
	K-5 Body
	K-6 Body
	K-7 Body
	K-8 Body
	K-9 Body

$LiAl_2 Si_8 O_{21}$
$Li_2 Al_2 Si_{10} O_{24}$
LiK Body
Petalite
Lithium Aluminosilicates
Lithium Aluminosilicate Bodies, Barium Modified
Lithium Aluminosilicates with Lead Bisilicate
Lithium Aluminosilicates with Lead Borates
Petalite
QC 6 Frit

VII-E-7   Borosilicate Glass Bond

VII-E-8   Phosphate Glass Bond

VII-E-9   Alumina Fire Brick

K-30 Insulating Brick
K-28 Insulating Brick

VII-E-10   Basic Brick

Basic Refractory
Basic Schamotte Brick
Chrome - Magnesite Brick
Forsterite Brick
Magnesite Brick

VII-E-11   Silica Brick

Coke Oven Brick
Silicrete

VII-E   Other Vitreous Bonded Crystalline Ceramics

Vitreous Bonded Aluminum Titanate

VII-F   Inorganic Cements and Adhesives

Lightweight Concrete
Portland Cement-Barytes Aggregate
Portland Cement

VIII.	CERMETS
	(Nominal refractory phase is that which is greatest weight fraction of total refractory phase.)
VIII-A	Cermets Containing Carbides as Major Refractory Phase
VIII-A-1	Tungsten Carbide as Major Refractory Phase

Carbide Tool Steel, CA-2
Carbide Tool Steel, CA-4
Carbide Tool Steel Kennametal K2S
Carbide Tool Steel Kennametal K-138
Carbide Tool Steel Kennametal K-6
Carboloy
Carboloy 44A
Carboloy 55A
Tungsten Carbide Cermet, Cobalt Bonded
Tungsten Carbide Cermet, Nickel Bonded

VIII-A-2   Titanium Carbide as Major Refractory Phase

Kennametal K-138A
Kennametal K-138
Kennametal K-151
Kennametal K-151A
Titanium Carbide Cermet, Cobalt Bonded
Titanium Carbide Cermet, Nickel Bonded
Titanium Carbide Cermet, Molybdenum Bonded
Titanium Carbide Cermet, Tungsten Bonded

VIII-A-3   Chromium Carbide as Major Refractory Phase

VIII-A-4   Zirconium Carbide As Major Refractory Phase

Hafnium Carbide Cermet

VIII-A-5   Silicon Carbide as Major Refractory Phase

Silicon Carbide Cermet, Cr-Mo Bonded
Silicon Carbide Cermet, Al-Ni Bonded
Silicon Carbide Cermet, Vitallium Bonded

VIII-A   Other Carbide Cermets

Boron Carbide Cermet, Iron Bonded
Boron Carbide Cermet, Aluminum Bonded
Manganese Carbide Cermet
Molybdenum Carbide Cermet
Niobium Carbide Cermet
Plutonium Carbide Cermet
Tantalum Carbide Cermet, Iron Bonded
Thorium Carbide Cermet
Uranium Carbide Cermet
Vanadium Carbide Cermet
Yttrium Carbide Cermet
Binary Carbide Cermets
Ternary Carbide Cermets

VIII-B   Cermets Containing Oxides or Suboxides as Major Refractory Phase

VIII-B-1   Aluminum Oxide as Major Refractory Phase

Aluminum Oxide Cermet, Chromium Bonded
Aluminum Oxide Cermet, Iron Bonded
Aluminum Oxide Cermet, Stainless Steel Bonded
Fiber Cermet
Metamic LT - 1

VIII-B-2	Magnesium Oxide as Major Refractory Phase
	Magnesium Oxide Cermet, NiAl Bonded
	Magnesium Oxide Cermet, Tungsten Bonded
VIII-B-3	Uranium Oxide as Major Refractory Phase
	Uranium Oxide Cermet, Zirconium Bonded
VIII-B-4	Thorium Oxide as Major Refractory Phase
	Thorium Oxide Cermet, Tungsten Bonded
VIII-B-5	Beryllium Oxide as Major Refractory Phase
	Beryllium Oxide Cermet, Beryllium Bonded
	Beryllium Oxide Cermet, Niobium Bonded
VIII-B	Other Oxide Cermets
	Boron Oxide Cermet, Boron Bonded
	Chromium Oxide Cermet, Cr$_2$Ti Bonded
	Silicon Oxide Cermet, Aluminum Bonded
	Silicon Oxide Cermet, Stainless Steel Bonded
	Titanium Oxide Cermet, Cr-Ti Bonded
	Zirconium Oxide Cermet, Titanium Bonded
	Zirconium Oxide Cermet, Zirconium Bonded
VIII-C	Cermets Containing Borides as Major Refractory Phase
VIII-C-1	Zirconium Boride Cermet
	Zirconium Diboride Cermet (Borolite)
	Borolite I, Grade F
	Borolite I, Grade G
	Borolite I, Grade S
VIII-C	Other Boride Cermets
	Borolite IV
	Chromium Boride Cermet, CrMo Bonded
	Titanium Boride Cermet, Aluminum Bonded
	Titanium Boride Cermet, Stellite 31 Bonded
VIII-D	Cermets Containing Silicides as Major Refractory Phase
	Chromium-Molybdenum-Silicon Cermet
	Chromium Silicide Cermet, Chromium Bonded
	Chromium Silicide Cermet, Kanthal Bonded
	Chromium-Titanium-Silicon Cermet
	Molybdenum Silicide Cermet, Copper Bonded
	Molybdenum Silicide -Alumina-Calcia Cermet
	Molybdenum-Titanium-Silicon Cermet
VIII-E	Cermets Containing Nitrides as Major Refractory Phase
	Titanium Nitride Cermet, Chromium + Titanium Bonded
	Titanium Nitride Cermet, Cr$_3$Ti Bonded
VIII-F	Cermets Containing Hydrides as Major Refractory Phase
VIII	Other Cermets
	Chromium Titanide Cermet, Molybdenum Bonded
	Nickel Aluminide Cermet, Chromium Bonded
	Nickel-Aluminum- Titanium Cermet

IX.	INTERMETALLICS
	(Nominal intermetallic, or nominal intermetallic greatest weight fraction with one or more other intermetallics. Also see section VII-D and respective alloy system.)
IX-A	Carbide Systems
IX-A-1	Tungsten Carbide, WC
IX-A-2	Titanium Carbide, TiC
IX-A-3	Chromium Carbide, Cr_3C_2
	Grade 608 Cr_3C_2
IX-A-4	Zirconium Carbide, ZrC
	Hafnium Carbide, HfC
IX-A-5	Tantalum Carbide, TaC
	$UTa_{10}C_4$
IX-A-6	Molybdenum Carbide, MoC, Mo_2C
IX-A-7	Uranium Carbide, UC, U_2C_3
IX-A	Other Carbides
	Iron Carbide, Fe_3C
	Manganese Carbide, Mn_3C, Mn_7C_3
	Niobium Carbide, NbC
	Plutonium Carbide, PuC
	Thorium Carbide, ThC
	Vanadium Carbide, VC
	Yttrium Carbide, YC
IX-B	Silicide Systems
IX-B-1	Molybdenum Silicide, $MoSi_2$, Mo_3Si, Mo_5Si_3
IX-B-2	Uranium Silicide, USi, USi_2, USi_3, U_3Si, U_3Si_2
IX-B	Other Silicides
	Chromium Silicide, CrSi, Cr_3Si
	Magnesium Silicide, Mg_2Si
	Neptunium Silicide
	Niobium Silicide, Nb_5Si_3
	Plutonium Silicide
	Rhenium Silicide, ReSi, $ReSi_2$, Re_3Si
	Tantalum Silicide, Ta_2Si, $TaSi_2$, Ta_5Si_3
	Thorium Silicide, $ThSi_2$
	Titanium Silicide
	Tungsten Disilicide, WSi_2
	Vanadium Silicide
	Zirconium Silicide
	Binary Silicide Systems
	Ternary Silicide Systems or Larger
	Silicide Base Systems with Other Intermetallics
IX-C	Boride Systems
IX-C-1	Magnesium Boride, MgB_2, MgB_4
IX-C-2	Titanium Boride, TiB, TiB_2
	TiB_2 + TiN
IX-C-3	Zirconium Boride, ZrB_2, ZrB_{12}
	Hafnium Boride, HfB_2
IX-C	Other Borides
	Aluminum Boride
	Beryllium Boride, BeB, Be_2B
	Cerium Boride, CeB_4
	Chromium Boride, CrB, CrB_2
	Gadolinium Boride, GdB_6

173

IX-F-1   Antimonides

           Aluminum Antimonide, AlSb

           Indium Antimonide, InSb

           Magnesium Antimonide, Mg_3Sb_2

           Manganese Antimonide, MnSb

           Tellurium Antimonide, Sb_2Te_3

           Thorium Antimonide, ThSb, $ThSb_2$, Th_3Sb_4

           Zinc Antimonide, ZnSb

IX-F-2   Tellurides

           Antimony Telluride, Sb_2Te_3

           Barium Telluride, BaTe

           Bismuth Telluride, Bi_2Te_3

           Cadmium Telluride, CdTe

           Iron Telluride, $FeTe_4$

           Lead Telluride, PbTe

           PbTe + PbSe

           Silicon Telluride, SiTe

           Tin Telluride, SnTe

IX-F   Arsenides

           Indium Arsenide, InAs

           Zinc Arsenide

IX-F   Phosphides

           Gallium Phosphide

           Nickel Phosphide

           Iron Phosphide

           Thallium Phosphide

IX-G   Intermetallics Involving a Light Metal (Al, Be, Mg, Ti)

IX-G-1   Aluminides

           Cerium Aluminide, CeAl, $CeAl_2$, $CeAl_4$, Ce_3Al_2

           Chromium Aluminide, CrAl

           Iron Aluminide

           Lanthanum Aluminide, LaAl, $LaAl_4$, La_3Al_2

           Nickel Aluminide, NiAl, Ni_3Al

           Titanium Aluminide, TiAl

           Uranium Aluminide, UAl_2

           Binary Aluminide Systems or Larger

           Aluminide Base Systems with Other Intermetallics

IX-G-2   Beryllides

           Beryllium Boride, BeB, BeB_6, Be_2B

           Molybdenum Beryllide, $MoBe_{12}$

           Palladium Beryllide, $PdBe_{12}$

           Platinum Beryllide, $PtBe_{12}$

           Plutonium Beryllide, $PuBe_{13}$

           Titanium Beryllide, TiBe, $TiBe_2$

           Uranium Beryllide, UBe_{13}

IX-G-3   Magnesium Intermetallics

           Cerium-Magnesium Intermetallic, CeMg, $CeMg_3$, $CeMg_9$, Ce_4Mg

           Cadmium-Magnesium Intermetallic, Mg_3Cd

           Lanthanum-Magnesium Intermetallic, LaMg, $LaMg_3$, $LaMg_9$, La_4Mg

           Lead-Magnesium Intermetallic, Mg_2Pb

           Magnesium Germanide, Mg_2Ge

           Magnesium Stannide, Mg_2Sn

IX-G-4   Titanium Intermetallics

           Titanium Aluminide, TiAl

           Titanium Beryllide, TiBe, $TiBe_2$

           Titanium Carbide, TiC

           Titanium-Gold Intermetallic, Ti_3Au, TiAu, $TiAu_2$

           Titanium-Iron Intermetallic, FeTi

           Titanium-Uranium Intermetallic, U_2Ti

IX-H   Intermetallics Involving a Rare Earth (Atomic Numbers 57-71)

IX-H-1   Cerium Intermetallics

Aluminum-Cerium Intermetallic, $CeAl$, $CeAl_2$, $CeAl_4$, Ce_3Al_2

Copper-Cerium Intermetallic, $CeCu$, $CeCu_2$, $CeCu_4$, $CeCu_6$

Gold-Cerium Intermetallic, $CeAu$, $CeAu_2$, $CeAu_3$, Ce_2Au

Lead-Cerium Intermetallic, $CePb_3$, Ce_2Pb

Magnesium-Cerium Intermetallic, $CeMg$, $CeMg_3$, $CeMg_9$, Ce_4Mg

Thallium-Cerium Intermetallic, $CeTl$, $CeTl_3$, Ce_2Tl

Tin-Cerium Intermetallic, $CeSn_3$, Ce_2Sn, Ce_2Sn_3

Silver-Cerium Intermetallic, $CeAg$, $CeAg_2$, $CeAg_3$

IX-H-2   Dysprosium Intermetallics

IX-H-3   Erbium Intermetallics

IX-H-4   Europium Intermetallics

IX-H-5   Gadolinium Intermetallics

IX-H-6   Holmium Intermetallics

IX-H-7   Lanthanum Intermetallics

Aluminum-Lanthanum Intermetallic, $LaAl$, $LaAl_2$, $LaAl_4$, La_3Al_2

Boron-Lanthanum Intermetallic, LaB_6

Copper-Lanthanum Intermetallic, $LaCu_4$, $LaCu_6$, $LaCu$, $LaCu_2$

Gold-Lanthanum Intermetallic, $LaAu$, $LaAu_2$, La_2Au, La_3Au

Lead-Lanthanum Intermetallic, $LaPb$, $LaPb_3$, La_2Pb

Magnesium-Lanthanum Intermetallic, $LaMg$, $LaMg_3$, $LaMg_9$, La_4Mg

Silver-Lanthanum Intermetallic, $LaAg$, $LaAg_2$, $LaAg_3$

Thallium-Lanthanum Intermetallic, $LaTl$, $LaTl_3$, La_2Tl

Tin-Lanthanum Intermetallic, $LaSn_3$, La_2Sn, La_2Sn_3

IX-H-8   Lutetium Intermetallics

IX-H-9   Neodymium Intermetallics

IX-H-10   Praseodymium Intermetallics

Aluminum-Praseodymium Intermetallic, $PrAl$, $PrAl_2$, $PrAl_4$, Pr_3Al_2

Copper-Praseodymium Intermetallic, $PrCu$, $PrCu_2$, $PrCu_4$, $PrCu_6$

Gold-Praseodymium Intermetallic, $PrAu$, $PrAu_2$, $PrAu_3$, Pr_2Au

Lead-Praseodymium Intermetallic, $PrPb$, $PrPb_3$, Pr_2Pb

Magnesium-Praseodymium Intermetallic, $PrMg$, $PrMg_3$, $PrMg_9$, Pr_4Mg

Praseodymium Boride, PrB_6

Silver-Praseodymium Intermetallic, $PrAg$, $PrAg_2$, $PrAg_3$

Thallium-Praseodymium Intermetallic, $PrTl$, $PrTl_3$, Pr_2Tl

Tin-Praseodymium Intermetallic, $PrSn_3$, Pr_2Sn, Pr_2Sn_3

IX-H-11   Promethium Intermetallics

IX-H-12   Samarium Intermetallics

IX-H-13   Terbium Intermetallics

IX-H-14   Thulium Intermetallics

IX-H-15   Ytterbium Intermetallics

IX-J   Intermetallics Involving a Refractory Metal (Cr, Co, Hf, Ni, Nb, Ta, Th, W, V, Zr)

IX-J-1   Chromium Intermetallics

Boron-Chromium Intermetallic, CrB, CrB_2

Hafnium-Chromium Intermetallic, $HfCr_2$

Niobium-Chromium Intermetallic

Tantalum-Chromium Intermetallic

IX-J-2   Cobalt Intermetallics

Niobium-Cobalt Intermetallic

Hafnium-Cobalt Intermetallic, $HfCo_2$

Tantalum-Cobalt Intermetallic, $TaCo_2$

Tungsten-Cobalt Intermetallic

Uranium-Cobalt Intermetallic, UCo, U_6Co

Zirconium-Cobalt Intermetallic, $ZrCo_2$

IX-J-3   Hafnium Intermetallics
          Boron-Hafnium Intermetallic, HfB_2
          Chromium-Hafnium Intermetallic, $HfCr_2$
          Cobalt-Hafnium Intermetallic, $HfCo_2$
          Iron-Hafnium Intermetallic, $HfFe_2$
          Manganese-Hafnium Intermetallic, $HfMn_2$
          Molybdenum-Hafnium Intermetallic, $HfMo_2$
          Nickel-Hafnium Intermetallic, $HfNi_2$
          Vanadium-Hafnium Intermetallic, HfV_2

IX-J-4   Molybdenum Intermetallics
          Boron-Molybdenum Intermetallic, MoB_2
          Hafnium-Molybdenum Intermetallic, $HfMo_2$
          Molybdenum Germanide, Mo_3Ge
          Silicon-Molybdenum Intermetallic, $MoSi_2$, Mo_3Si

IX-J-5   Nickel Intermetallics
          Hafnium-Nickel Intermetallic, Ni_2Hf
          Iron-Nickel Intermetallic, Ni_3Fe
          Manganese-Nickel Intermetallic, Ni_3Mn
          Nickel Selenide, $NiSe$, $NiSe_2$
          Plutonium-Nickel Intermetallic, $PuNi$, $PuNi_2$, $PuNi_5$
          Uranium-Nickel Intermetallic, UNi_2, U_6Ni

IX-J-6   Niobium Intermetallics
          Boron-Niobium Intermetallic, NbB_2
          Cobalt-Niobium Intermetallic, $NbCo_2$
          Chromium-Niobium Intermetallic, $NbCr_2$
          Germanium-Niobium Intermetallic, $GeNb_3$, Ge_2Nb
          Iron-Niobium, $NbFe_2$
          Manganese-Niobium Intermetallic, $NbMn_2$
          Niobium Silicide, Nb_5Si_3

IX-J-7   Tantalum Intermetallics
          Boron-Tantalum Intermetallic, TaB_2
          Chromium-Tantalum Intermetallic, $TaCr_2$
          Cobalt-Tantalum Intermetallic, $TaCo_2$
          Germanium-Tantalum Intermetallic, Ta_4Ge
          Iron-Tantalum Intermetallic, $TaFe_2$
          Silicon-Tantalum Intermetallic, $TaSi_2$

IX-J-8   Thorium Intermetallics
          Antimony-Thorium Intermetallic, $ThSb$, $ThSb_2$, Th_3Sb_4
          Manganese-Thorium Intermetallic, $ThMn_{12}$, Th_6Mn_{23}
          Thorium Nitride, ThN
          Thorium Silicide, $ThSi_2$

IX-J-9   Tungsten Intermetallics
          Tungsten Boride, WB_2, W_2B_2
          Cobalt-Tungsten Intermetallic, WCo_2
          Tungsten Silicide, WSi_2

IX-J-10   Vanadium Intermetallics
          Hafnium-Vanadium Intermetallic, HfV_2
          Manganese-Vanadium Intermetallic, VMn_2
          Vanadium-Aluminide, Al_3V
          Vanadium-Boride, VB_2
          Zirconium-Vanadium Intermetallic, ZrV_2

IX-J-11   Zirconium Intermetallics
          Cobalt-Zirconium Intermetallic, $ZrCo_2$
          Iron-Zirconium Intermetallic, $ZrFe_2$
          Vanadium-Zirconium Intermetallic, ZrV_2
          Zirconium Boride, ZrB_2, ZrB_{12}
          Zirconium Carbide, ZrC

For Intermetallics not listed above, see Respective Alloy System in Volume II.

X. POLYMERIC MATERIALS
(INCLUDING PLASTICS AND FILLED PLASTICS)

X-A   Polyesters

X-A-1   Cellulose Acetate
               Chemaco SPZ-325
               Chemaco SPZ-326
               Chemaco SPZ-327
               Chemaco SPZ-329
               Chemaco SPZ-330
               Chemaco SPZ-331
               Chemaco SPZ-332
               Tenite I

X-A-2   Cellulose Propionate
               Forticel 28238
               Forticel 28227

X-A-3   Cellulose Acetate Butyrate
               Tenite G204-H2
               Tenite I 204-MS
               Tenite Q264-H-2
               Tenite S 264-MS
               Tenite II

X-A-4   Cellulose Nitrate

X-A-5   Ethyl Cellulose
               Chemaco 342
               Chemaco 343
               Chemaco 344
               Chemaco 345
               Chemaco 346

X-A-6   Polyvinyl Acetals

X-A-7   Polyvinyl Acetate

X-A-8   Copolyvinyl Chloride-Acetate
               Vinylite VMCH
               Vinylite VYDR

X-A-9   Isocyanate Elastomers
               Diisocyanate Polyester Elastomer
               Vulcollan

X-A-10   Polyurethane Foams
               Alkyd Isocyanate Foams
               Armofoam
               Goodyear Foam in Place
               Hamilton Standard Foam in Place
               Isofoam
               Lockfoam
               MIL-C-8087

X-A-11   Unsaturated Polyester
               Laminac 4129
               Selectron 5026

X-A   Other Polyesters
               Polyvinyl Carbazole (Luvican)
               Trolitul Luv-M-150 (German)

X-B   TAC Polyesters (Tri-Allyl Cyanurate)
               Castolite
               Paraplex P-43
               Vibrin 135

X-C   Phenolics

X-C-1   Phenol Formaldehyde
               Catalin

X-C-1   (Continued)
               Phenol Formaldehyde, Asbestos Filled
               Bakelite BM-13335
               Bakelite BM-261
               Phenol Formaldehyde, Cord Filled
               Bakelite- BM-13014
               Bakelite BM-15140
               Phenol Formaldehyde, Cottonflock Filled
               Bakelite BM-13080
               Bakelite BM-14726
               Bakelite BM-16468
               Bakelite BM-17711
               Phenol Formaldehyde, Fabric Filled
               Bakelite BM-3510
               Phenol Formaldehyde, Wood Flour Filled
               Bakelite BM-704
               Bakelite BM-14316
               Phenolic Resin, Stupalith Filled

X-C-2   Furfural Formaldehyde
               Wood Flour Filled BM-17849

X-C-3   Urea Formaldehyde
               Urea Formaldehyde, Alpha Cellulose Filled
               Beetle

X-C   Other Phenolic Resins
               Alberit 1005
               Alberit 8291-SO
               Bakelite BM-17849
               Conolon 506
               Cresol Resin
               Type 31 Phenolic Resin
               Phenolic Novolak

X-D   Epoxides
               Araldite Casting Resin 501
               Epon Resins
               Hysol 6000-OP

X-E   Melamines
               Melmac 592
               Melmac 1077
               Melmac 1502
               Melamine Formaldehyde
               Melamine Formaldehyde, Alpha Cellulose Filled
               Melamine Formaldehyde, Mineral Filled
               Resimene 814 Resin

X-F   Acrylics
               Acrylate
               American Phenolic Grade 912A
               Lucite
               Methacrylate
               Plexiglass 11
               Plexiglass An-P-44A
               Polymethyl Methacrylate
               Polymethyl Methacrylate, Filled
               Selectron 400 Acrylic Resin
               Vinylidene

X-G   Polyethylene and Halogenated Polyethylenes
               Alathon-10
               Bakelite DYNH
               Filled Teflon

X-G   (Continued)

Fluorothene (Chlorotrifluoroethylene)
Kel-F
Marlex 20
Marlex 50
PE-575
Polychlorotrifluoroethylene
Polyethylene
Polytetrafluoroethylene (Teflon)
Polythene
Polythene PM-1
Teflon Type TF-1

X-H   Polyamide (Nylon)

Polycaprolactam
Nylon 6
Nylon 9
Nylon 11
Nylon 66

X-J   Natural and Synthetic Rubber

Buna N
Buna S(GR-S)
Butadiene - Acrylonitrile Copolymer
Butadiene - Styrene Copolymer
Butyl (GR-1)
Cellular Rubber Board
Dihydro Perfluorobutylacrylate
GMGA - 5003
Hard Rubber
Hard Rubber Board No. 2266
Hycar PA-21
Isoprene-Isobutylene Copolymer
Natural Rubber
Neoprene
Neoprene GN
Neoprene W
Perbunan 18
Perbunan 26
Perbunan 35
Polybutadiene
Polyfluorobutyl acrylate
Polyisoprene
Polystyrene-Butadiene
Silastic 160
Silastic 180
Silicone Rubber

X   Other Polymers

Aniline Resin
Casein
Dow Corning R-7001
Dow Corning R-7002
Dow Corning R-7091
Eccofoam LM
Isotactic Polymer
Lustrex L-2020 Polystyrene
Moplen
Opalon 300-FM
Penton 1215 Chlorinated Polyether

X   (Continued)
Polypropylene
Polystyrene
Polyvinyl Chloride
Silicone Foams

XI. COMPOSITE MATERIALS

(The word "ceramic", as used below, includes any material which is inorganic and nonmetallic. Semiorganic materials, such as silicones, are included in the term "organic".)

XI-A   Composite Organic Materials; Sandwich Structures
(Any layer may be pure, filled, or reinforced.)

XI-A-1   Plastic Skin, Plastic Foam Core
Foam Sandwich Panel

XI-A-2   Plastic Skin, Plastic Honeycomb Core
Phenolic Honeycomb Panel
Polyester Honeycomb Panel
Reinforced TAC Polyester Skin, Phenolic Honeycomb Core

XI-A-3   Solid Plastic Layers

XI-B   Composite Metallic Materials

XI-B-1   Metal Skin, Metal Honeycomb Core
Alclad Skin and Honeycomb Core
Stainless Steel Skin and Honeycomb Core

XI-B-2   Unbonded Metal Layers
Aluminum-Uranium Joint

XI-B-3   Fusion Bonded Metal Layers
Aluminum Sprayed on Stainless Steel
Brazed Metals
Hot Dipped Metals
Stainless Steel Sprayed on Copper

XI-B-4   Mechanically Bonded Metal Layers
Riveted Joints
Riveted Aluminum Joints
Riveted Aluminum Alloy Joints

XI-B-5   Clad Metals
Alclad 24ST = Alclad 2024
Stainless Clad Steel Plate

XI-B-6   Plated Metals

XI-C   Composite Ceramic Materials
Corning E.C. Coat on 1722 Glass
Electro conducting Glass 547-26
Electro conducting Glass LOF-81E-19778
Electro conducting Glass LOF-PB-19195
Graphite Coated with Silicon Carbide
Graphite - Graphite Joint
Graphite - Uranium Oxide Joint
Laminated Transparent Glasses
Nesacoat on Glass
Pyroceram 9606
Pyroceram 9608
Safety Glass
Sierra Cote I on Glass

XI-D   Composite Organic-Metallic Materials; Sandwich Structures
(Any organic layer may be pure, filled, or reinforced.)

XI-D-1   Plastic Skin, Metal Honeycomb Core
Reinforced Polyester Skin, Aluminum Honeycomb Core

XI-D-2   Metal Skin, Plastic Honeycomb Core
Aluminum Skin, Phenolic Honeycomb Core

XI-D-3   Metal Skin, Plastic Foam Core
Aluminum Skin, Plastic Foam Core

XI-D-4	<u>Adhesive Bonded Metal Layers</u>
	Adhesive Bonded Aluminum Layers
XI-D	<u>Other Composite Organic-Metallic Materials</u>
	Aluminum Coated with Alcyd-Base Clear Lacquer
	Aluminum Coated with Clear Silicone Vehicle
	Aluminum Coated with Varnish-Base Clear Lacquer
	Aluminum Painted with Camouflage Green Paint
	Aluminum Painted with Zinc Chromate
	Dow Metal Coated with Alcyd Base Clear Lacquer
	Dow Metal Coated with Clear Silicone Vehicle
	Dow Metal Coated with Varnish-Base Clear Lacquer
	Inconel Painted with Aluminum Paint
	Mild Steel Coated with Clear Silicone Vehicle
	Stainless Steel Coated with Clear Silicone Vehicle
XI-E	<u>Composite Metallic-Ceramic Materials</u>
	Aluminum Oxide Coated Metal
	Beryllium with Oxide or Nitride Film
	Boral Thermal Neutron Shield
	Ceramic Coated Mild Steel
	Coated Magnesium Alloy
	Coated Molybdenum
	Coated Stainless Steel
	Enamel Coated Inconel
	Metal-Ceramic Joint
	Steel-Uranium Carbide Joint
	Steel-Uranium Oxide Joint
	Uranium-Graphite Joint
	Zirconia Flame Sprayed on Inconel
XI-F	<u>Composite Organic-Ceramic Materials; Sandwich Structures</u>
	(Any organic layer may be pure, filled, or reinforced.)
XI-G	<u>Composite Organic-Metallic-Ceramic Materials; Sandwich Structures</u>
	(Any organic layer may be pure, filled, or reinforced.)
XI-H	<u>Reinforced Organic Materials</u>
XI-H-1	<u>Reinforced Teflon</u>
	Duroid 5600
	Glass Fabric Reinforced Teflon
XI-H-2	<u>Reinforced Melamine Formaldehyde</u>
	Asbestos Fabric Reinforced Melamine-Formaldehyde
	Cellulose Paper Reinforced Melamine-Formaldehyde
	Cotton Fabric Reinforced Melamine-Formaldehyde
	Glass Fabric Reinforced Melamine-Formaldehyde
	Glass Mat Reinforced Melamine-Formaldehyde
XI-H-3	<u>Reinforced Phenolics</u>
	<u>Alpha Cellulose Paper Reinforced Phenolic</u>
	Phenolite Nema XP
	Phenolite Nema XXX
	Phenolite Nema XXXP
	Phenolite XXXP-454
	<u>Cotton Fabric Reinforced Phenolic</u>
	Panelyte Rod Grade 942
	Phenolite Nema C
	Phenolite Nema L
	Phenolite LE

XI-H-3   (Continued)
Asbestos Fabric Reinforced Phenol-Formaldehyde
Asbestos Paper Reinforced Phenol-Formaldehyde
Cotton Web Reinforced Phenol-Formaldehyde
Glass Fabric Reinforced Phenolics
Glass Fiber Reinforced Phenolic Fiberite 4030-190
Conolon N-1 Laminate
Kraft Paper Reinforced Phenolic
Phenolite Nema
Nylon Fabric Reinforced Phenol-Formaldehyde
Nylon Flock Reinforced Phenolic LM1-304 (Loven)
Plyophen 5023
Plyophen Resin No. 1001, Reinforced
Reinforced Copolymer of Phenolic and Epoxide Resins
Epon Reinforced
Reinforced Copolymer (Epoxide-Phenolic)
Reinforced Phenolic Formaldehyde
Reinforced Phenolics
Insurok XXX-T-640
Insurok-C-T-601
Lamicoid-C-6030
Wood Base, Phenol-Formaldehyde

XI-H-4   Reinforced Diallyl Phthalate
Cotton Fabric Reinforced Diallyl Phthalate
Diall-50-01
Diall-50-51
Diall-50-52
Diall-52-20-30
Diall-52-01
Durez 16694 (Orlon Filled)
Glass Fabric Reinforced Diallyl Phthalate

XI-H-5   Reinforced Polyesters and TAC Polyesters
Dynakon Rod F
Dynakon Sheet A3A
Glass Fabric Reinforced Polyester
Glass Fabric Reinforced TAC Polyester
Glass Fiber Reinforced Polyester
Glass Mat Reinforced Polyester
Paper Reinforced Polyester
Reinforced Vibrin-135
Reinforced Vibrin-X-1068
Triallyl Cyanurate Modified Polyester Resin
with Reinforcement

XI-H-6   Reinforced Silicones
2106 Silicone Resin, Reinforced
Silicone Laminate, Reinforced
Asbestos Fabric Reinforced Silicone Laminate
Glass Fabric Reinforced Silicone Laminate
Glass Fiber Reinforced Silicone Laminate

XI-H-7	Reinforced Epoxides
	Epon Resin 828, Glass Reinforced
	Fabric Reinforced Epoxide
	Reinforced Epoxide X-12100
XI-H	Other So-called "Plastic Laminates"
	Resin Impregnated Glass Fabric, Cotton Duck Laminate
XI-J	Reinforced Ceramic Materials
	Glass Bonded Mica
	Molybdenum Reinforced Alumina
	Supramica 557 (Mycalex)

This index lists the names of ALL materials for which some property is reported in the handbook, and shows their location in the volumes which are arranged by materials. The names are those given by the authors of the original articles.

The index also lists some of the more common trade names, even if NO DATA are reported for them in the handbook. To assist the reader most of the optional variations of material names have been listed, but it is obviously impossible to list each and every possible permutation and abbreviation of material names.

Material Index Number	Material Name
X-J	1,1 Dihydroperfluorobutyl Acrylate
VII-B-2-e	2 BeO . SiO$_2$
VII-B-6	2 BeO . TiO$_2$
VII-B-5	2 CaO . B$_2$O$_3$
VII-A-4-a	2 CeO$_2$. V$_2$O$_4$
VII-B-2-e	2 MgO . SiO$_2$
VII-C-1-m	2 PbO . 3 SiO$_2$
VII-C	2 TeO$_2$. MoO$_3$ Glass
X-A	3,3 Bichloro-methyl-oxetane
VII-B-1	3 Al$_2$O$_3$. 2 SiO$_2$, Mullite
VII-B-3-b	3 BeO . Al$_2$O$_3$. 6 SiO$_2$
VII-B-6-f	3 CaO . 2 TiO$_2$
VII-B-7-d	3 CaO . Al$_2$O$_3$
VII-B-5	3 CaO . B$_2$O$_3$
VII-C-1-m	3 PbO . 2SiO$_2$
V-A-5	3S Aluminum Alloy
VII-B-6	4 BeO . TiO$_2$
V-A-5	4S Aluminum Alloy
VII-B-6	6 BeO . TiO$_2$
VII-A-9	6 HfO$_2$. Ta$_2$O$_5$
V-A-1	11S Aluminum Alloy
VII-B-7-d	12 CaO . 7 Al$_2$O$_3$
V-A-2	13 Aluminum Alloy
V-A-1	14S (R30 1) Aluminum Alloy
II-D-3	17-7 P.H. Stainless Steel
V-A-1	17S Aluminum Alloy
II-D-2	18-8 Stainless Steel
XI-B	18-8 Stainless Steel Sprayed on Copper
V-A-1	18S Aluminum Alloy
II-D-3	19-9 DL
II-D-3	19-9 W-Mo
V-A-1	24S Aluminum Alloy
I-A-2	24ST Aluminum Alloy
V-A-1	25S Aluminum Alloy
V-A-2	32S Aluminum Alloy
V-A-4	40E Aluminum Alloy
V-A-2	43 Aluminum Alloy

Material Index Number	Material Name
V-A-3	50S Aluminum Alloy
V-A-2	51S Aluminum Alloy
V-A-3	52S Aluminum Alloy
V-A-3	53S Aluminum Alloy
V-A-3	56S Aluminum Alloy
V-A-3	61S Aluminum Alloy
V-A-3	63S Aluminum Alloy
IV-B-1	73J
V-A-2	85 Aluminum Alloy
IV-A-3	100 N T-2
IV-A-4	100 NT-2
IV-A-5	100 NT-2
V-A-1	108 Aluminum Alloy
IV-B-1	111 VT 2-2
V-A-1	113 Aluminum Alloy
V-A-1	122 Aluminum Alloy
V-A-1	138 Aluminum Alloy
V-A-1	142 Aluminum Alloy
V-A-1	195 Aluminum Alloy
V-A-3	214 Aluminum Alloy
V-A-3	218 Aluminum Alloy
V-A-3	220 Aluminum Alloy
II-D-3	234 A-5
II-D-3	302B Stainless Steel
V-A-2	319 Aluminum Alloy
II-D-3	321 Stainless Steel
V-A-2	355 Aluminum Alloy
V-A-2	356 Aluminum Alloy
V-A-2	360 Aluminum Alloy
V-A-2	380 Aluminum Alloy
V-A-3	406 Aluminum Alloy
II-D-1	446 Stainless Steel
II-D-9	815 Steel (German)
IV-A-1	1040 Alloy
XI-H-6	2106 Silicone Resin, Reinforced
II-C-1	2515 Low Alloy Steel
IV-B-1	6059
V-A-2	A-108 Aluminum Alloy
V-C-1	A-110-AT Titanium Alloy
V-A-2	A 132 Aluminum Alloy
V-A-3	A 214 Aluminum Alloy
I-A-1	Ac
X-A-3	Acetate Butyrate
I-C-3-p	Acetylene Soot
I-C-3	Acheson Graphite
IV-A-4-a	ACI-HU Alloy

Material Index Number	Material Name
II-D-3	ACI-CA-15
II-D-3	ACI -CA-40
II-D-6	ACI-CM-25
II-D-6-a	ACI-CN-7
II-D-6	ACI-CT-7
II-D-6-a	ACI-HN
II-D-6	ACI-HP
II-D-6	ACI-HS
II-D-6	ACI-HT
II-D-6	ACI-HU
II-D-3	ACI Type CA-15
II-C-3	ACI Type CA-40
II-D-2	ACI Type CB-30
II-D-2	ACI Type CC-50
II-D-3	ACI Type CE-30
II-D-3	ACI Type CF-8
II-D-3	ACI Type CF-16F
II-D-3	ACI Type CF-20
II-D-3	ACI Type CG
II-D-3	ACI Type CH-10
II-D-3	ACI Type CH-20
II-D-3	ACI Type CK-20
II-D-3	ACI Type HB
II-D-3	ACI Type HC
II-D-3	ACI Type HD
II-D-3	ACI Type HE
II-D-3	ACI Type HF
II-D-3	ACI Type HH
II-D-3	ACI Type HI
II-D-3	ACI Type HK
II-D-3	ACI Type HL
X-F	Acrylate
X-F	Acrylic Resin
X-F	Acrylics
X-J	Acrylonite-Butadiene Copolymer
I-A-1	Actinium
VI	Actinium Intermetallic
VII-A-1-a	Activated Alumina
XI-D-4	Adhesive Bonded Aluminum Layers
XI-D-4	Adhesive Bonded Metal Layers
III-D	Admiraly Nickel
III-D	Advance
I-S-4	Ag
VI-B-1	Ag + Al + X

Material Index Number	Material Name
VI-B	Ag + Au + X
VI-B-2	Ag + Cd + X
VI-B-3	Ag + Cu + X
VI-B	Ag + Mg + X
VI-B	Ag + Mn + X
VI-B	Ag + Pb + X
VI-B-4	Ag + Pd + X
VI-B	Ag + Pt + X
VI-B	Ag + Zn + Au
VI-B	Ag + Zn + Be
VI-B	Ag + Zn + X
II-C-7	Air Hardening High Alloy, High Chromium Tool Steel
II-C-7	Air Hardening Low Alloy, Chromium Tool Steel
II-C-7	Air Hardening Low Alloy, High Manganese Tool Steel
II-C-6	AISI-7Cr Type Steel
II-C-7	AISI-9Cr Steel
II-D-2	AISI-301 Stainless Steel
II-D-2	AISI-302 Stainless Steel
II-D-3	AISI-302B High Temperature Scale Resistant Stainless Steel
II-D-3	AISI-303 Free Cutting Stainless Steel
II-D-2;II-D-3	AISI-304 Weldable Stainless Steel
II-D-2	AISI-308 Stainless Steel
II-D-2	AISI-309 Stainless Steel
II-D-2, 3	AISI-310 Stainless Steel
II-D-3	AISI-316 Chemical Corrosion Resistant Stainless Steel
II-D-3	AISI-317 Chemical Corrosion Resistant Stainless Steel
II-D-3	AISI-321 Stabilized Stainless Steel
II-D-6	AISI-330 Stainless Steel
II-D-3	AISI-347 Stabilized Stainless Steel
II-D-1	AISI-403 Steel
II-D-4	AISI-405 Steel
II-D-4	AISI-406 Stainless Steel
II-D-1	AISI-410 Stainless Steel
II-D-2	AISI-414 Stainless Steel
II-D-4	AISI-416 Stainless Steel
II-D-1	AISI-420 Steel
II-D-1	AISI-430 Stainless Steel
II-D-2	AISI-431 Steel
II-D-4	AISI-440A Steel
II-D-1	AISI-442 Steel
II-D-4	AISI-443 Steel
II-D-1	AISI-446 Stainless Steel
II-C-6	AISI-501 Steel
II-C-6	AISI-502 Steel

Material Index Number	Material Name
II-A-1, 2	AISI-1010 Steel
II-A-1	AISI-1020 Steel
II-A-2	AISI-1320 Steel
II-A-2	AISI-1330 Steel
II-A-3	AISI-1340 Steel
II-C-1	AISI-2300 Series Steel
II-C-2	AISI-3100 Series Low Alloy Steel
II-C-5	AISI-4000 Series Steel
II-C-7	AISI-4100 Series Steel
II-C-7	AISI-4130 Steel
II-C-2	AISI-4300 Series Low Alloy Steel
II-C-3	AISI-4600 Series Low Alloy Steel
II-C-3	AISI-4800 Series Low Alloy Steel
II-C-6	AISI-5045 Steel
II-C-6	AISI-5046 Steel
II-C-6	AISI-5100 Series Steel
II-C-6	AISI -6100 Series Steel
II-C-2	AISI-8600 Series Low Alloy Steel
II-C-6	AISI-8653 Steel
II-C-2	AISI-8700 Series Low Alloy Steel
II-C-9	AISI-9200 Series Steel
II-A-3	AISI-A-1345 Steel
II-A-1	AISI-C-1005 to C-1019 Steel
II-A-2	AISI-C-1020 to 1038
II-A-3	AISI-C-1039 to 1057
II-A-4	AISI-C-1058 to 1078
II-A-5	AISI-C-1080 to 1095
II-C-6	AISI-E-50100 Steel
II-C-6	AISI-E-51100 Steel
II-C-6	AISI-E-52100 Steel
II-C-2	AISI-E-9310 Steel
II-C-2	AISI-E-9315 Steel
II-C-2	AISI-E-9317 Steel
II-C-2	AISI-E-9437 to 9445
II-C-3	AISI-9747 Low Alloy Steel
II-C-3	AISI-9763 Low Alloy Steel
II-C-2	AISI-9840 Thru 9850 Low Alloy Steel
I-A-2	Al
VII-A-1-a	Al_2O_3
VII-A-1-b	$Al_2O_3 + Cr_2O_3 + X$
VII-A-1	$Al_2O_3 + MgO + BeO + X$
VII-A-1	$Al_2O_3 + Nb_2O_5$
VII-A-1	$Al_2O_3 + ThO_2$
VII-A-1	$Al_2O_3 + ThO_2 + BeO + X$

189

Material Index Number	Material Name
VII-A-1	$Al_2O_3 + UO_2$
VII-A-1	$Al_2O_3 + ZrO_2 + BeO$
VII-B-6-d	Al_2TiO_5
IX-J-10 also IX-G-1	Al_3V
V-A-6	$Al + Ag + X$
X-G	Alathon-10
X-C	Alberit 1005
X-C	Alberit 8291-SO
V-A	$Al + Be + X$
VII-B-3-h	Albite
I-A-2 also XI-B-5	Alclad
XI-B-5 also I-A-2	Alclad 24 St
XI-B-5 also I-A-2	Alclad 2024
XI-D	Alclad 2024 Painted with Zinc Chromate
XI-D	Alclad 2024 Painted with Green Paint
V-A-1	$Al + Cu + Mg + X$
V-A-1	$Al + Cu + Ni + Mg + X$
V-A-1	$Al + Cu + Si + X$
V-A-1	$Al + Cu + X$
X	Aliphatic Olefin Polymer
VII-B-3	Alkali and Alkaline-Earth Aluminosilicate (Feldspar)
VII-D-3	Alkali and Alkaline Earth Carbides
VII-E-6	Alkaline Aluminosilicate Glass Bond
VII-E-5	Alkaline Earth Aluminosilicate Glass Bond, other
VII-C-2	Alkaline Earth Borate Glass
VII-E-1	Alkaline Earth Silicate Glass Bond
VII-E-2	Alkali Silicate Glass Bond
X-A-10	Alkyd Isocyanate Foam
XI-D	Alkyd Lacquer Coated Aluminum Alloy 24 ST
XI-D	Alkyd Lacquer Coated Aluminum Alloy 75 ST
XI-D	Alkyd Lacquer Coated Dow Metal
V-A-2-a	Allcast
II-D-3	Allegheny Metal 18-8m
V-A-1	Alloy 14S
V-A-4	Alloy 75S
V-A-1	Alloy 195
V-A-3	Alloy 220
V-A-2	Alloy 356
V-A-1	Alloy 2014
V-A-1	Alloy 2024-5
V-A-4	Alloy 7075
V-A-1	Alloy C-46
IV-A-4-a	Alloy-ACI-HU

Material Index Number	Material Name
IV-A-4	Alloy HW, ACI Type
V-A-3	Al + Mg
V-A-3	Al + Mg + Mn + X
V-A-3	Al + Mg + Ni + Si + X
V-A-3	Al + Mg + X
V-A-5	Al + Mn + X
V-A	Al + Ni + Cu + Mn + X
V-A	Al + Ni + Mn + Cu + X
V-A	Al + Ni + X
V-A-2-b	Alpax Gamma Aluminum Alloy (British)
XI-H-3	Alpha Cellulose Paper Reinforced Phenolic
VII-B-5	Al PO_4 LiF
IX-F-1	Al Sb
V-A-2-a	Al + Si + Cu + X
V-A-2-a	Al + Si + Cu + Fe + Ni + X
V-A-2-a	Al + Si + Cu + Mg
V-A-2-a	Al + Si + Cu + Mg + X
V-A-2-a	Al + Si + Cu + Ni + Mg + X
V-A-2	Al + Si + Fe + X
VII-B-2-e	Al Si Mag 196 Steatite
V-A-2-b	Al + Si + Mg + Mn + Fe
V-A-2-b	Al + Si + Mg + X
V-A-2	Al + Si + Ni + X
V-A-2	Al + Si + X
V-A-4	Al + Zn + X
VII-A-1-a	Alumina
VII-E-9	Alumina Brick
VII-E-9	Alumina Firebrick
VII-A-1	Alumina + Magnesia + Beryllia + X
XI-J	Alumina, Molybdenum Reinforced
VII-A-1	Alumina + Niobium Pentoxide
VII-B-7	Aluminate Spinel
VII-A-1	Alumina + Thoria
VII-A-1	Alumina + Thoria + Beryllia + X
VII-A-1	Alumina + Uranium Dioxide
VII-A-1	Alumina + Zirconia + Beryllia
VII-A-1	Alumina + Zirconia + X
IX-G-1	Aluminide
IX-G-1	Aluminide Base Intermetallics
IX-G-1	Aluminides of Nickel
IX-G-1 also IX-G-4	Aluminides of Titanium
VII-B-1	Alumino-Silicate
VII-B-1	Aluminosilicate , non-hydrous (Mullite, Kyanite)
I-A-2	Aluminum

Material Index Number	Material Name
XI-D	Aluminum, Alkyd Lacquer Coated
V-A	Aluminum Alloy
See Alloy. . . .	Aluminum Alloy . . . . .
XI-D	Aluminum Alloy 24ST, Lacquer Coated
I-A-2	Aluminum Alloy 25
IX-F-1	Aluminum Antimonide
V-A	Aluminum-Base Alloy
V-A	Aluminum + Beryllium + X
IX-C	Aluminum Boride
III-A	Aluminum Brass
III-E	Aluminum Bronze
VII	Aluminum Carbide
IX-H-1	Aluminum -Cerium Intermetallic
XI-D	Aluminum Coated with Alkyd-Base Clear Lacquer
XI-D	Aluminum Coated with Clear Silicone Vehicle
XI-D	Aluminum Coated with Varnish-Base Lacquer
V-A-1	Aluminum + Copper + Magnesium + X
V-A-1	Aluminum + Copper + Nickel + Magnesium + X
V-A-1	Aluminum + Copper + Silicon + X
V-A-1	Aluminum + Copper + X
IX-H-7 also IX-G-1	Aluminum Lanthanum Intermetallic
V-A-3	Aluminum + Magnesium
V-A-3	Aluminum + Magnesium + Manganese + X
V-A-3	Aluminum + Magnesium + Nickel + Silicon + X
VII-C-5	Aluminum Magnesium Zinc Borosilicate Glass
V-A-5	Aluminum + Manganese + X
V-A	Aluminum + Nickel + Copper + Manganese + X
V-A	Aluminum + Nickel + Manganese + Copper + X
VIII	Aluminum-Nickel -Titanium Cermet
V-A	Aluminum + Nickel + X
VII-A-1-a	Aluminum Oxide
VIII-B-1	Aluminum Oxide as a Major Refractory Phase of Cermet
VIII-B-1	Aluminum Oxide Cermet
VIII-B-1	Aluminum Oxide Cermet-Chromium Bonded
VIII-B-1	Aluminum Oxide Cermet-Iron Bonded
VIII-B-1	Aluminum Oxide Cermet-Stainless Steel Bonded
VII-A-1-b	Aluminum Oxide + Chromium Oxide + X
XI-E	Aluminum Oxide Coated Metal
VII-A-1	Aluminum Oxide + Magnesium Oxide + Beryllium Oxide + X
VII-A-1	Aluminum Oxide + Niobium Oxide + X
VII-A-1	Aluminum Oxide + Thorium Oxide + X
VII-A-1	Aluminum Oxide + Thorium Oxide + Beryllium Oxide + X
VII-A-1	Aluminum Oxide + Uranium Oxide + X
VII-A-1	Aluminum Oxide + Zirconium Oxide + Beryllium Oxide
VII-A-1	Aluminum Oxide + Zirconium Oxide + X

Material Index Number	Material Name
XI-D	Aluminum Paint on Inconel
IX-H-10 also IX-G-1	Aluminum-Praseodymium Intermetallic
V-A-2-a	Aluminum+Silicon + Copper + Iron + Nickel + X
V-A-2-a	Aluminum + Silicon + Copper + Magnesium
V-A-2-a	Aluminum + Silicon + Copper + Magnesium + X
V-A-2-a	Aluminum + Silicon + Copper + Nickel + Magnesium + X
V-A-2-a	Aluminum + Silicon + Copper + X
XI-D	Aluminum-Silicone Coated
V-A-2	Aluminum + Silicon + Iron + X
V-A-2-b	Aluminum + Silicon + Magnesium + Manganese + Iron
V-A-2-b	Aluminum + Silicon + Magnesium + X
V-A-2	Aluminum + Silicon + Nickel + X
V-A-2	Aluminum + Silicon + X
V-A-6	Aluminum + Silver - X
XI-B-1	Aluminum Skin and Honeycomb Core
XI-D-2	Aluminum Skin, Phenolic Honeycomb Core
XI-D-3	Aluminum Skin, Plastic Foam Core
XI-B	Aluminum Sprayed on Stainless Steel
VII-B-6-d	Aluminum Titanate
VII-E	Aluminum Titanate, Bonded
XI-B-2	Aluminum-Uranium Joint
IX-J-10	Aluminum-Vanadium Intermetallic
XI-D	Aluminum-Varnish Lacquer Coated
V-A-4	Aluminum + Zinc + Magnesium + Copper + X
V-A-4	Aluminum + Zinc + X
VII-A-1-a	Alundum
V-A-4	Al + Zn + Mg + Cu + X
I-A-3	Am
II-D-3	AM-350 Alleghany Metal Stainless Steel
VII-B-5	Amblygonite
X-F	American Phenolic Grade 912A
I-A-3	Americium
VII-D-5-a	Americium Fluoride
VI	Americium Intermetallic
VII-D-5-a	Americium Trifluoride
VII-D-5-a	AmF_3
I-C-3	Amorphous Carbon
VII-B-1	Amphibole
IV-B-1	AMS-5375
II-D-3-a	AMS-5376, a Low Carbon Multimet Alloy
IV-A-3-a	AMS-5378
IV-B-1	AMS-5380
IV-B-1	AMS-5382
IV-B-1	AMS-5385

Material Index Number	Material Name
IV-A-2	AMS-5530, Hastelloy C
II-D-3-b	AMS-5532b, Multimet Alloy NR-21
VII-A-8	Anatase
VII-B-1	Andalusite
I-N-3	"A" Nickel
X	Anilin Resin
V-B-1	AN-M-29 Magnesium Alloy
VII-B-3-c	Anorthite
II-C also II-D	Anti-Friction Alloy
IX-F-1	Antimonide
I-A-4	Antimony
VII-A-13	Antimony Oxide
IX-F-2	Antimony Telluride
IX-J-8	Antimony-Thorium Intermetallic
VII-B	Aragonite
X-D	Araldite
X-D	Araldite Casting Resin 501
I-J-2	Armco Ingot Iron
I-J-2	Armco Iron
X-A-10	Armofoam
I-A-5	Arsenic
VII-C-4	Arsenic Oxide Glass
IX-F-3	Arsenide
I-C-3-a	Artificial Graphite
I-A-5	As
XI-H-2	Asbestos Fabric Reinforced Melamine Formaldehyde
XI-H-3	Asbestos Fabric Reinforced Phenol Formaldehyde
XI-H-6	Asbestos Fabric Reinforced Silicone Laminate
VII-B-10	Asbestos Minerals
XI-H-3	Asbestos Paper Reinforced Phenol Formaldehyde
I-A-6	Astatine
V-B-2	ASTM A8
V-B-2	ASTM A10
II-D-9	ASTM A-128-33
V-B-2	ASTM AM11
V-B-1	ASTM-AZ-31A
V-B-1	ASTM-AZ-31B
V-B-1	ASTM-AZ-31X
V-B-2	ASTM-AZ-51X
V-B-1	ASTM-AZ-61X
V-B-1	ASTM-AZ-63
V-B-1	ASTM-AZ-80X
V-B-1	ASTM-AZ-81
V-B-1	ASTM-AZ-91
V-B-1	ASTM-AZ-92
IV-A-4-a	ASTM-B83-46

Material Index Number	Material Name
V-B-3	ASTM-EK-30
V-B-3	ASTM-EK-32A
V-B-3	ASTM-EK-33A
V-B-3	ASTM-EK-41
V-B-3	ASTM-EZ-33A
V-B-4	ASTM-HK-31
V-B-4	ASTM-HK-31A
V-B-4	ASTM-HK-31XA
V-B-4	ASTM-HM-21XA
V-B-3	ASTM-HM-31XA
V-B-4	ASTM-HZ-32XA
V-B	ASTM-M1
VII-E-9	ASTM-No. 16 Insulating Firebrick
VII-E-9	ASTM-No. 20 Insulating Firebrick
VII-E-9	ASTM-No. 23 Insulating Firebrick
VII-E-9	ASTM-No. 26 Insulating Firebrick
VII-E-9	ASTM-No. 28 Insulating Firebrick
VII-E-9	ASTM-No. 30 Insulating Firebrick
IV-A-4-a	ASTM-No. B-83-46
V-B	ASTM-ZK-60A
I-A-6	At
II-D-3	A.T.S. (German)
I-G-3	Au
VI-A	Au_2Mn
VI-A	Au_3Cu
VI-A	Au + Ag + X
VI-A-1	Au + Cd + X
VI-A-2	Au + Co + Pd + X
VI-A	Au + Cu + X
VI-A	Au + Cu + Zn
VI-A	Au + Fe
VI-A-5	Au + Mn + X
VI-A-4	Au + Ni + X
VI-A-3	Au + Pd
VI-A-3	Au + Pd + Co + X
VI-A	Au + Pt
II-A-3, 5	Austenite
IX-G-4	AuTi
IX-G-4	$AuTi_3$
VI-A	Au + U
VI-A	Au + Zn + X
V-B-1	AX-81-8A Magnesium Alloy
V-B-1	AZ-31A Magnesium Alloy
V-B-1	AZ-61-X Magnesium Alloy

Material Index Number	Material Name
V-B-1	AZ-63A Magnesium Alloy
V-B-1	AZ-81 Cast Magnesium Alloy
V-B-1	AZ-92-A Magnesium Alloy
I-B-4	B
VII-A-13	B_2O_3
VII-C-2	B_2O_3
VII-D-2	B_4C
V-A-1	B 195 Aluminum Alloy
V-A-3	B 214 Aluminum Alloy
II-D-4	B-759 (German)
I-B-1	Ba
VII-B-6-e	Ba_2TiO_4
VII-B-7-b	$Ba\,Al_2O_4$
VII-B-2-a	$Ba\,CO_3$
VII-A-9-b	Baddeleyite
X-C-1	Bakelite BM-261
X-C-1	Bakelite BM-704
X-C-1	Bakelite BM-3510
X-C-1	Bakelite BM-14316
X-C-1	Bakelite BM-13014
X-C-1	Bakelite BM-13080
X-C-1	Bakelite BM-13335
X-C-1	Bakelite BM-14726
X-C-1	Bakelite-15140
X-C-1	Bakelite BM-16468
X-C-1	Bakelite BM-17711
X-C-1	Bakelite BM-17849
X-G	Bakelite Dynh
VII-E-3-g	Ball Clay
VII-A-13	BaO
VII-B-7-b	$BaO \cdot Al_2O_3$
VII-B-6-c	$BaO \cdot ZrO_2$
I-B-1	Barium
VII-B-6-e	Barium Beryllium Titanate
VII-C-2	Barium Borate Glass
VII-B-2-a	Barium Calcium Silicate
VII-C-1-k	Barium Crown Glass
VII-B-3-a	Barium Feldspar
VII-C-2	Barium Fluoborate Glass
VII-C-1-m	Barium Lead Silicate Glass
VII-B-6-e	Barium-Lead Titanate
VII-B-2-a	Barium Magnesium Silicate
VII-B-6-e	Barium Magnesium Titanate
VII-B-9	Barium Mica

Material Index Number	Material Name
VII-E-3-j	Barium Modified Magnesium Aluminosilicate
VII-A-13	Barium Oxide
VII-D-6	Barium Selenide
VII-B-2-a	Barium Silicate
VII-B-6-e	Barium-Strontium Titanate
IX-F-2	Barium Telluride
VII-B-6-e	Barium Titanate
VII-C-1-k	Barium Titanium Silicate Glass
VII-C	Barium Vanadate Glass
VII-C-5	Barium-Zinc-Borosilicate Glass
VII-B-6-c	Barium Zirconate
VII-D-6	BaSe
VII-E-10	Basic Brick
VII-C-3	Basic Phosphate Glass
VII-C-3	Basic Phosphate Glass + Neodymia
VII-E-10	Basic Refractory
VII-E-10	Basic Schamotte Brick
IX-F-2	BaTe
VII-B-6-e	$BaTiO_3$
VII-B-6-e	$BaTiO_4$
I-B-3	Be
IX-G-2 also IX-C	Be_2B
VII-D-3-a	Be_2C
IX-D	Be_3N_2
V-D	Be + Al + X
IX-C also IX-G-2	BeB
IX-G-2 also IX-C	BeB_6
X-C-3	Beetle
VII-D-5-a	BeF_2
VII-B-1	Bentonite
VII-A-2-a	BeO
VII-B-7-c	$BeO \cdot Al_2O_3$
VII-A-2	$BeO + Al_2O_3 + MgO + X$
VII-A-2	$BeO + Al_2O_3 + ThO_2 + MgO$
VII-A-2	$BeO + Al_2O_3 + ThO_2 + X$
VII-E-4	BeO Porcelain
VII-B-6	$BeO \cdot TiO_2$
VII-A-2	$BeO + UO_2 + X$
I-B-2	Berkelium
VI	Berkelium Intermetallics
VII-B-3-b	Beryl
VII-A-2-a	Beryllia
VII-A-2	Beryllia + Alumina + Magnesia + X

Material Index Number	Material Name
VII-A-2	Beryllia + Alumina + Thoria + Magnesia
VII-A-2	Beryllia + Alumina + Thoria + X
VII-A-2	Beryllia + Uranium Dioxide
IX-G-2	Beryllides
I-B-3	Beryllium
VII-B-7-c	Beryllium Aluminate
VII-B-3-b	Beryllium Alumino Silicate
V-D	Beryllium + Aluminum + X
V-D	Beryllium-Base Alloy
IX-C also IX-G-2	Beryllium Boride
VII-D-3	Beryllium Carbide
III-G	Beryllium Copper No. 175
VII-D-5-a	Beryllium Difluoride
VII-D-5-a	Beryllium Fluoride
VII-E-3-f	Beryllium Modified Magnesium Aluminosilicate
IX-D	Beryllium Nitride
VII-A-2-a	Beryllium Oxide
VIII-B-5	Beryllium Oxide Cermet
VIII-B-5	Beryllium Oxide Cermet-Beryllium Bonded
VIII-B-5	Beryllium Oxide Cermet-Beryllium + Molybdenum Bonded
VIII-B-5	Beryllium Oxide Cermet-Beryllium + Silicon Bonded
VIII-B-5	Beryllium Oxide Cermet-Niobium Bonded
VII-B-2-b	Beryllium Silicate
VII-D-6	Beryllium Sulfide
VII-B-6	Beryllium Titanate
VII-D-6	BeS
VII-B-6	$Be\,TiO_3$
I-B-2	Bk
VII-B	$Bi_2Sn_3O_9$
VII-B	$Bi_2(SnO_3)_3$
IX-F-2	Bi_2Te_3
VI	Bi_2U
VI	Bi_4U_3
VI	Bi_5U_4
IX-G	Binary Aluminide Systems
IX-C	Binary Boride Systems
VIII-A	Binary Carbide Cermets
IX-D	Binary Nitride Systems
IX-B	Binary Silicide Systems
VII-B-9	Biotite
VI	Bismuth-Base Alloys
VII-A-13	Bismuth Oxide
VII-B	Bismuth Stannate
IX-F-2	Bismuth Telluride
VI	Bismuth + Uranium

Material Index Number	Material Name
VI	BiU
VI	Bi + U
VII-B-9	Black Mica
VII-D-4	BN
VIII-E	Bonded Aluminum Titanate
XI-E	Boral Thermal Neutron Shield
VII-B-5	Borate
VII-C-2	Borate Glass
VII-B-5	Borax
VII-C-2	Borax Glass
IX-C	Boride Base Systems with Other Intermetallics
IX-C	Borides
IX-C	Borides of Aluminum and Iron-Aluminum
IX-C	Borides of Chromium
IX-C	Borides of Hafnium
IX-C	Borides of Molybdenum
IX-C	Borides of Niobium
IX-C	Borides of Tantalum
IX-C-2	Borides of Titanium
IX-C	Borides of Tungsten
IX-C	Borides of Vanadium
IX-C-3	Borides of Zirconium
IX-C	Boride Systems
VIII-C-1	Borolite
VIII-C-1	Borolite I, Grade F
VIII-C-1	Borolite I, Grade G
VIII-C-1	Borolite I, Grade S
I-B-4	Boron
VII-D-2	Boron Carbide
VIII-A	Boron Carbide Cermet
VIII-A	Boron Carbide Cermet-Iron Bonded
X-G	Boron Carbide Filled Teflon
IX-J-1	Boron-Chromium Intermetallic
IX-J-3	Boron-Hafnium Intermetallic
IX-H-7	Boron-Lanthanum Intermetallic
IX-J-4	Boron-Molybdenum Intermetallic
IX-J-6	Boron-Niobium Intermetallic
VII-D-4	Boron Nitride
VII-A-13	Boron Oxide
VIII-B	Boron Oxide Cermet
VII-C-2	Boron Oxide Glass
VII-B-5	Boron Phosphate
IX-J-7	Boron-Tantalum Intermetallic
VII-C-5	Borosilicate Crown Glass
VII-C-5	Borosilicate Glass

Material Index Number	Material Name
VII-E-7	Borosilicate Glass Bond
VII-A-13	Boric Oxide
I-C-3-1	Bort Diamond
III-A-1	Brass
III-A-3	Brass
III-A-3	Brass α phase
III-A-1	Brass, β phase
III-A-1	Brass, Free Cutting
III-A-1	Brass, Leaded
XI-B-3	Brazed Metal
VII-A-6	Brazilian Quartz
VI-C	Brazing Alloy GE-76
IV-A-5	Brazing Compound GEH-62V
VII-E-4	Brick
VII-A-2-a	Bromellite
III-B-1 also III-B-3	Bronze
III-E	Bronze, Aluminum
III-B-3	Bronze, Porous
VII-A-8	Brookite
X-J	Buna Rubber
X-J	Buna-S (GR-S)
VII-A-14	Bunsenite
I-J-2	Bureau of Standards Iron
I-C-7	Bus Bar Copper
X-J	Butadiene
X-J	Butadiene-Acrylonite Copolymer
X-J	Butadiene-Styrene Copolymer
X-J	Butyl GR-1
X-A-3	Butyrate
X	BV-17085
I-C-3	C
V-C-2	C 110M
V-A-1	C 113 Aluminum Alloy
V-C-1 also V-C-2	C-130 AM Titanium Alloy
I-C-1	Ca
VIII-A-1	CA-2
VII-B-8-d	$Ca_2Fe_2O_5$
VII-B-2-c	Ca_2SiO_4
VII-B-2-c	$Ca_3Si_2O_7$
VII-B-2-c	Ca_3SiO_5
VII-B-6-f	$Ca_3Ti_2O_7$
VIII-A-1	CA-4
VII-D-3	CaC_2
VII-B	$CaCO_3$

Material Index Number	Material Name
VII-C-1-m	Cadmium Lead Silicate Glass
IX-G-3	Cadmium-Magnesium Intermetallic
VII-A-13	Cadmium Oxide
VI	Cadmium + Silver + X
VII-D-6	Cadmium Sulfide
IX-F-2	Cadmium Telluride
VII-D-5-a	CaF_5
VII-B-8-d	$Ca\ Fe_2O_4$
VII-B-6-a	$Ca\ Hf\ O_3$
VII-A-3	Calcia
VII-A-3	Calcia + Titania
VII-A-3	Calcia + Titanium Dioxide
VII-A-5-a	Calcined Magnesite
I-C-1	Calcium
VII-B-7-d	Calcium Aluminate
VII-E-4	Calcium Aluminosilicate Glass Bond (Porcelain)
VII-B-3-c	Calcium-Aluminum Silicate
VII-B-5	Calcium Borate
VII-C-2	Calcium Borate Glass
X-G	Calcium Boride Filled Teflon
VII-D-3	Calcium Carbide
VII-B-3-c	Calcium Feldspar
VII-B-8-d	Calcium Ferrite
VII-B-6-a	Calcium Hafnate
VII-B-2-c	Calcium Magnesium Silicate
VII-B-6-f	Calcium Metatitanate
VII-E-3-g	Calcium Modified Magnesium Aluminosilicate
VII-B-2-c	Calcium Ortho-Silicate
VII-A-3	Calcium Oxide
VII-A-3	Calcium Oxide + Titanium Oxide
VII-B-2-c	Calcium Silicate
VII-B-5	Calcium Silico-Phosphate
VII-B	Calcium Stannate
VII-B-6-f	Calcium Titanate
VII-C	Calcium Uranate
VII-B-6-c	Calcium Zirconate
I-C-2	Californium
VI	Californium Intermetallics
VII-B-2-c	$Ca\ Mg\ (SiO_4)_2$
I-C-3	Canadian Natural Graphite Flake
VII-A-3	CaO
VII-B-7-d	$Ca\ O\ .\ 2\ Al_2O_3$
VII-B-5	$CaO\ .\ 2\ B_2O_3$
VII-B-7-d	$CaO\ .\ Al_2O_3$

Material Index Number	Material Name
VII-B-5	$CaO \cdot B_2O_3$
VII-B-8-d	$CaO \cdot Fe_2O_3$
VII-A-3	$CaO + TiO_2$
IX-A	Carbide Systems
VIII-A-1	Carbide Tool Steel CA-2
VIII-A-1	Carbide Tool Steel CA-4
VIII-A-1	Carbide Tool Steel Kennametal K-2S
VIII-A-1	Carbide Tool Steel Kennametal K-6
VIII-A-1	Carbide Tool Steel Kennametal K-138
VII-D-1-a	Carbofrax
VIII-A-1	Carboloy
VIII-A-1	Carboloy 44A
VIII-A-1	Carboloy 55A
I-C-3	Carbon
I-C-3-b	Carbon Block
II-C-6	Carbon-Chromium Tool Steel
I-C-3-b	Carbon Electrode
I-C-3-b	Carbon, Extruded Acheson Amorphous Carbon
I-C-3-c	Carbon, Extruded Acheson Graphite, Carbon Impregnated
I-C-3-a	Carbon, Extruded Acheson Graphite, Multicrystalline
I-C-3-h	Carbon, Pyrolytic
II-A	Carbon Steel
II-A-5 to 8	Carbon Tool Steel
II-C	Carbon-Vanadium Tool Steel
I-J-2	Carbonyl Iron
I-N-3	Carbonyl Nickel
VII-D-1-a	Carborundum
VII-B-3-c	Carnegiete
X-	Casein
VII-B	$Ca Sn O_3$
VII-A-15	Cassiterite
II-B	Cast Iron
II-B-2	Cast Iron, Gray Alloyed
II-B-1	Cast Iron, Gray Low Alloy
II-B-4	Cast Iron, White Alloyed
II-B-5	Cast Iron, Malleable Ferritic
II-B-6	Cast Iron, Malleable Pearlitic
II-B-7	Cast Iron, Nodular Ferritic
II-B-8	Cast Iron, Nodular Pearlitic
II-B-3	Cast Iron, White Low Alloy
IV-A-1	Cast Monel
IV-A	Cast Nickel
X-B	Castolite
X-C-1	Catalin

Material Index Number	Material Name
VII-B-6-f	$Ca\,TiO_3$
VII-C	$CaUO_4$
VII-B-6-c	$CaZrO_3$
I-N-4	Cb
VI	$Cd + Ag + X$
VII-A-13	CdO
I-C-4	Ce
IX-H-1	Ce_2Au
IX-H-1	Ce_2Pb
VII-D-6	Ce_2S_3
IX-H-1	Ce_2Sn
IX-H-1	Ce_2Sn_3
IX-H-1	Ce_2Tl
IX-G-1 also IX-H-1	Ce_3Al_2
VII-D-6	Ce_3S_4
IX-G-3 also IX-H-1	Ce_4Mg
IX-G-1 also IX-H-1	$Ce\,Al_4$
IX-H-1	$CeAg$
IX-H-1	$Ce\,Ag_2$
IX-H-1	$Ce\,Ag_3$
IX-G-1 also IX-H-1	$Ce\,Al$
IX-G-1 also IX-H-1	$Ce\,Al_2$
IX-G-1 also IX-H-1	$Ce\,Al_4$
IX-H-1	$Ce\,Au$
IX-H-1	$Ce\,Au_2$
IX-H-1	$Ce\,Au_3$
IX-C	$Ce\,B_4$
VII-D-5	$Ce\,Br_3$
VII-D-5	$Ce\,Cl_3$
IX-H-1	$Ce\,Cu$
IX-H-1	$Ce\,Cu_2$
IX-H-1	$Ce\,Cu_4$
IX-H-1	$Ce\,Cu_6$
X-J	Cellular Rubber Board No. 2266
X-A-5	Cellulose
X-A-1	Cellulose Acetate
X-A-3	Cellulose Acetate Butyrate
X-A-4	Cellulose Nitrate
XI-H-3	Cellulose Paper Reinforced Phenolic
X-A-2	Cellulose Propionate
IX-G-3 also IX-H-1	$Ce\,Mg$
IX-G-3 also IX-H-1	$Ce\,Mg_3$
IX-G-3 also IX-H-1	$Ce\,Mg_9$
VII-A-4-a	$Ce\,O_2$

Material Index Number	Material Name
VII-A-4-a	$Ce\,O_2 + UO_2$
IX-H-1	$Ce\,Pb_3$
XI-E	Ceramic Coated Mild Steel
VII-A-4-a	Ceria
VII-A-4-a	Ceria + Uranium Dioxide
VII-B-9	Cericite
I-C-4	Cerium
IX-G-1 also IX-H-1	Cerium Aluminide
IX-C	Cerium Boride
VII-D-5	Cerium Bromide
VII-D-5	Cerium Chloride
IX-H-1	Cerium Intermetallics
VI	Cerium + Iron + X
IX-G-3 also IX-H-1	Cerium-Magnesium Intermetallic
VII-A-4-a	Cerium Oxide
VII-A-4-a	Cerium Oxide + Uranium Oxide
VII-D-6	Cerium Sulfide
VI	Cerium + Zinc + Iron + X
VIII	Cermets
VIII-C	Cermets Containing Borides as Major Refractory Phase
VIII-A	Cermets Containing Carbides as Major Refractory Phase
VIII-F	Cermets Containing Hydrides as Major Refractory Phase
VIII-E	Cermets Containing Nitrides as Major Refractory Phase
VIII-B	Cermets Containing Oxides or Suboxides as Major Refractory Phase
VIII-D	Cermets Containing Silicides as Major Refractory Phase
VII-D-6	$Ce\,S$
VII-B-3-d	Cesium Alumino-Silicate
VII-E-3-e	Cesium Modified Magnesium Aluminosilicate
IX-H-1	$Ce\,Sn_3$
IX-H-1	$Ce\,Tl$
IX-H-1	$Ce\,Tl_3$
I-C-3-j	Ceylon Block Graphite
I-C-2	Cf
IV-B-1	CF-43
VII-A-13	CH. D. A Brand (Russian)
X-A-5	Chemaco 342
X-A-5	Chemaco 343
X-A-5	Chemaco 345
X-A-5	Chemaco 346
X-A-1	Chemaco SPZ-325
X-A-1	Chemaco SPZ-326
X-A-1	Chemaco SPZ-327
X-A-1	Chemaco SPZ-329
X-A-1	Chemaco SPZ-330

Material Index Number	Material Name
X-A-1	Chemaco SPZ-331
X-A-1	Chemaco SPZ-332
VII-E-4	China
VII-B-1	China Clay
X-G	Chlorotrifluoroethylene
VII-C-1-b	Chrome Green Container Glass
VII-E-10	Chrome Magnesite Brick
IV-A-5	Chromel A
IV-A-4	Chromel C
VII-B-8-a	Chrome Magnesia
I-C-5	Chrome Metal
VII-B	Chromite
I-C-5	Chromium
IX-G-1	Chromium Aluminide
IV-F	Chromium-Base Alloy
IX-C	Chromium Boride
IX-C	Chromium Boride + X
IX-A-3 also IX-J-1	Chromium Carbide
VIII-A-3	Chromium Carbide as Major Refractory Phase in Cermet
IX-C	Chromium Diboride
I-C-5	Chromium Flake, Electrolytic
IX-J-3	Chromium-Hafnium Intermetallic
II-C-7	Chromium Hotwork Tool Steel
IX-J-1	Chromium Intermetallic
IV-F	Chromium + Iron
IV-F	Chromium + Iron + Molybdenum + X
II-C-6	Chromium-Manganese Tool Steel
II-C-7	Chromium-Molybdenum Hotwork Tool Steel
IV-F	Chromium + Molybdenum + Iron + X
II-C-7	Chromium-Molybdenum-Manganese Tool Steel
VIII-D	Chromium-Molybdenum-Silicon Cermet
II-C-7	Chromium-Molybdenum Tool Steel
IV-F	Chromium + Molybdenum + X
IV-F-1	Chromium + Nickel + X
IX-J-6	Chromium-Niobium Intermetallic
IX-D	Chromium Nitride
VII-A-13	Chromium Oxide
VII-A-13	Chromium Oxide + Aluminum Oxide
VIII-B	Chromium Oxide Cermet, Cr_2Ti Bonded
VII-A-13	Chromium Oxide + Magnesium Oxide + Aluminum Oxide
IX-B	Chromium Silicide
VIII-D	Chromium Silicide Cermet-Chromium Bonded
VIII-D	Chromium Silicide Cermet-Kanthal Bonded
IX-J-7	Chromium-Tantalum Intermetallic

Material Index Number	Material Name
IV-F	Chromium + Tellurium + X
VIII	Chromium Titanide Cermet-Molybdenum Bonded
VIII-D	Chromium-Titanium-Silicon Cermet
II-C-6	Chromium Tool Steel
II-C-6 also II-C-8	Chromium-Tungsten Hotwork Tool Steel
IV-F	Chromium + Tungsten + Iron + Molybdenum
IV-F	Chromium + Tungsten + Iron + X
IV-F	Chromium + Tungsten + X
II-C-6	Chromium-Vanadium Stock Resisting Tool Steel
IV-F	Chronin
VII-B-7-c	Chrysoberyl
VII-E-6	Clay
I-C-8	Cm
IV-F	CM-469
I-C-6	Co
VII-A-13	Co_3O_4
I-C-7	Coalesced Copper
XI-D	Coated Alclad 24ST
XI-D	Coated Aluminum Alloy 24ST
XI-D-	Coated Aluminum Alloy 75ST
XI-D	Coated Dow Metal
XI-E	Coated Inconel
XI-E	Coated Magnesium Alloy
XI-E	Coated Metal, Aluminum Oxide
XI-E	Coated Molybdenum
XI-E	Coated Stainless Steel
IV-B	Co + Au
IV-B	Co + Au + Pd + X
I-C-6	Cobalt
II-D-3-a	Cobalt Alloy N-155
VII-B-7	Cobalt Aluminate
IV-B	Cobalt Base Alloy
IV-B-1	Cobalt + Chromium + Molybdenum + Nickel + Iron
IV-B-1	Cobalt + Chromium + Molybdenum + X
IV-B-1	Cobalt + Chromium + Nickel + Tungsten + Iron
IV-B-1	Cobalt + Chromium + Nickel + Vanadium + X
IV-B-1	Cobalt + Chromium + Nickel + X
IV-B-1	Cobalt + Chromium + Tungsten + Nickel + X
IV-B-1	Cobalt + Chromium + X
VII-B-8-m	Cobalt Ferrite
IV-B	Cobalt + Gold
IV-B	Cobalt + Gold + Platinum + X
IX-J-3 also IX-J-2	Cobalt-Hafnium Intermetallic

Material Index Number	Material Name
IX-J-2	Cobalt Intermetallic
IV-B-3	Cobalt + Iron + V
VII-C-1-m	Cobalt Lead Silicate Glass
IX-J-6	Cobalt-Niobium Intermetallic
VII-A-13	Cobalt Oxide
IX-J-7	Cobalt-Tantalum Intermetallic
IX-J-9	Cobalt-Tungsten Intermetallic
IX-J-2	Cobalt-Uranium Intermetallic
IX-J-11	Cobalt-Zirconium Intermetallic
IV-B-1	Co + Cr
IV-B-1	Co + Cr + X
IV-B-1	Co + Cr + Mo + Ni + Fe
IV-B-1	Co + Cr + Mo + X
IV-B-1	Co + Cr + Ni + V + X
IV-B-1	Co + Cr + Ni + W + Fe
IV-B-1	Co + Cr + Ni + X
IV-B-1	Co + Cr + W + Ni + X
IV-B-1	Co + Cr + W + X
IV-B	Co + Cu + Pd
IV-B	Co + Cu + Pd + X
IV B-3	Co + Fe
VII-B-8-m	$Co\ Fe_2O_4$
IV-B-3	Co + Fe + Cr + Ni + X
IV-B-3	Co + Fe + Cr + X
IV-B-3	Co + Fe + X
I-C-3	Coke
VII-E-11	Coke Oven Silica Brick
VII-B-5	Colemanite
I-A-2	Commercially Pure Aluminum
XI-C	Composite Ceramic Material
XI-E	Composite Metallic-Ceramic Material
XI-B	Composite Metallic Material
XI-F	Composite Organic-Ceramic Materials; Sandwich Structures
XI-A-1, 2	Composite Organic Material
XI-A-1	Composite Organic Materials; Sandwich Structures
XI-G	Composite Organic-Metallic-Ceramic Materials
XI-G	Composite Organic-Metallic-Ceramic Materials;Sandwich Structures
XI-D-1, 2, 3	Composite Organic-Metallic Materials; Sandwich Structures
XI-D-1, 2, 3	Composite Organic-Metallic Material
I-C-3-1	Commercial Diamond Powder
XI-B-5	Clad Metal
IV-B-2	Co + Ni + X
X-C	Conolon 506
XI-H-3	Conolon N-1 Laminate

Material Index Number	Material Name
VII-C-1	Container Glass
IV-A-4	Contracid
VII-A-13	CoO
VII-B-7	$CoO \cdot Al_2O_3$
VII-A-13	CoO - CuO Inverse Spinel
VII-B-8-m	$CoO \cdot Fe_2O_3$
VII-A-13	CoO - Ni_2O Inverse Spinel
IV-B-4	CO + Pd + Au + X
IV-B-4	Co + Pd + Cu + X
X	Copolymer
XI-H-3	Copolymer of Phenolic and Epoxideresins Reinforced
X-A-8	Copolyvinyl Chloride-Acetate
I-C-7	Copper
III-E	Copper + Aluminum + X
III	Copper Base Alloy
III-G	Copper + Beryllium + X
IX-H-1	Copper-Cerium Intermetallic
I-C-7	Copper, Electrolytic Tough Pitch
VII-B-8	Copper Ferrite
III	Copper + Iron
IX-H-7	Copper-Lanthanum Intermetallic
III-C	Copper + Lead + X
III-H	Copper + Manganese + X
III-D	Copper + Nickel + X
VII-A-13	Copper Oxide
IX-H-10	Copper-Praseodymium Intermetallic
III-F	Copper + Silicon + X
III	Copper + Silver + X
III-B-3	Copper + Tin
III	Copper + Titanium
III	Copper + Uranium
III-A-3	Copper + Zinc
III-A	Copper + Zinc + X
III-L	Copper + Zirconium
VII-E-3	Cordierite
VII-E-3	Cordierite 202
VII-E-3	Cordierite Body
VII-C-1-b	Corning 0080 Soda-Lime-Silica Glass
VII-C-1-m	Corning 0120 Lead Silicate Glass
VII-C-1	Corning 1723 Aluminum Silicate Glass
VII-C-5	Corning 7740 Borosilicate Glass
VII-C-6	Corning 7940 Silica Glass
XI-C	Corning E. C. Coaton 1722 Glass
VII-A-1-a	Corundum

Material Index Number	Material Name
XI-H-4	Cotton Fabric Reinforced Diallyl Phthalate
XI-H-2	Cotton Fabric Reinforced Melamine Formaldehyde
XI-H-3	Cotton Fabric Reinforced Phenolic
XI-H-3	Cotton Fabric Reinforced Phenol Formaldehyde
IX-J-2	CoU
IX-J-2	CoU_6
VII-D also IX	Covalent Ceramic Structures
I-C-5	Cr
VII-A-13	Cr_2O_3
VII-A-13	$Cr_2O_3 + Al_2O_3$
VII-A-13	$Cr_2O_3 + MgO + Al_2O_3$
IX-A-3 also IX-J-1	Cr_3C_2
IX-B	Cr_3Si
IX-G-1	Cr Al
IX-C also IX-J-1	Cr B
IX-C also IX-J-1	$Cr B_2$
IX-C	$Cr B_2 + Ti B_2$
IX-C	$Cr B_2 + VB_2$
X-C	Cresol Resin
IV-F	Cr + Fe + Mo + X
IV-F	Cr + Fe + X
IV-F-2	Cr + Mo + Fe + X
IV-F-2	Cr + Mo + X
IV-F-1	Cr + Ni + Mo + X
IV-F-1	Cr + Ni + X
VII-C-1-k	Crown Glass
IX-B	Cr Si
IV-F	Cr + W + Fe + Mo
IV-F	Cr + W + Fe + X
IV-F	Cr + W + X
I-T-6	Crystal Bar Titanium
VII-B-3-e	Crystalline Lithium Aluminosilicate
VII-A-6	Crystobalite
I-C-7	Cu
VI-A	Cu_3Au
III	Cu + Ag + X
III-E	Cu + Al
VI-A	$Cu Au_3$
III-G	Cu + Be
III	Cu + Co + Pd
III-K	Cu + Cr
III	Cu + Fe
III	Cu + Ge
III-H	Cu + Mg
III-H	Cu + Mn

209

Material Index Number	Material Name
III-H	Cu + Mn + Ni + X
III-D	Cu + Ni
III-D	Cu + Ni + Be
VII-A-13	Cu O
VII-B-8	Cu O . Fe_2O_3
III	Cu + P
III-C	Cu + Pb
III	Cu + Pd
III	Cu + Pd + Co
III	Cu + Pt
I-C-8	Curium
VI	Curium Intermetallics
III-F	Cu + Si
III-B-3	Cu + Sn
III-B-1	Cu + Sn + Pb
III-B	Cu + Sn + X
III-B-2	Cu + Sn + Zn
III-J	Cu + Te
III	Cu + Ti
III	Cu + U
III-A-3	Cu + Zn
III-A	Cu + Zn + Ni
III-A-1	Cu + Zn + Pb
III-A-2	Cu + Zn + Sn
III-A	Cu + Zn + X
III-L	Cu + Zr
VII-D-2	D-11, 776-2 Boron Carbide
VII-D-2	D-11, 798-1 Boron Carbide
XI-H-6	DC-301 Silicone - Glass Fiber Filled
VII-A-5-a	Deadburned Magnesite
VII-C-1-m	Dense Flint Glass
I-C-7	Deoxidized Copper
XI-H-4	Di all-50-01
XI-H-4	Diall-50-51
XI-H-4	Diall-50-52
XI-H-4	Diall-52-01
XI-H-4	Diall-52- 20-30
XI-H-4	Diallyl Phtalate, Reinforced
I-C-3-1	Diamond
I-C-3-1	Diamond Powder
X-C	Diboride of ..
II-A-3	Die Iron Tool Steel
X-A-9	Diisocyanate Polyester Elastomer
X-J	Dimethyl Siloxane Polymer
VII-B-2-c	Diopside

Material Index Number	Material Name
IV-A	D-Nickel
VII-B	Dolomite
X	Dow Corning R-7001
X	Dow Corning R-7002
X	Dow Corning R-7091
XI-D	Dowmetal-Alcyd Base Lacquer Coated
V-B-1	Dowmetal C
V-B-1	Dowmetal FS-1
V-B-1	Dowmetal J
V-B	Dowmetal M, Contains Mn
XI-D	Dowmetal-Silicone Coated
XI-D	Dowmetal-Varnish Base Lacquer Coated
I-C-5	Ductile Chromium
V-A-1	Duralite
V-A-1	Duralumin
X-C	Dures 16274 Mineral Filled Phenolic
XI-H-4	Dures 16694
XI-H-1	Duroid 5600
II-D-6	DVL-4/V 869 (German)
II-D-3	DVL-30 (German)
II-D-6	DVL-31 (German)
IV-A-3-a	DVL-32 (German)
II-D-3-a	DVL-46 (German)
II-D-3-a	DVL-47 (German)
II-D-3-a	DVL-48 (German)
II-D-3-a	DVL-49 (German)
II-D-3-a	DVL-50 (German)
II-D-3	DVL-51 (German)
II-D-3	DVL-52 (German)
IV-A-3-a	DVL-321a (German)
IV-A-3-a	DVL-321i (German)
IV-A-3-a	DVL-325a (German)
I-D-1	Dy
VII-A-4-b	Dy_2O_3
XI-H-5	Dynakon Rod F
XI-H-5	Dynakon Sheet A-3
VII-A-4-b	Dysprosia
I-D-1	Dysprosium
IX-H-2	Dysprosium Intermetallics
VII-A-4-b	Dysprosium Oxide
I-E-1	E
II-C-1	E-2512 Low Alloy Steel
II-C-1	E-2517 Low Alloy Steel
VII-E-4	Earthenware
XI-C	E. C. Coat on Corning 1722 Glass
X	Eccofoam LM
V-B-2	Eclipsaloy 130
VII-E-3-g	Edgar Plastic Kaolin
I-E-1	Einsteinium

Material Index Number	Material Name
VI	Einsteinium Intermetallics
V-B-3	EK-30A Magnesium Alloy
V-B-3	EK-32-A Magnesium Alloy
V-B-3	EK-33-A Magnesium Alloy
V-B-3	EK-41 Cast Magnesium Alloy
VII-E-4	Electrical Porcelain
II-D-6	Electric Resistance Alloy
II-D-4	Electric Resistance Alloy Furnace Element
XI-C	Electroconducting Glass 547-26
XI-C	Electroconducting Glass LOF-81-E-19778
XI-C	Electroconducting Glass LOF-PB-19195
I-C-3	Electrode Carbon
I-....	Electrolytic.... see ......
I-C-5	Electrolytic Chromium
I-C-5	Electrolytic Flake Chromium
I-J-2	Electrolytic Iron
I-N-3	Electrolytic Nickel
I-C-7	Electrolytic Tough Pitch Copper
I-N-3	Electronickel
II-D-3	EME
VII-A-1-a	Emery
II-C-1	EN-8 (British)
II-C-6	EN-19 (British)
II-C-6	EN-31 (British)
XI-E	Enamel Coated Inconel
II-C-6	Enduro 18-8B Steel
VII-B-2-e	Enstatite
VII-E-3-g	EPK Clay
XI-H-3	Epon, Reinforced
X-D	Epon Resin
XI-H-7	Epon Resin 828, Glass Reinforced
X-D	Epoxide
XI-H-7	Epoxide, Reinforced
I-E-2	Er
VII-A-4-c	Erbia
I-E-2	Erbium
IX-H-3	Erbium Intermetallics
VII-A-4-C	Erbium Oxide
X-A-5	Ethyl Cellulose
I-E-3	Eu
VII-A-4-d	Eu_2O_3
VII-B-3-b	Euclase
VII-B-3-e	Eucryptite
VII-E-6	Eucryptite, Fired
VII-A-4-d	Europia

Material Index Number	Material Name
I-E-3	Europium
IX-H-4	Europium Intermetallics
VII-A-4-d	Europium Oxide
IV-A-5	Evanohm
VII-D-1-a	Exolon Type Si C
X-A-1	Expanded Cellulose Acetate
I-C-3-h	EYX 4 Pyrolytic Carbon
V-B-3	EZ - 33-A Magnesium Alloy
IV-A-5	F-342
IV-B-1	F-484
XI-H-7	Fabric Reinforced Epoxide
XI-H-3	Fabric Reinforced Phenolic
II-D-9	FCM (German)
I-J-2	Fe
VII-B-7	$Fe_2O_3 \cdot 2\ Al_2O_3$
VII-B-8-d	$Fe_2O_3 \cdot CaO$
VII-B-8-m	$Fe_2O_3 \cdot CoO$
VII-B-8	$Fe_2O_3 \cdot CuO$
VII-B-8-a	$Fe_2O_3 \cdot MgO$
VII-B-8-n	$Fe_2O_3 \cdot NiO$
VII-B-8-p	$Fe_2O_3 \cdot ZnO$
VII-B-2-d	$Fe_2\ SiO_4$
IX-A	$Fe_3\ C$
VII-A-13	Fe_3O_4
II-C	Fe + Al, 0-10% Al
VII-B-7	$Fe\ Al_2\ O_4$
II-D-7	Fe + Al, 10-50% Al
II-C	Fe + Al + Cr
II-D-9	FCM (German)
II-D	Fe + Co
VII-B-8	$Fe\ Co_2O_4$ Spinel
II-D	Fe + Co + Cr + Ni
II-C	Fe + Co Low Alloy Steel
II-C-6	Fe + Cr, 0-10% Cr
II-D-1	Fe + Cr, 10-50% Cr
II-D-4	Fe + Cr + Al
II-D-4	Fe + Cr + Co
II-D-4	Fe + Cr + Mn + Si
II-D-4	Fe + Cr + Mn + X
II-C-7	Fe + Cr + Mo + X, Low Alloy
II-D-2	Fe + Cr + Ni
II-D-3	Fe + Cr + Ni + Al
II-D-3	Fe + Cr + Ni + B + X
II-D-3-a	Fe + Cr + Ni + Co + X
II-D-3	Fe + Cr + Ni + Mn

Material Index Number	Material Name
II-D-3	Fe + Cr + Ni + Mo
II-D-3	Fe + Cr + Ni + Nb
II-D-3	Fe + Cr + Ni + Ti
II-D-3	Fe + Cr + Ni + X (X ≠ O)
II-D-3	Fe + Cr + Ni + W + X
II-D-4	Fe + Cr + Si
II-D-4	Fe + Cr + V + X
II-C-6	Fe + Cr + X, Low Alloy
II-D-4	Fe + Cr + X (X, ≠ O, Ni) High Alloy
II-D	Fe + Cu + Graphite Anti-Friction Alloy
III-E	Fed. Spec. QQ-B-667 Composition 3
III-E	Fed. Spec. QQ-B-667 Composition 5
I-C-7	Fed. Spec. QQ-C-502 Tough Pitch Copper
I-C-7	Fed. Spec. QQ-C-576 Electrolytic Tough Pitch Copper
VII-B-3	Feldspar
VII-E-6	Feldspar Porcelain
II-D-9	Fe + Mn, High Alloy
II-C	Fe + Mn, Low Alloy
II-D-9	Fe + Mn + Cr
II-D-9	Fe + Mn + Cr + Mo + Ni + X
II-D	Fe + Mo + X, High Alloy
II-C-5	Fe + Mo, Low Alloy
II-C-5	Fe + Mo + Cr
II-D-9	Fe + Mn + Cr + Si
II-D-9	Fe + Mn + Cr + X
II-D-9	Fe + Mn + Ni + X
II-D-9	Fe + Mn + X
II-D-5	Fe + Ni, High Alloy
II-C-1	Fe + Ni, Low Alloy
II-D-5	Fe Ni - 36 (German)
II-D-6	Fe + Ni + Al
II-D-6	Fe + Ni + Co + X
II-D-6-a	Fe + Ni + Cr
II-D-6-a	Fe + Ni + Cr + Co
II-D-6-a	Fe + Ni + Cr + Mo
II-D-6-a	Fe + Ni + Cr + Ti + X
II-D-6-a	Fe + Ni + Cr + W
II-D-6-a	Fe + Ni + Cr + X, High Alloy
II-C-2	Fe + Ni + Cr + X, Low Alloy
II-D-6	Fe + Ni + Mn + Cr
II-D-6	Fe + Ni + Mn + X
II-C-4	Fe + Ni + X, Low Alloy
II-D-6	Fe + Ni + X (X ≠ O), High Alloy
VII-A-13	Fe O

Material Index Number	Material Name
VII-B-7	$FeO \cdot Al_2O_3$
VII-B-8	$FeO \cdot Co_2O_3$ Spinel
II-D	$Fe + Pt$
I-F-1	Fermium
VII-B-8-n, p	Ferramic E Nickel-Zinc Ferrite Spinel
VII-B-8	Ferrite Spinel
II-B-5	Ferritic Malleable Cast Iron
II-B-7	Ferritic Nodular Cast Iron
I-F-1	Fermium
VI	Fermium Intermetallics
IV-D	Ferromolybdenum
IV-C	Ferrotungsten
VII-B-2-d	Ferrous Silicate
II-C also IV-G	Ferrovanadium
II-D	$Fe + Si$, High Alloy
II-C-9	$Fe + Si$, Low Alloy
II-B-8	$Fe + Si$, Nodular Cast Iron
II-C	$Fe + Te$
IX-F-2	$Fe Te_2$
IX-G-4	$Fe Ti$
VII-B-6-g	$Fe TiO_3$
II-D	$Fe + V$, High Alloy
II-C	$Fe + V$, Low Alloy
II-D-8	$Fe + W$
II-D-8	$Fe + W + Cr$, High Alloy
II-C-8	$Fe + W + Cr$, Low Alloy
II-D-8	$Fe + W + X$
VII-B-1	Fiber Cermet
XI-H-3	Fiberite 4030-190 Glass Fiber Reinforced Phenolic
X-C	Filled Phenolic Resin
X-F	Filled Polymethyl Methacrylate
X-G	Filled Teflon
II-C-8	Finishing Tool Steel
IV-A-5	Firearmor
XI-E	Fired Enamel on Inconel
VII-E-3	Fired Magnesium Alumino-Silicate
VII-E-3-c	Fired Steatite
VI-F-2	Fissium Alloy
I-B-3	Flake Beryllium
I-C-5	Flake Chromium, Electrolytic
I-C-3	Flake Graphite
I-M-2	Flake Manganese
XI-E	Flame Sprayed Zirconia on Inconel

Material Index Number	Material Name
VII-A-6	Flint
VII-C-1-b	Flint Container Glass
VII-C-1-b	Flint Glass
VII-E-3	Florida Kaolin
VII-C	Fluoborate Glass
VII-D-5-a	Fluorides
X-G	Fluorothene
VII-D-5-a	Fluorite
I-F-1	Fm
X-A-9	Foam
XI-A-1	Foam Sandwich Panel
X-C	Formaldehyde
X-E	Formaldehyde, Melamine
XI-H-2	Formaldehyde, Reinforced Melamine
VII-E-10 also VII-B-2-e	Forsterite
X-A-2	Forticel 28227
X-A-2	Forticel 28238
I-F-2	Fr
I-F-2	Francium
III-A-1	Free Cutting Leaded Brass
II-D-2	Free Cutting Stainless Steel AISI-303
III-J	Free Cutting Te Copper
V-B-1	FS-1 Magnesium Alloy
X-C-2	Furfural Formaldehyde
X-C-2	Furfural Formaldehyde, Wood Flour Filled
VII-A-1-a	Fused Alumina
VII-C-2	Fused Boric Oxide
VII-C-6	Fused Quartz
VII-C-6	Fused Silica
XI-B-3	Fusion Bonded Metal Layers
II-D-3-a	G-18B Steel, Jessop (British)
IV-A-5	G-157
VII-A-13	Ga_2O_3
VII-A-4-e	Gadolinia
I-G-1	Gadolinium
IX-C	Gadolinium Boride
IX-H-5	Gadolinium Intermetallic
VII-A-4-e	Gadolinium Oxide

Material Index Number	Material Name
VII-A-13	Gallium Oxide
VII	Gallium Phosphide
IX-F-2	Gallium Telluride
V-A-2-b	Gamma, Alpax Aluminum Alloy (British)
I-C-3-b	Gas Baked Coke, Indexrod Extruded Acheson Amorphous Carbon
I-C-1	Gd
IX-C	$Gd\ B_6$
VII-A-4-e	$Gd_2\ O_3$
I-G-2	Ge
IV-A-5	GE-62 Brazing Alloy
VI-C	GE-76 Brazing Alloy
IV-A-2	GE-B-129
IV-A-5	GEH-62 V Brazing Compound
VII-C	Gels
I-C-3-1	Gem Quality Diamond
VI	Germanides
I-G-2	Germanium
VII-D	Germanium Carbide
VII-A-13	Germanium Dioxide
IX-J-6	Germanium-Niobium Intermetallic
VII-A-13	Germanium Oxide
VII-C	Germanium Oxide Glass
VI	Germanium + Silicon + X
VII-B-5	Gerstly Borate
VI	Ge + Si + X
XI-J	Glass Bonded Mica
XI-J	Glass Bonded Synthetic Mica
XI-H-3	Glass Fabric Reinforced Copolymer
XI-H-4	Glass Fabric Reinforced Diallyl Phthalate
XI-H-7	Glass Fabric Reinforced Epoxide
XI-H-2	Glass Fabric Reinforced Melamine Formaldehyde
XI-H-3	Glass Fabric Reinforced Phenolic
XI-H-5	Glass Fabric Reinforced Polyester
XI-H-6	Glass Fabric Reinforced Silicone
XI-H-5	Glass Fabric Reinforced Tac Polyester
XI-H-6	Glass Fiber Filled Silicone
XI-H-3	Glass Fiber Reinforced Phenolic Fiberite 4030-190
XI-H-5	Glass Fiber Reinforced Polyester
VII-C-2	Glassy Boron Sesquioxide
VII-D-1-a	Globar Recrystallized Silicon Carbide

Material Index Number	Material Name
X-J	GMGA-5003
I-G-3	Gold
VI-A	Gold-Base Alloy
VI-A-1	Gold + Cadmium + X
IX-H-1	Gold-Cerium Intermetallic
VI-A-2	Gold + Cobalt + Palladium + X
VI-A	Gold + Copper
VI-A	Gold + Copper + Palladium + X
VI-A	Gold + Copper + Zinc
VI-A	Gold + Platinum
VI-A	Gold + Copper + Silver + X
VI-A	Gold + Copper + X
IX-H-7	Gold-Lanthanum Intermetallic
VI-A	Gold + Iron
VI-A-5	Gold + Manganese + X
VI-A	Gold + Nickel + Copper + Zinc + X
VI-A-4	Gold + Nickel + X
VI-A-3	Gold + Palladium
VI-A-3	Gold + Palladium + Cobalt + X
IX-H-10	Gold-Praseodymium Intermetallic
VI-A	Gold + Silver + X
VI-A	Gold + Silver + Copper + Nickel + Zinc
VI-A	Gold + Silver + Platinum + X
VI-A	Gold + Uranium
VI-A	Gold + Zinc + X
X-A-10	Goodyear Foam-Inplace
IX-A-3 and IX-J-1	Grade 608 Cr_3C_2
I-C-3-a	Grade A, Artificial Extruded Acheson Graphite
I-N-3	Grade A Nickel
I-C-3-a	Grade B, Artificial Extruded Acheson Graphite
I-C-3-d	Grade C, Artificial Molded Graphite
I-C-3-a	Grade CS Extruded Acheson Graphite
IV-A	Grade Z Duranickel, contains Al
I-C-3	Graphite
XI-C	Graphite Coated with Silicon Carbide
I-C-3-n	Graphite Crystal
XI-C	Graphite-Graphite Joint
I-C-3-h	Graphite, Pyrolytic
XI-C	Graphite-Uranium Oxide Joint
II-B-1	Gray Cast Iron

Material Index Number	Material Name
II-B-2	Gray Cast Iron, Alloyed
II-B-1	Gray Cast Iron - Ferritic
II-B-1	Gray Cast Iron, Low Alloy
II-B-1	Gray Cast Iron, Pearlitic
II-B-1	Gray Cast Iron, Unalloyed
XI-D	Green Camouflage Paint on Alclad 2024
VII-C-1-b	Green Container Glass
II-D-9	Hadfields Chromium-Manganese Steel
II-D-9	Hadfields Manganese Steel
VII-B-6-a	Hafnate
VII-B-6	Hafnates; Niobates; Titanates; Zirconates
VII-A-9-a	Hafnia
VII-A-9-a	Hafnia + Tantalum Pentoxide
I-H-1	Hafnium
IV-K	Hafnium, Alloyed
IV-K	Hafnium-Base Alloy
IX-C-3	Hafnium Boride
IX-A-4	Hafnium Carbide
IX-J-1 also IX-J-3	Hafnium-Chromium Intermetallic
IX-J-2 also IX-J-3	Hafnium-Cobalt Intermetallic
IX-C-3 also IX-J-3	Hafnium Diboride
VII-A-9-a	Hafnium Dioxide
IX-E-2	Hafnium Hydride
IX-J-3	Hafnium Intermetallic
IX-J-3	Hafnium-Iron Intermetallic
IX-J-3	Hafnium-Manganese Intermetallic
IX-J-3 also IX-J-4	Hafnium-Molybdenum Intermetallic
IX-J-5 also IX-J-3	Hafnium-Nickel Intermetallic
IX-D-3	Hafnium Nitride
VII-A-9-a	Hafnium Oxide
VII-A-9-a	Hafnium Oxide + Tantalum Oxide
VII-A-9-a	Hafnium Oxide-Stabilized
VII-A-9-a	Hafnium Oxide-Unstabilized
VII-B-4-a	Hafnium Silicate
IX-J-3 also IX-J-10	Hafnium-Vanadium Intermetallic
VII-B-4-a	Hafnon
VII-D-5	Halides and Oxyhalides
X-G	Halogenated Polyethylene
X-A-10	Hamilton Standard Foam-in-Place
X-J	Hard Cellular Rubber Board No. 2266

Material Index Number	Material Name
X-J	Hard Rubber
X-J	Hard Rubber Board No. 2266
IV-A-6	Haskins Alloy 667
IV-A-2	Hastelloy A
IV-A-2	Hastelloy B
IV-A-2 also IV-A-5	Hastelloy C
IV-A	Hastelloy D, Contains Si
IV-A-5	Hastelloy X, Contains Fe
IV-A-5	Hastelloy R
IV-A-5-a	Hastelloy R-235
IV-A-2	Hastelloy W
IV-A-5-a	Hastelloy X
IV-B-1	Haynes Alloy No. 25, Contains W
IV-B-1	Haynes Alloy No. 36, Contains Ni
	Haynes Stellite....see Stellite ...
IV-B-1	HE-1049
II-D-7	Heat Resisting Alloy
IV-C	Heavy Alloy
VII-B-5	Hebronite
I-H-1 see also IV-K	Hf
IX-C-3 also IX-J-3	$Hf B_2$
IX-A-4	$Hf C$
IX-J-2 also IX-J-3	$Hf Co_2$
IX-J-1 also IX-J-3	$Hf Cr_2$
IX-J-3	$Hf Fe_2$
II-D-2	HF Grade Alloy
IX-J-3	$Hf Mn_2$
IX-J-3 als IX-J-4	$Hf Mo_2$
IX-J-3	$Hf Ni_2$
VII-A-9-a	$Hf O_2$
VII-A-9-a	$Hf O_2 + Ta_2 O_5$
IX-J-3 also IX-J-10	$Hf V_2$
II-C-6	HGT - 3 Steel (British)
VII-B-3-e	Hiddenite
II-D	High Alloy Steel
VII-E-3	High Aluminum Magnesium Alumino-Silicate
IV-F	High Carbon Ferrochromium
II-D-4	High Chromium High-Carbon Cold Work Tool Steel
II-C-2	High-Chromium, Nickel Tool Steel
II-D-1	High Chromium Tool Steel

Material Index Number	Material Name
II-C-9	High Silicon, Manganese Shock Resisting Tool Steel
II-C-5	High Speed Steel M-10
II-C-5	High Speed Steel M-1
II-C-8	High Speed Steel M-2
II-D-8	High Speed Steel (Ti)
VII-E-4	High Tension Electrical Porcelain
II-C-5	High Speed Tool Steel
VII-B-2-c	Hillebrandite
IV-A-4	Hipernik
I-H-2	Ho
I-H-2	Holmium
IX-H-6	Holmium Intermetallic
VII-A-4-f	Holmium Oxide
XI-A-1	Honeycomb Sandwich Panel
VII-B-1	Hornblende
XI-B-3	Hot Dipped Metal
II-C-6 also II-C-7	Hot Work Tool Steel
X	Hycar PA-21
I-C-5	Hydride Process Chromium
IX-E	Hydrides
IX-E	Hydride Systems
I-J-2	Hydrogen-Purified Iron
V-A-3	Hydronalium 5 Aluminum Alloy (German)
V-A-3	Hydronalium 7 (German)
V-A-3	Hydronalium 51 (German)
V-B-2	Hydronalium 71 Magnesium Alloy (German)
IV-A-4	Hyperm
X-D	Hysol 6000-OP
IV-B-1	I-336
X	Igelit - PCU, Polyvinyl Chloride Resin
VII-B-9	Illite
IV-A-5	Illium Alloy
IV-A-5	Illium D
IV-B-1	Illium G
IV-A-5	Illium R
IV-B-1	Illium X
VII-B-6-g	Ilmenite
IX-F	In As
IV-A-5-a	Inconel, Contains Fe
IV-A-5-a	Inconel B

Material Index Number	Material Name
XI-D	Inconel with Aluminum Paint
IV-A-5-a	Inconel - X
XI-E	Inconel-Zirconia Coated
I-C-3-b	Index Rod Extruded Acheson Amorphous Carbon
IX-F-1	Indium Antimonide
IX-F	Indium Arsenide
I-C-3-1	Industrial Diamond
I-J-2	Ingot Iron
IV-A-2	INOR- 8
VII-F	Inorganic Cements and Adhesives
I-S-4	Inquartation Silver
IX-F-1	In Sb
VII-E-9	Insulating Brick
XI-H-3	Insurok - C - T -601
XI-H-3	Insurok XXX - T - 640
IX	Intermetallics as Intermediate Phases in Binary Metal-Non-Metal Systems
IX	Intermetallics as Intermediate Phases in Binary Metal-Metal Systems
IX	Intermetallics as Intermediate Phases in Ternary or Higher Order Metal-Non Metal Systems
IX	Intermetallics as Intermediate Phases in Ternary or Higher Order Metallic Systems
IX-G	Intermetallics of a Light Metal (Al, Be, Mg, Ti)
IX-H	Intermetallics of a Rare Earth (Atomic Numbers 57-71)
IX-J	Intermetallics of a Refractory Metal (Cr, Co, Hf, Mo, Ni, Nb, Ta, Th, W, V, Zr)
IX-H-1	Intermetallics of Cerium
IX-J-1	Intermetallics of Chromium
IX-J-2	Intermetallics of Cobalt
VI	Intermetallics of Germanium
IX-J-3	Intermetallics of Hafnium
II	Intermetallics of Iron
IX-H-7	Intermetallics of Lanthanum
IX-G-3	Intermetallics of Magnesium
VI	Intermetallics of Manganese
IX-J-4	Intermetallics of Molybdenum
IX-J-5	Intermetallics of Nickel
IX-J-6	Intermetallics of Niobium
IX-H-10	Intermetallics of Praseodymium
VI	Intermetallics of Rhenium
IX-J-7	Intermetallics of Tantalum

Material Index Number	Material Name
IX-J-8	Intermetallics of Thorium
IX-G-4	Intermetallics of Titanium
IX-J-9	Intermetallics of Tungsten
VI-F or IX	Intermetallics of Uranium
IX-J-10	Intermetallics of Vanadium
IX-J-11	Intermetallics of Zirconium
II-D-6 also II-D-5	Invar
I-T-6	Iodide Process Titanium
I-Z-1	Iodide Process Zirconium
I-T-6	Iodide Titanium
I-Z-1	Iodide Zirconium
I-J-1	Ir
I-J-1	Iridium
I-J-2	Iron
VII-B-7	Iron Aluminate Spinel
IX-G-1	Iron Aluminide
II-C	Iron + Aluminum, 0-10% Al
II-D-7	Iron + Aluminum, 10-50% Al
IX-C	Iron-Aluminum Boride
II-C	Iron + Aluminum + Chromium
II	Iron Base Alloy
II-C	Iron-Base, Porous Sintered Material
II-C	Iron-Base, Sintered Porous Material
IX-A	Iron Carbide
II-C-6	Iron + Chromium, 0-10% Cr
II-D-1	Iron + Chromium, 10-50% Cr
II-D-2	Iron-Chromium Corrosion Resistant Casting
II-D-4	Iron + Chromium + Manganese + Silicon
II-D-4	Iron + Chromium + Manganese + X
II-C-7	Iron + Chromium + Molybdenum + X
II-D-2	Iron + Chromium + Nickel
II-D-3	Iron + Chromium + Nickel + Aluminum
II-D-3	Iron + Chromium + Nickel + Boron + X
II-D-3-a	Iron + Chromium + Nickel + Cobalt + X
II-D-3	Iron-Chromium-Nickel Corrosion Resistant Casting
II-D-3	Iron + Chromium + Nickel + Molybdenum
II-D-3	Iron + Chromium + Nickel + Niobium
II-D-3	Iron + Chromium + Nickel + Tungsten + X
II-D-3	Iron + Chromium + Nickel + X

Material Index Number	Material Name
II-D-4	Iron + Chromium + Silicon
II-D-4	Iron + Chromium + Vanadium + X
II-D-4	Iron + Chromium + X, High Alloy
II-C-6	Iron + Chromium + X, Low Alloy
II-D	Iron + Cobalt + Chromium + Nickel
VII-B-8	Iron Cobaltite
II-D	Iron + Cobalt + X, High Alloy
IX-F-2	Iron Ditelluride
X-G	Iron Filled Teflon
II-C	Iron + Graphite Antifriction Alloy
IX-J-3	Iron-Hafnium Intermetallic
II	Iron Intermetallic
VII-C-1-m	Iron Lead Silicate Glass
II-D-9	Iron + Manganese + Chromium + Molybdenum + Nickel + X
II-D-9	Iron + Manganese + Chromium + Silicon
II-D-9	Iron + Manganese + Chromium + X
II-D-9	Iron + Manganese, High Alloy
II-D-9	Iron + Manganese + Nickel + X
II-D-5	Iron + Nickel, High Alloy
II-C-1	Iron + Nickel, Low Alloy
II-D-6	Iron + Nickel + Aluminum
II-D-6-a	Iron + Nickel + Chromium + Cobalt
II-D-6-a	Iron + Nickel + Chromium, High Alloy
II-D-6-a	Iron + Nickel + Chromium + Molybdenum
II-D-6-a	Iron + Nickel + Chromium + Titanium
II-D-6-a	Iron + Nickel + Chromium + Titanium + X
II-D-6-a	Iron + Nickel + Chromium + Tungsten
II-D-6-a	Iron + Nickel + Chromium + X, High Alloy
II-C-2	Iron + Nickel + Chromium + X, Low Alloy
II-D-6	Iron + Nickel + Cobalt + X
IX-J-5	Iron-Nickel Intermetallic
II-D-6	Iron + Nickel + Manganese + Chromium
II-D-6	Iron + Nickel + Manganese + X
II-C-4	Iron + Nickel + X
IX-J-6	Iron-Niobium Intermetallic
VII-A-13	Iron Oxide
IX-F-4	Iron Phosphide
VII-B-2-d	Iron Silicate
II-D	Iron + Silicon, High Alloy
II-C-9	Iron + Silicon, Low Alloy

Material Index Number	Material Name
IX-J-7	Iron-Tantalum Intermetallic
IX-F-2	Iron Telluride
II-C	Iron + Tellurium
VII-B-6-g	Iron Titanate
II-D	Iron + Vanadium, High Alloy
II-C	Iron + Vanadium, Low Alloy
IX-J-11	Iron-Zirconium Intermetallic
X-A-10	Isocyanate Foam
X-A-9	Isocyanate Elastomer
X-A-10	Isofoam
X-J	Isoprene-Isobutylene Copolymer
X	Isotactic Polypropylene
IV-B-2	J-1570
IV-A-5	J-8100 Brazing Alloy
II-D-3-a	Jessop G-18-B Steel (British)
II-D-3	Jessop G-21 (British)
IV-B-1	Jessop G-32 Alloy
IV-B-1	Jessop G-34 Alloy (British), contains Fe
II-C-6	Jessop H-40 Steel (British)
II-C-6	Jessop No. 40 Steel (British)
II-D-4	Jessop No. 46 Steel (British)
II-D-3	Jessop R-20 Steel (British)
XI	Joints
VII-C	$K_2 UO_4$
VII-E-6	K-3 Body
VII-E-6	K-5 Body
VII-E-6	K-6 Body
VII-E-6	K-7 Body
VII-E-6	K-8 Body
VII-E-6	K-9 Body
VII-E-9	K-30 Insulating Brick
IV-A-3	K-42-B (Type 5)
VIII-A-1	K-138
VIII-A-2	K-138A
VIII-A-2	K-151
VIII-A-2	K-151A
I-J-2	Kahlbaum Iron
II-D-4	Kanthal

Material Index Number	Material Name
VII-B-1 also VII-E-3-g	Kaolin
VII-B-1	Kaolinite
X-G	Kel-F
I-C-3	Kendall Coke
I-C-3	Kendall Graphite
VIII-A-1	Kennametal K25
VIII-A-1	Kennametal K6
VIII-A-1	Kennametal K-138
VIII-A-2	Kennametal K-138A
VIII-A-2	Kennametal K-151
VIII-A-2	Kennametal K-151A
VII-C-1-b	Kimble . N-51A Glass
IV-A-2	Kinsalloy
IV-A-1	K-Monel, Contains Al
IV-A-3	Konel
II-D-6	Kovar
XI-H-3	Kraft Paper Reinforced Phenolic
VII-B-3-e	Kunzite
VII-B-1	Kyanite
IV-B-1	L-251
IV-B-1	L-605
X	L-2020 Lustrex Polystyrene
I-L-1	La
IX-H-7	$La_2 Au$
VII-A-4-g	$La_2 O_3$
IX-H-7	$La_2 Pb$
IX-H-7	$La_2 Sn$
IX-H-7	$La_2 Sn_3$
IX-H-7	$La_2 Tl$
IX-G-1 also IX-H-7	$La_3 Al_2$
IX-H-7	$La_3 Au$
IX-G-3 also IX-H-7	$La_4 Mg$
V-A-4	L'A-Z56 Aluminum Alloy (French)
IX-G-1 also IX-H-7	La Al
IX-G-1 also IX-H-7	$La Al_2$
IX-G-1 also IX-H-7	$La Al_4$
IX-H-7	La Ag
IX-H-7	$La Ag_2$

Material Index Number	Material Name
IX-H-7	La Ag$_3$
IX-H-7	La Au
IX-H-7	La Au$_2$
IX-C also IX-H-7	La B$_6$
VII-D-5	La Br$_3$
VII-B-3-c	Labradorite
VII-D-5	La Cl$_3$
XI-D	Lacquer Coated Aluminum Alloy 75 ST
IX-H-7	La Cu
IX-H-7	La Cu$_2$
IX-H-7	La Cu$_4$
IX-H-7	La Cu$_6$
IX-E	La H$_2$
IX-E	La H$_3$
IX-G-3 also IX-H-7	La Mg
IX-G-3 also IX-H-7	La Mg$_3$
IX-G-3 also IX-H-7	La Mg$_9$
XI-H-3	Lamicoid-C-6030
X-A	Laminac 4129
XI-C	Laminated Transparent Glass
I-C-3-p	Lampblack
I-C-3-g	Lampblack-base Carbon
I-C-3-g	Lampblack-base Graphite
I-C-3-g	Lampblack-base Graphite, Molded
I-C-3-g	Lampblack Graphite
I-C-3-p	Lampblack Powder
VII-A-4-g	Lanthana
I-L-1	Lanthanum
IX-G-1 also IX-H-7	Lanthanum Aluminide
IX-C	Lanthanum Boride
VII-D-5	Lanthanum Bromide
VII-D-5	Lanthanum Chloride
IX-E	Lanthanum Hydride
IX-H-7	Lanthanum Intermetallic
IX-G-3 also IX-H-7	Lanthanum-Magnesium Intermetallic
VII-A-4-g	Lanthanum Oxide
IX-H-7	La Pb
IX-H-7	La Pb$_3$

Material Index Number	Material Name
IX-H-7	La Sn$_3$
IX-H-7	La Tl
IX-H-7	La Tl$_3$
V-A-4	L'A - 25 G (French)
VII-E-3-k	Lead-Barium Cordierite
VII-C-2	Lead Borate Glass
VII-C-5	Lead Borosilicate Glass
IX-H-1	Lead-Cerium Intermetallic
VI	Lead + Copper
VII-E-3-k	Lead Cordierite
III-B-1 also III-C	Leaded Bronze
VII-C-1-m	Lead Glass
IX-G-3	Lead-Magnesium Intermetallic
VI	Lead + Plutonium
IX-H-10	Lead-Praseodymium Intermetallic
IX-H-7	Lead-Lanthanum Intermetallic
VII-E-3-k	Lead Modified Magnesium Aluminosilicate
VII-A-14	Lead Oxide
VII-D-6	Lead Selenide
VII-C-1-j	Lead Strontium Silicate Glass
VII-D-6	Lead Sulfide
IX-F-2	Lead Telluride
VII-C	Lead Uranate
VI	Lead + Uranium
VII-C	Lead Vanadate Glass
VI-G-1	Leboite
VII-A-6	Lechatelierite
VII-E-6	Li$_2$ Al$_2$ Si$_{10}$ O$_{24}$
VII-E-6	Li$_2$O $\cdot$ Al$_2$O$_3$ $\cdot$ 10 Si O$_2$
VII-B-6-h	Li$_2$ TiO$_3$
VII-C	Li$_2$ U O$_4$
VII-E-6	Li Al$_2$ Si$_8$ O$_{21}$
VII-B-5	Li Al $\cdot$ FPO$_4$
VII-D-5-a	Li F
VII-F	Lightweight Concrete
IX-E-1	Li H
VII-E-6	Li K Body
VII-A-3	Lime

Material Index Number	Material Name
VII-B	Limestone
VII-C-1-h	Lime Window Glass
VII-C-2	Lindemann Xray Transmitting Glass
X-G	Linear Polyethylene
VII-E-G	$Li O_2 \cdot Al_2 O_3 \cdot 8 Si O_2$
VII-C-2	$Li O_2 - Al_2 O_3 - B_2 O_3$ Glass
VII-C-2	$Li O_2 - Be O - B_2 O_3$ Glass
VII-B-3-e	$Li O \cdot Al_2 O_3 \cdot 4 Si O_2$
X-G	Litharge Filled Teflon
VII-B-7-f	Lithium Aluminate
VII-E-6	Lithium Alumino-Silicate Bodies, Barium Modified
VII-C-1-a	Lithium Aluminosilicate Glass
VII-C-2	Lithium Aluminum Borate Glass
VII-C-1-a	Lithium Aluminum Silicate Glass
VII-B-3-e also VII-E-6	Lithium Alumino Silicate
VII-E-6	Lithium Aluminosilicate with Lead Bisilicate
VII-E-6	Lithium Aluminosilicate with Lead Borate
VII-C-2	Lithium Beryllium Borate Glass
VII-C-2	Lithium Borate Glass
VII-C-1-a	Lithium Calcium Silicate Glass
VII-B-3-e	Lithium Feldspar
VII-D-5-a	Lithium Fluoride
IX-E-1	Lithium Hydride
VII-C-1-m	Lithium Lead Silicate Glass
VII-C-1-a	Lithium-Lime-Silicate Glass
VII-C-1-a	Lithium-Magnesium-Barium Silicate Glass
VII-B-6-h	Lithium Metatitanate
VII-E-3-a	Lithium Modified Magnesium Aluminosilicate
VII-B-3-e	Lithium Potassium Feldspar
VII-E-2	Lithium Silicate-Quartz Body
VII-C-1-a	Lithium Sodium Silicate Glass
VII-B-6-h	Lithium Titanate
VII-C	Lithium Uranate
XI-H-3	LMI-304 Nylon Flock Filled Phenolic
I-N-3	"L" Nickel
X-A-10	Lockfoam
VII-A-14	Lodestone
V-A-2-a	Lo-ex Aluminum Alloy (British)
XI-C	LOF-81-E-19778 Electroconducting Glass

Material Index Number	Material Name
XI-C	LOF-PB-19195 Electroconducting Glass
XI-C	LOF Sierracote I on Glass
III-D	LOHM
II-C	Low Alloy Steel
II-C-7	Low Alloy Steel Fe + Cr + Mo + X
II-C-6	Low Alloy Steel Fe + Cr + X ($X_1 \neq$ Mo)
II-C-5	Low Alloy Steel Fe + Mo + X
II-C-1	Low Alloy Steel Fe + Ni
II-C-2	Low Alloy Steel Fe + Ni + Cr + X
II-C-3	Low Alloy Steel Fe + Ni + Mo + X
II-C-4	Low Alloy Steel Fe + Ni + X ($X_1 \neq$ Mo, Cr)
II-C-9	Low Alloy Steel Fe + Si + X
II-C-8	Low Alloy Steel Fe + W + X
IV-F	Low Carbon Ferrochromium
II-A-1	Low Carbon Steel
II-C-2	Low Chromium, Nickel Tool Steel
II-D-5	Low Expansion Alloy
VII-C-1-b	Low Iron Flint Glass
II-C-9	Low Silicon, Manganese, Shock Resisting Tool Steel
I-L-2	Lu
X-F	Lucite
X	Lustrex L-2020 Polystyrene
VII-A-4-h	Lutetia
I-L-2	Lutetium
IX-H-8	Lutetium Intermetallic
VII-A-4-h	Lutetium Oxide
X-A	Luvican
X-A	Luv-M-150 Polyester (German)
IV-B-2	M-203
IV-B-2	M-204
IV-B-3	M-205
IV-A-5	M-600
VII-A-5-a	Magnesia
VII-A-5	Magnesia + Alumina + Beryllia + X
VII-A-5	Magnesia + Beryllia
VII-E-10	Magnesia Brick
VII-A-5	Magnesia + Nickel Oxide
VII-A-5	Magnesia + Silica + X

Material Index Number	Material Name
VII-A-5	Magnesia + Silicon Dioxide
VII-A-5	Magnesia + Tin Oxide + X
VII-A-5	Magnesia + Titania
VII-A-5	Magnesia + Titanium Dioxide
VII-A-5	Magnesia + Urania
VII-B-8-a	Magnesiochromite
VII-B-8-a	Magnesioferrite
VII-A-5-a	Magnesite
VII-A-5-a	Magnesite A, B or C
VII-E-10	Magnesite Brick "HÜ" (German)
VII-A-5-a	Magnesite C
VII-E-10	Magnesite-Chrome Brick
VII-A-5-a	Magnesite, Dead Burned
I-M-1	Magnesium
V-B-. . .	Magnesium Alloy . . .
XI-E	Magnesium Alloy, Coated
VII-B-7-a	Magnesium Aluminate
VII-E-3	Magnesium Alumino-Cordierite
VII-E-3	Magnesium Aluminosilicate Glass Bond (Cordierite, Steatite)
V-B-2	Magnesium + Aluminum + Manganese
VII-C-1-g	Magnesium Aluminum Silicate Glass
V-B-2	Magnesium + Aluminum + Silicon
V-B-1	Magnesium + Aluminum + Zinc
VII-C-5	Magnesium Aluminum Zinc Borosilicate Glass
IX-F-1	Magnesium Antimonide
V-B	Magnesium-Base Alloy
VII-C-2	Magnesium Borate Glass
IX-C-1	Magnesium Boride
IX-G-3	Magnesium-Cadmium Intermetallic
IX-H-1	Magnesium-Cerium Intermetallic
VII-B	Magnesium Chromite
VII-D-5	Magnesium Diboride
VII-B-8-a	Magnesium Ferrite
IX-G-3	Magnesium Germanide
IX-E	Magnesium Hydride
IX-G-3	Magnesium Intermetallics
IX-H-7 also IX-G-3	Magnesium-Lanthanum Intermetallic
VII-C-1-m	Magnesium Lead Silicate Glass

Material Index Number	Material Name
VII-B-2-e	Magnesium Metasilicate
VII-B-9	Magnesium Mica
VII-B-6-b	Magnesium Niobate
IX-D	Magnesium Nitride
VII-B-2-e	Magnesium Orthosilicate
VIII-B-2	Magnesium Oxide as Major Refractory Phase of Cermet
VII-A-5-a	Magnesium Oxide
VII-A-5	Magnesium Oxide + Beryllium Oxide
VIII-B-2	Magnesium Oxide Cermet
VIII-B-2	Magnesium Oxide Cermet-Ni Al Bonded
VIII-B-2	Magnesium Oxide Cermet— Tungsten Bonded
VII-A-5	Magnesium Oxide + Nickel Oxide
VII-A-5	Magnesium Oxide + Silicon Oxide + X
VII-A-5	Magnesium Oxide + Tin Oxide + X
VII-A-5	Magnesium Oxide + Titanium Oxide
VII-A-5	Magnesium Oxide + Uranium Oxide
VII-A-5	Magnesium Oxide + Zinc Oxide + X
IX-H-10 also IX-G-3	Magnesium-Praseodymium Intermetallic
V-B-3	Magnesium + Rare Earth + Zinc + X
VII-B-2-e	Magnesium Silicate
IX-B	Magnesium Silicide
VII-B	Magnesium Stannate
IX-G-3	Magnesium Stannide
V-B-4	Magnesium + Thorium + X
VII-B-6-j	Magnesium Titanate
VII-E-4	Magnesium Titanate Porcelain
VII-C	Magnesium Uranate
V-B-6	Magnesium + Zinc
V-B-6	Magnesium + Zinc + Zirconium + X
II-C-9	Magnetic Alloy
II-C-1 also II-C-4	Magnetic Alloy Steel
II-D-5	Magnetically Soft Alloy
VII-A-13	Magnetite
VII-B-2-c	Malacolite
II-B-5	Malleable Cast Iron, Ferritic
II-B-6	Malleable Cast Iron, Pearlitic
I-M-2	Manganese
IX-F-1	Manganese Antimonide

Material Index Number	Material Name
VI-E	Manganese-Base Alloy
III-A-2	Manganese Bronze No. 937
IX-A	Manganese Carbide
VI-E-1	Manganese + Copper + Nickel + X
VI-E-1	Manganese + Copper + X
VII-B-8	Manganese Ferrite
IX-J-3	Manganese-Hafnium Intermetallic
VI	Manganese Intermetallics
VI-E	Manganese + Iron + X
IV-A-6	Manganese Nickel
VI-E-2	Manganese + Nickel + Copper + X
VI-E-2	Manganese + Nickel + X
IX-J-5	Manganese-Nickel Intermetallic
IX-J-6	Manganese-Niobium Intermetallic
VII-A-14	Manganese Oxide
VII-A-14	Manganese Sesquioxide
VI-E	Manganese + Titanium
III-H	Manganin
VII-B-2-f	Manganous Silicate
VII-B-2-f	Manganese Silicate
IX-J-3	Manganese-Thorium Intermetallic
VI-E	Manganese + Titanium + X
II-C-7	Manganese Tool Steel
IX-J-10	Manganese-Vanadium Intermetallic
VII-A-14	Manganosite
VII-B	Marble
X-G	Marlex 20
X-G	Marlex 50 Linear Polyethylene
V-B	Mazlo AM 3 S
I-M-1	Mazlo AM 25 Magnesium
V-B	Mazlo AM 403
V-B-1	Mazlo AM-C52S
VII-B-6-g	Menaccanite
XI-B-4	Mechanically Bonded Metal Layers
IV-A-4	Megaperm 6510
X-E	Melamine
X-E	Melamine Formaldehyde
X-E	Melamine Formaldehyde, Alpha Cellulose Filled
XI-H-2	Melamine Formaldehyde, Asbestos Paper Reinforced

Material Index Number	Material Name
X-E	Melamine-Formaldehyde, Filled
X-E	Melamine Formadehyde, Mineral Filled
XI-H-2	Melamine Formaldehyde, Reinforced
X-E	Melmac 592 Mineral Filled Melamine
X-E	Melmac 1077 Melamine
X-E	Melmac 1079 Melamine
X-E	Melmac 1502 Melamine
I-M-3	Mendelevium
VI	Mendelevium Intermetallics
XI-E	Metal-Ceramic Joint
XI-B-1	Metal Skin, Metal Honeycomb Core
XI-D-3	Metal Skin, Plastic Foam Core
XI-D-2	Metal Skin, Plastic Honeycomb Core
VIII-B-1	Metamic LT-1
X-F	Methacrylate
I-M-1	Mg
IX-G-3	$Mg_2 Ge$
IX-G-3	$Mg_2 Pb$
IX-B	$Mg_2 Si$
VII-B-2-e	$Mg_2 Si O_4$
IX-G-3	$Mg_2 Sn$
VII-B-6-j	$Mg_2 Ti O_4$
IX-G-3	$Mg_3 Cd$
IX-D	$Mg_3 N_2$
IX-F-1	$Mg_3 Sb_2$
V-B-2	$Mg + Al$
VII-B-7-a	$Mg Al_2 O_4$
V-B-2	$Mg + Al + Mn + X$
V-B-2	$Mg + Al + Si$
V-B-2	$Mg + Al + X (X_1 \neq Zn)$
V-B-1	$Mg + Al + Zn$
V-B-1	$Mg + Al + Zn + X$
IX-C-1	$Mg B_2$
IX-C-1	$Mg B_4$
IX-G-3 also IX-H-1	$Mg Ce$
VII-B	$Mg C O_3$
VII-B	$Mg Cr_2 O_4$
VII-B-8-a	$Mg Fe_2 O_4$
IX-E	$Mg H_2$

Material Index Number	Material Name
IX-G-3 also IX-H-7	Mg La
V-B-5	Mg + Li + X
VII-A-5-a	Mg O
VII-B-7-a	Mg O · Al_2O_3
VII-A-5	Mg O + Al_2O_3 + Be O + X
VII-C-2	Mg O + B_2O_3 + Al_2O_3 Glass
VII-C-2	Mg O + B_2O_3 + Be O Glass
VII-C-2	Mg O + B_2O_3 Glass
VII-A-5	Mg O + Be O
VII-B	Mg O · Cr_2O_3
VII-B-8-a	Mg O · Fe_2O_3
VII-A-5	Mg O + Ni O
VII-A-5	Mg O + Si O_2
VII-A-5	Mg O + Si O_2 + X
VII-A-5	Mg O + Sn O_2 + X
VII-A-5	Mg O + Ti O_2
VII-A-5	Mg O + U O_2
VII-A-5	Mg O + Zn O + X
V-B-3	Mg + Rare Earth + X
V-B-3	Mg + R E
V-B-3	Mg + R E + Zn
VII-B-2-e	Mg. Si O_3
VII-B	Mg Sn O_3
V-B-4	Mg + Th + X
VII-B-6-j	Mg Ti_2O_5
VII-B-6-j	Mg Ti O_3
VII-C	Mg U O_4
V-B	Mg + Zn + X
V-B-6	Mg + Zn + Zr + X
VII-B-9	Mica
XI-J	Mica, Glass Bonded
VII-B-3-g	Microcline
IV-A-4	Midvale BTG
X-A-9	MIL-C-8087
II-A-1	Mild Steel
XI-D	Mild Steel - Silicone Coated
II-D-3	MIL-S-5059A
II-D-3	MIL-S-6721 A
VII-B-1	Mineral Alumino-Silicate
VII-B also VII-A and VII-E	Mineral Ceramic

Material Index Number	Material Name
I-S-4	Mint Proof Silver
X-A, B, C, D, F	Miscellaneous Plastics
VI	Mischmetal
VII-A-4	Mixed Rare Earth Oxides
IV-B-1	ML-1700
I-M-2	Mn
VII-A-14	$Mn_2 O_3$
IX-A	$Mn_3 C$
IX-A	$Mn_7 C_3$
VI-E-1	$Mn + Cu + Ni + X$
VI-E-1	$Mn + Cu + X$
VII-B-8	$Mn Fe_2 O_4$
VI-E	$Mn + Fe + C + X$
VII-A-14	$Mn O$
VII-B-8	$Mn O \cdot Fe_2 O_3$
VI-E-2	$Mn + Ni + Cu + X$
VI-E-2	$Mn + Ni + X$
IX-F-1	$Mn Sb$
VI-E	$Mn + Ti + X$
I-M-4	Mo
IX-C	$Mo_2 B$
IX-C	$Mo_2 B_5$
IX-A-6	$Mo_2 B + Mo_2 C$
IX-C	$Mo_2 B + Mo Si_2$
IX-C	$Mo_2 B + Nb_5 Si_3$
IX-C	$Mo_2 B + Ta_5 Si_3$
IX-C	$Mo_2 B + Ta Si_2$
IX-C	$Mo_2 B + Ti C$
IX-A-6	$Mo_2 C$
IX-A-6	$Mo_2 C + Mo_2 B$
IX-A-6	$Mo_2 C + Mo Si_2$
IX-A-6	$Mo_2 C + Nb_5 Si_3$
IX-A-6	$Mo_2 C + Ta_5 Si_3$
IX-A-6	$Mo_2 C + Ta Si_2$
IX-A-6	$Mo_2 C + Ti B_2$
IX-A-6	$Mo_2 C + X$
IX-A-6	$Mo_2 C + Zr B_2$
IX-J-4	$Mo_3 Ge$
IX-J-6	$Mo_3 Si$

Material Index Number	Material Name
IX-3-1	$Mo_3 Si$
IX-B-1	$Mo_4 C Si_3$
IX-B-1	$Mo_5 Si_3$
IX-C also IX-J-4	$Mo B$
IX-C also IX-J-4	$Mo B_2$
IX-G-2 also IX-J-4	$Mo Be_{12}$
IX-A-6 also IX-J-4	$Mo C$
IX-B-1	$(Mo, Cr) Si_2$
IV-D	$Mo + Fe$
I-C-3-e	Molded Acheson Amorphous Carbon
I-C-3-f	Molded Acheson Graphite, Carbon Impregnated
I-C-3-d	Molded Acheson Graphite, Multicrystalline
I-C-3-g	Molded Lampblack Base Graphite
VII-D-6	Molybdenite
I-M-4	Molybdenum
IV-D	Molybdenum-Base Alloy
IX-G-2	Molybdenum Beryllide
IX-C	Molybdenum Boride
IX-A-6 also IX-J-4	Molybdenum Carbide
VIII-A	Molybdenum Carbide Cermet
IX-B-1	Molybdenum Disilicide
IX-C also IX-J-4	Molybdenum Diboride
IX-J-4	Molybdenum Germanide
IX-J-3 also IX-J-4	Molybdenum-Hafnium Intermetallic
II-C-5	Molybdenum High Speed Tool Steel
II-C-8	Molybdenum, High Tungsten, High Speed Tool Steel
II-C-5	Molybdenum Hot Worked Tool Steel
IX-E	Molybdenum Hydride
IX-J-4	Molybdenum Intermetallics
IV-D	Molybdenum + Iron
II-C-5	Molybdenum, Low Tungsten, Vanadium High Speed Tool Steel
IV-D	Molybdenum + Nickel + Copper
IV-D	Molybdenum + Niobium + Titanium + X
IX-D	Molybdenum Nitride
VII-A-14	Molybdenum Oxide
XI-J	Molybdenum Reinforced Alumina
IX-B-1	Molybdenum Silicide
VIII-D	Molybdenum Silicide Cermet-Copper Bonded

Material Index Number	Material Name
IV-D	Molybdenum + Titanium + Niobium + X
IV-D	Molybdenum + Titanium + X
VII-A-14	Molybdenum Trioxide
II-C-5	Molybdenum-Vanadium High Speed Tool Steel
IV-D	Molybdenum + Zirconium + X
VII-A-14	Molybdite
IV-D	$Mo + Nb + Ti + X$
IV-A-1	Monel
IV-D	$Mo + Ni + Cu$
VII-B-1	Montmorillonite
VII-A-14	$Mo\ O_3$
X	Moplen
VII-D-6	$Mo\ S_2$
IX-B-1	$Mo\ Si_2$
IX-J-4	$Mo\ Si_2$
VIII-D	$Mo\ Si_2 - Al_2\ O_3 \cdot Ca\ O$ Cermet
IX-B-1	$Mo\ Si_2 + Mo_2\ B$
IX-A-6	$Mo\ Si_2 + Mo_2\ C$
IX-B-1	$Mo\ Si_2 + Ta\ C$
IX-B-1	$Mo\ Si_2 + Ti\ B_2$
IX-B-1	$Mo\ Si_2 + Zr\ B_2$
IV-D	$Mo + Ti + Nb + X$
IV-D	$Mo + Ti + X$
IV-D	$Mo + Zr + C$
IV-D	$Mo + Zr + X$
VII-B-1	Mullite
VII-E-9	Mullite Brick
IV-A-5	Multi-alloy
VII-C-6	Multiform 790 Leached Glass
II-D-3-a	Multimet Alloy
IV-A-4	Mumetal, Contains Cu
VII-B-9	Muscovite
I-M-3	Mv
II-D-3	N-153
II-D-3-a	N-155
II-D-3-a also II-D-4	N-155 Low Carbon
VII-B-2-c	$Na_2\ Ca\ Si\ O_4$
VII-C-2	$Na_2\ O + B_2\ O_3 + Be\ O$ Glass

Material Index Number	Material Name
VII-C-2	$Na_2 O + B_2 O_3$ Glass
VII-C-2	$Na_2 O + B_2 O_3 + Mg O$ Glass
VII-C-2	$Na_2 O + BeO\text{-}B_2 O_3$ Glass
VII-C-2	$Na_2 O - Mg O - B_2 O_3$ Glass
VII-C-1-b	$Na_2 Si O_3$
VII-C	$Na_2 U O_4$
VII-B-3-h	$Na\, Al\, Si\, O_4$
II-A-3	National Emergency Steel NE-1350
II-C-2	National Emergency Steel NE-8613
II	National Emergency Steel NE-9630
II-C-6	National Emergency Steel NE-52100 C
I-C-3-j	Natural Ceylon Block Graphite
I-C-3-j	Natural Graphite
I-C-3-k	Natural Graphite-Base Carbon
I-C-3-j	Natural Graphite-Base Graphite
I-C-3-n	Natural Graphite Flake
X-J	Natural Rubber
III-A-2	Naval Brass
III-A-2	Naval Brass No. 452
I-N-4	Nb
VII-A-14	$Nb_2 O_5$
VII-A-14	$Nb_2 O_5 + Ti O_2 + X$
VII-A-14	$Nb_2 O_5 + Zr O_2 + X$
IX-J-6	$Nb_3 Ge$
IX-J-6 also IX-B	$Nb_5 Si_3$
IX-B	$Nb_5 Si_3 + Mo_2 B$
IX-B	$Nb_5 Si_3 + Mo_2 C$
IX-B	$Nb_5 Si_3 + Ta\, C$
IX-B	$Nb_5 Si_3 + Ti\, B_2$
IX-J-6 also IX-C	$Nb\, B_2$
IX-C	$NbB_2 + ZrB_2$
IX-A also IX-J-6	NbC
IX-J-2 also IX-J-6	$NbCO_2$
IX-J-1 also IX-J-6	$NbCr_2$
IX-J-6	$NbFe_2$
IX-J-6	$NbGe_2$
IX-J-6	$NbMn_2$
IV-E	$Nb + Mo + Ti + X$

Material Index Number	Material Name
IX-D	NbN
IV-E	Nb + Ti + Mo + X
IV-E	Nb + Ti + X
I-N-1	Nd
VII-A-4-j	Nd_2O_3
VII-D-5	$NdCl_3$
IV-B-1	NDRC-61
IV-B-1	NDRC No. NR-10
IV-B-1	NDRC No. NR-12
IV-B-1	NDRC No. NR-71
II-A-3	NE 1350 Steel
II-C-2	NE-8613 National Emergency Steel
II	NE-9630 National Emergency Steel
II-C-6	NE-52100 C National Emergency Steel
I-N-1	Neodymium
VII-D-5	Neodymium Chloride
IX-H-9	Neodymium Intermetallics
VII-A-4-j	Neodymium Oxide
X-J	Neoprene
X-J	Neoprene GN
X-J	Neoprene W
VII-B-3-h	Nepheline Syenite
I-N-2	Neptunium
VII-D-5	Neptunium Bromide
VII-D-5	Neptunium Chloride
VII-A-14	Neptunium Dioxide
VI	Neptunium Intermetallics
IX-D	Neptunium Nitride
VII-A-14	Neptunium Oxide + X
IX-B	Neptunium Silicide
XI-C	NESA Coating on Glass
I-N-3	Ni
IX-J-5	Ni_2Hf
IX-J-5	Ni_2Pu
IX-J-5	Ni_2U
IX-G-1	Ni_3Al
IX-J-5	Ni_3Fe
IX-J-5	Ni_3Mn

Material Index Number	Material Name
IX-J-5	Ni_5Pu
IX-G-1	NiAl
IV-4	Ni + Al
VIII	NiAl Cermet, Chromium Bonded
IV-A-4	Nicaloi
IV-A-4-a	Nichrome
IV-A-5	Nichrome V
I-N-3	Nickel
IX-G-1	Nickel Aluminide
VIII	Nickel Aluminide Cermet, Chromium Bonded
IV-A	Nickel + Aluminum
VIII	Nickel-Aluminum-Titanium Cermet
IV-A	Nickel-Base Alloy
IV-A-5	Nickel + Chromium
IV-A-5	Nickel + Chromium + Aluminum + Copper
IV-A-5	Nickel + Chromium + Copper + Aluminum
IV-A-5-a	Nickel + Chromium + Iron
IV-A-5-a	Nickel + Chromium + Iron + Molybdenum
IV-A-5-a	Nickel + Chromium + Iron + Titanium
IV-A-5-a	Nickel + Chromium + Iron + X
IV-A-5	Nickel + Chromium + Molybdenum
II-C-2	Nickel - Chromium - Molybdenum Tool Steel
IV-A-5	Nickel + Chromium + Silicon
II-C-2	Nickel Chromium Tool Steel
IV-A-3	Nickel + Cobalt
IV-A-3-a	Nickel + Cobalt + Chromium + X
IV-A-1	Nickel + Copper + Aluminum
IV-A-1	Nickel + Copper + Iron + X
IV-A-1	Nickel + Copper + X
VII-B-8-n	Nickel Ferrite
I-N-3	Nickel, Grade A
IX-J-3 also IX-J-5	Nickel-Hafnium Intermetallic
IX-J-5	Nickel Intermetallic
IV-A-4	Nickel + Iron
IV-A-4-a	Nickel + Iron + Chromium + Silicon
IV-A-4-a	Nickel + Iron + Chromium + X
VII-C-1-m	Nickel-Lead Silicate Glass
IV-A-6	Nickel + Manganese

Material Index Number	Material Name
IV-A-6	Nickel + Manganese + Iron
IV-A-6	Nickel + Manganese + Silicon
VII-N-6	Nickel Metatitanate
IV-A-2	Nickel + Molybdenum + Chromium
IV-A-2	Nickel + Molybdenum + Copper + Iron
IV-A-2	Nickel + Molybdenum + Iron + X
VII-A-14	Nickel Oxide
VII-A-14	Nickel Oxide + Magnesium Oxide
IV-A	Nickel + Palladium + Chromium + X
IV-A	Nickel + Palladium + X
IX-F-4	Nickel Phosphide
IX-J-5	Nickel-Plutonium Intermetallic
VII-B-2-g	Nickel Silicate
III-A	Nickel Silver
III-D	Nickel Silver No. 719
IX-J-5	Nickel Selenide
VII-N-6	Nickel Titanate
IX-J-5	Nickel-Uranium Intermetallic
VII-B-8-n, p	Nickel-Zinc Ferrite Spinel
I-N-3	Ni + Co, Small Amounts of Co
IV-A-3	Ni + Co
IV-A-3-a	Ni + Co + Cr + Fe + X
IX-A-3-a	Ni + Co + Cr + X
IV-A-3	Ni + Co + X
IV-A-5	Ni + Cr
IV-A-5	Ni + Cr + Al + Cu
IV-A-5	Ni + Cr + Cu + Al
IV-A-5-a	Ni + Cr + Fe
IV-A-5-a	Ni + Cr + Fe + Mo + Ti
IV-A-5-a	Ni + Cr + Fe + Ti
IV-A-5-a	Ni + Cr + Fe + X
IV-A-5	Ni + Cr + Mo + X
IV-A-5	Ni + Cr + Si + X
IV-A-5	Ni + Cr + X
IV-A-1	Ni + Cu
IV-A-1	Ni + Cu + Al + X
IV-A-1	Ni + Cu + Fe + X
IV-A-1	Ni + Cu + X

Material Index Number	Material Name
IV-A-4	Ni + Fe
VII-B-8-n	$NiFe_2O_4$
IV-A-4-a	Ni + Fe + Cr + Si
IV-A-4-a	Ni + Fe + Cr + X
IV-A-4-	Ni + Fe + Mo + X
IV-A-4	Ni + Fe + X
IV-A-6	Ni + Mn
IV-A-6	Ni + Mn + Fe
IV-A-6	Ni + Mn + Si
IV-A-2	Ni + Mo + Cr + X
IV-A-2	Ni + Mo + Cr + Fe + X
IV-A-2	Ni + Mo + Cu + Fe
IV-A-2	Ni + Mo + Fe + X
IV-A-5-a	Nimonic 75 (British), contains Fe
IV-A-5	Nimonic 80 (British), contains Fe
IV-A-3-a	Nimonic 90
IV-A-3-a	Nimonic 100
IV-A-2	Ni + Mo + X
VII-A-14	NiO
VII-B-8-n	$NiO \cdot Fe_2O_3$
I-N-4	Niobium
IV-E	Niobium-Base Alloy
IX-C	Niobium Boride
IX-C	Niobium Boride + Zirconium Boride
IX-A also IX-J-7	Niobium Carbide, NbC
VIII	Niobium Carbide Cermet
IX-J-1	Niobium-Chromium Intermetallic
IX-J-2 also IX-J-6	Niobium-Cobalt Intermetallic
IX-C	Niobium Diboride
VII-A-14	Niobium Dioxide
IX-J-6	Niobium Germanide
IX-E	Niobium Hydride
IX-J-6	Niobium-Iron Intermetallic
IX-J-6	Niobium Intermetallic
IV-E	Niobium + Molybdenum + Titanium + X
VII-A-14	Niobium Monoxide
IX-D	Niobium Nitride
VII-A-14	Niobium Oxide

243

Material Index Number	Material Name
VII-A-14	Niobium Oxide + Aluminum Oxide + X
VII-A-14	Niobium Oxide + Beryllium Oxide
VII-A-14	Niobium Oxide + Magnesium Oxide
VII-A-14	Niobium Oxide + Titanium Oxide + X
VII-A-14	Niobium Oxide + Zirconium Oxide + X
VII-A-14	Niobium Pentoxide
VII-A-14	Niobium Sesquioxide
IX-J-6 also IX-B	Niobium Silicide
IX-B	Niobium Silicide + X
IV-E	Niobium + Titanium + Molybdenum + X
IV-E	Niobium + Titanium + X
VII-B-8-n	$NiO \cdot Fe_2O_3$
VII-A-14	NiO + MgO
IV-A	Ni + Pd
IV-A	Ni + Pd + Cr + X
IX-J-5	NiPu
IX-J-5	NiSe
IX-J-5	$NiSe_2$
IV-A	Ni + Si
VII-N-6	$NiTiO_3$
II-C-6	Nitralloy
II-C	Nitralloy 125 (type H)
II-C	Nitralloy 135 (type G)
II-C	Nitralloy 135 (modified)
II-C	Nitralloy 230 (Alamo)
II-C-6	Nitralloy EZ
II-C-2	Nitralloy N
IX-D	Nitride Base Systems with Other Intermetallics
XI-E	Nitride Coated Beryllium
IX-D	Nitrides of Niobium
IX-D	Nitrides of Thorium
IX-D-1	Nitrides of Titanium
IX-D-2	Nitrides of Uranium
IX-D	Nitrides of Vanadium
IX-D-3	Nitrides of Zirconium
IX-D	Nitride Systems
I-N-3	Nivac

Material Index Number	Material Name
IV-B-2	Ni + V
IX-J-5	NiU_6
I-N-5	No
VII-E-6	No. 4 Blend Clay
VII-E-4	No. 7A2 Porcelain
I-N-5	Nobelium
VI	Nobelium Intermetallics
II-B-7	Nodular Cast Iron, Ferritic
II-B-8	Nodular Cast Iron, Pearlitic
VII-E-3-g	North Carolina Kaolin
VII-A-1-a	Norton LA-603
VII-A-1-a	Norton RA-4213
VII-A-1-a	Norton Rokide.....see Rokide
X-C	Novolak
I-N-2	Np
VII-D-5	$NpBr_4$
VII-D-5	$NpCl_3$
VII-D-5	$NpCl_4$
VII-A-14	NpO_2
II-D-3-a	NR-21
IV-A-3-a	NR-60 Stellite
IV-A-3	NRDC-60
IV-B-1	NRDC-71, Stellite 31
X-H	Nylon
X-H	Nylon 6
X-H	Nylon 9
X-H	Nylon 11
X-H	Nylon 66
XI-H-3	Nylon Fabric Reinforced Phenol Formaldehyde
XI-H-3	Nylon Flock Filled Phenolic LMI-304
XI-H-3	Nylon Reinforced Phenolic
I-C-7	OFHC Copper
II-C-6	Oil Hardening, High Alloy, High Carbon, High Chromium Tool Steel
II-C-7	Oil Hardening, Low Alloy, High Manganese Tool Steel
II-C-6	Oil Hardening, Low Alloy, Low Manganese Tool Steel
II-C-8	Oil Hardening, Low Alloy, Tungsten Tool Steel
II-C-6	Oil Hardening Tool Steel

246

Material Index Number	Material Name
VI-D	Palladium + Silver
VI-D	Palladium + Silver + Copper + X
VI-D	Palladium + Silver + X
VI-D	Palladium + Uranium
XI-H-3	Panelyte Rod Grade 942
VII-A-14	PaO
XI-H-3	Paper Reinforced Phenolic
XI-H-5	Paper Reinforced Polyester
VII-A-13	Paramelaconite
X-B	Paraplex P-43 TAC Polyester
VII-B-2-e	Pass and Seymour Grade L-5 Steatite
VI	Pb_3U
VII-C-2	PbB_2O_4
VI	Pb + Cu
VII-C-2	$PbO \cdot B_2O_3$
VII-C-1-m	$PbO \cdot SiO_2$
VI	Pb + Pu
VII-D-6	PbS
VII-D-6	PbSe
IX-F-2	PbTe
IX-F-2	PbTe + PbSe
VI-F also VI	PbU
I-P-1	Pd
VI-D	Pd + Ag + X
VI-D-1	Pd + Au + Co + X
VI-D-2	Pd + Co + Au + X
VI-D-2	Pd + Co + Cu + X
VI-D-3	Pd + Cu + Co + X
VI-D	Pd + Ni + X
VI-D	Pd + Ag + X
IX-G-2	$PdBe_{12}$
VI-D-3	Pd + Cu + X
XI-D	Pd + Ni
VI-D	Pd + Rh + X
VI-D	Pd + Ru + Rh + X
VI-D	Pd + Ru + X
VI-D	Pd + U

Material Index Number	Material Name
II-B-6	Pearlitic Malleable Cast Iron
II-B-8	Pealitic Nodular Cast Iron
VII-B	Pearl Spar
X	Penton 1215
X-J	Perbunan 18
X-J	Perbunan 26
X-J	Perbunan 35
X-J	Perbunan Rubber
VII-A-5-a	Periclase
VII-B-2-e	Peridot
IV-A-4	Permafy
IV-A-4	Permalloy
II-D-6	Permanent Magnet Material (Alnico Series)
VII-B-6-f	Perovskite
VII-E-3-a also VII-E-6	Petalite
II-D-3	P.H. 15-7 Mo Armco Steel
VII-B-2-b	Phenacite
X-C-1	Phenol Formaldehyde, Fabric Filled
X-C-1	Phenol Formaldehyde
X-C-1	Phenol Formaldehyde, Asbestos Filled
XI-H-3	Phenol Formaldehyde, Cellulose Paper Base
X-C-1	Phenol Formaldehyde, Cord Filled
XI-H-3	Phenol Formaldehyde, Cotton Fabric Base
X-C-1	Phenol Formaldehyde, Cotton Flock Filled
XI-H-3	Phenol Formaldehyde, Glass Fabric Reinforced
X-C-1	Phenol Formaldehyde, Wood Flour Filled
XI-H-3	Phenolic Formaldehyde, Reinforced
XI-A-2	Phenolic Honeycomb Panel
X-C	Phenolic Novolak
XI-H-3	Phenolics, Reinforced
X-C	Phenolic Resin
X-C	Phenolic Resin, Ceramic Filled
X-C	Phenolic Resin, Stupalith Filled
X-C	Phenolics
XI-H-3	Phenolite NEMA C
XI-H-3	Phenolite NEMA L
XI-H-3	Phenolite NEMA LE
XI-H-3	Phenolite NEMA X

Material Index Number	Material Name
XI-H-3	Phenolite NEMA XP
XI-H-3	Phenolite NEMA XXX
XI-H-3	Phenolite NEMA XXXP
XI-H-3	Phenolite XXXP-454
XI-H-2	Phenolite, Reinforced
VII-B-9	Phlogopite
VII-C-5	Phoenix Glass
III-D	Phosnic Bronze
VII-B-5	Phosphate
VII-C-3	Phosphate Glass
VII-E-8	Phosphate Glass Bond
IX-F-4	Phosphides
III-B-3	Phosphor Bronze
I-C-7	Phosphorized Copper
III	Phosphorized Deoxidized Copper
VII-B	Picro-Chromite
XI-C	Pittsburgh NESA Coating on Glass
VII-C-5	Pittsburgh No. 3235 Borosilicate Glass
II-A	Plain Carbon Steel
II-A-1	Plain Carbon Steels $0.02 < C \leq 0.20\%$
II-A-2	Plain Carbon Steels $0.20 < C \leq 0.40\%$
II-A-3	Plain Carbon Steels $0.40 < C \leq 0.60\%$
II-A-4	Plain Carbon Steels $0.60 < C \leq 0.80\%$
II-A-5	Plain Carbon Steels $0.80 < C \leq 1.00\%$
II-A-6	Plain Carbon Steels $1.00 < C \leq 1.20\%$
II-A-7	Plain Carbon Steels $1.20 < C \leq 1.50\%$
II-A-8	Plain Carbon Steels $1.50 < C \leq 2.00\%$
VII-E-3-g	Plastic Kaolin
X	Plastics
XI-D-1	Plastic Skin, Metal Honeycomb Core Sandwich Material
XI-A-1	Plastic Skin, Plastic Foam Core Sandwich Material
XI-A-2	Plastic Skin, Plastic Honeycomb Core Sandwich Material
X-A, B, C, D, E, F	Plastics, Miscellaneous
XI-B-6	Plated Metals
VII-C-1-b	Plate Glass
I-P-2	Platinum
VI-C	Platinum-Base Alloy
IX-G-2	Platinum Beryllide

Material Index Number	Material Name
VI-H	Platinum + Copper + X
VI-C	Platinum + Iridium
VI-C	Platinum + Iron + X
VI-C	Platinum + Nickel + X
I-P-2	Platinum, Thermocouple Grade
VI-C	Platinum + Palladium + Ruthenium + X
VI-C	Platinum + Rhodium + X
VI-C	Platinum + Ruthenium + X
VI-C	Platinum + Tungsten + X
X-F	Plexiglass 11
X-F	Plexiglass AN-P-44A
VII-A-11	Plutonia
I-P-3	Plutonium
VI	Plutonium + Aluminum + X
VI	Plutonium Base Alloy
IX-G-2	Plutonium Beryllide
VII-D-5	Plutonium Bromide
IX-A	Plutonium Carbide
VIII	Plutonium Carbide Cermet
VII-D-5	Plutonium Chloride
VII-D-5-a	Plutonium Fluoride
VI	Plutonium Intermetallics
VII-D-5	Plutonium Iodide
VI	Plutonium + Iron
VI	Plutonium + Manganese
IX-J-5	Plutonium-Nickel Intermetallic
IX-D	Plutonium Nitride
VI	Plutonium + Osmium
VII-A-11	Plutonium Oxide
IX-B	Plutonium Silicide
VI	Plutonium + Thorium
VII-D-5-a	Plutonium Trifluoride
VI	Plutonium + X
XI-H-3	Plyophen 5023
XI-H-3	Plyophen Resin No. 1001, Reinforced
I-P-6	Pm
I-P-4	Po
I-P-4	Polonium

Material Index Number	Material Name
X-H	Polyamide (nylon)
X-J	Polybutadiene
X-H	Polycaprolactam
X-G	Polychlorotrifluoroethylene
X-A	Polyester
XI-A-2	Polyester Honeycomb Panel
XI-H-5	Polyester, Reinforced
X-A	Polyester Resin No. P-43
X-B	Polyester-TAC
X-G	Polyethylene
X-J	Polyfluorobutyl Acrylate Rubber
X-J	Polyisoprene
X-J	Polyisoprene-Isobutylene Copolymer
X-F	Polymethyl Methacrylate
X-F	Polymethyl Methacrylate-Alumina Filled
X-F	Polymethyl Methacrylate-Boron Phosphate Filled
X-F	Polymethyl Methacrylate-Calcium Carbonate Filled
X-F	Polymethylmethacrylate-Silica Filled
X-F	Polymethylmethacrylate-Zinc Oxide Filled
X	Polypropylene
X	Polystyrene
X-J	Polystyrene-Butadiene
X-G	Polytetrafluoroethylene
X-G	Polythene
X-G	Polythene-Iron Oxide Filled
X-G	Polythene-Oxide Filled
X-G	Polythene PM-1
X-A-10	Polyurethane
X-A-10	Polyurethane Foam
X-A-6	Polyvinyl Acetal
X-A-7	Polyvinyl Acetate
X-A	Polyvinyl Carbazole
X	Polyvinyl Chloride
X-A-8	Polyvinyl Chloride Acetate
VII-E-4	Porcelain
VII-E-4	Porcelain 576
III-B-3	Porosint
VII-F	Portland Cement

251

Material Index Number	Material Name
VII-F	Portland Cement-Barytes Aggregate
III-B-3	Porous Bronze
III-B-3	Porous Cu + Sn
II-C	Porous Iron-Base
II-D	Porous Iron + Copper + Graphite Anti-Friction Alloy
II-C	Porous Iron + Graphite Anti-Friction Alloy
II-C	Porous Sintered Low Alloy Steel
VII-C-2	Potassium Borate Glass
VII-B-3-f	Potassium Feldspar
VII-B-3-f	Potassium Feldspar, Anisotropic
VII-B-3-f	Potassium Feldspar, Crystalline
VII-B-3-f	Potassium Feldspar, Glassy
VII-B-3-f	Potassium Feldspar, Isotropic
VII-C-1-m	Potassium Lead Silicate Glass
VII-B-9	Potassium Mica
VII-E-3-c	Potassium Modified Magnesium Aluminosilicate
VII-C	Pottasium Uranate
VII-A-6	Pottery Flint
XI-C	PPG-NESA Coating on Glass
I-P-5	Pr
IX-H-10	Pr_2Au
IX-H-10	Pr_2Pb
IX-H-10	Pr_2Sn
IX-H-10	Pr_2Sn_3
IX-H-10	Pr_2Tl
IX-H-10 also IX-G-1	Pr_3Al_2
IX-H-10 also IX-G-3	Pr_4Mg
VII-A-4-m	Pr_6O_{11}
IX-H-10	$PrAg$
IX-H-10	$PrAg_2$
IX-H-10	$PrAg_3$
IX-H-10 also IX-G-1	$PrAl$
IX-H-10 also IX-G-1	$PrAl_2$
IX-H-10 also IX-G-1	$PrAl_4$
I-P-5	Praseodymium
IX-C also IX-H-10	Praseodymium Boride
VII-D-5	Praseodymium Bromide

Material Index Number	Material Name
VII-D-5	Praseodymium Chloride
IX-H-10	Praseodymium Intermetallic
VII-A-4-k	Praseodymium Oxide
IX-H-10	PrAu
IX-H-10	$PrAu_2$
IX-H-10	$PrAu_3$
IX-C also IX-H-10	PrB_6
VII-D-5	$PrBr_3$
VII-D-5	$PrCl_3$
IX-H-10	PrCu
IX-H-10	$PrCu_2$
IX-H-10	$PrCu_4$
IX-H-10	$PrCu_6$
IX-H-10 also IX-G-3	PrMg
IX-H-10 also IX-G-3	$PrMg_3$
IX-H-10 also IX-G-3	$PrMg_9$
I-B-3	Process Q Beryllium
I-P-6	Promethium
IX-H-11	Promethium Intermetallic
VII-A-4-1	Promethium Oxide
X-A-2	Propionate
I-P-7	Protactinium
VI	Protactinium Intermetallic
VII-A-14	Protactinium Oxide
IX-H-10	PrPb
IX-H-10	$PrPb_3$
IX-H-10	$PrSn_3$
IX-H-10	PrTl
IX-H-10	$PrTl_3$
I-P-2	Pt
IX-G-2	$PtBe_{12}$
VI-H	Pt + Cu + X
VI-C	Pt + Fe + X
VI-C	Pt + Ni + X
VI-C	Pt + Pd + Ru + X
VI-C	Pt + W + X
I-P-3	Pu
IX-A	Pu_2C_3

253

Material Index Number	Material Name
VI	Pu_6Fe
VI	$Pu + Al + X$
IX-G-2	$PuBe_{13}$
VII-D-5	$PuBr_3$
VII-D-5	$PuCl_3$
VII-D-5-a	PuF_3
VI	$Pu + Fe$
VI	$PuFe_2$
VII-D-5	PuI_3
VI	$Pu + Mn$
VI	$PuMn_2$
IX-J-5	$PuNi$
IX-J-5	$PuNi_2$
IX-J-5	$PuNi_5$
VII-A-11	PuO
VII-A-11	PuO_2
VII-A-11	PuO_3
VI	$Pu + O_s$
VI	$PuOs_2$
VI	$PuPb_3$
I-.....	Pure ...
VI	$Pu + Th$
VI	$Pu + X$
VII-C-5	Pyrex
VII-C-5	Pyrex 774
XI-C	Pyroceram 9606
XI-C	Pyroceram 9608
I-C-3-h	Pyrolytic Carbon
I-C-3-h	Pyrolytic Graphite
X	Q-103 Styrofoam Polystyrene
VII-A-6	Quartz
I-C-7	QQC-576 Electrolytic Tough Pitch Copper
VII-E-6	QC6 Frit
V-A-1	R 317 Aluminum Alloy
I-R-1	Ra
I-R-1	Radium
V-A	RAE-40 Aluminum Alloy (British)
V-A	RAE-47 Aluminum Alloy (British)

Material Index Number	Material Name
V-A	RAE-47 Aluminum Alloy (British)
V-A	RAE-55 Aluminum Alloy (British)
V-A	RAE470 Aluminum Alloy (British)
V-A-2-a	RAE-SA-1 Aluminum Alloy (British)
V-A-2-a	RAE-SA-44 Aluminum Alloy (British)
IX-C	Rare Earth Borides
VII-D-5	Rare Earth Bromides
VII-A-4	Rare Earth Oxides
VII-D-5-a	RbF
V-C-2	RC-130-A Titanium Alloy
V-C-1 also V-C-2 also V-C-5	RC-130-B Titanium Alloy
IV-A-3	RCA-N91
IV-A-3	RCA-N97
I-R-2	Re
IX-B	Re_3Si
VI	Re + W + X
V-A-3	Recidal
III-A-2	Red Brass
V-A-2-a	Red X-8 Aluminum Alloy
V-A-2	Red X-13 Aluminum Alloy
IV-A-3-a	Refractaloy 26
IV-B-1	Refractaloy 70
IV-C through IV-L	Refractory Metal-Base Alloy
VII-C-6	Refrasil
XI - - -	Reinforced - - - -
XI-J	Reinforced Alumina
XI-H-3	Reinforced Copolymer (Epoxide-Phenolic)
XI-H-3	Reinforced Copolymer of Phenolic and Epoxide Resins
XI-H-4	Reinforced Diallyl Phthalate
XI-H-7	Reinforced Epoxide
XI-H-7	Reinforced Epoxide X-12100
XI-H-2	Reinforced Melamine Formaldehyde
XI-H	Reinforced Organic Material
XI-H-3	Reinforced Phenolic
XI-H-3	Reinforced Phenolic Formaldehyde
XI-H-2	Reinforced Phenolite
XI-H-5	Reinforced Polyester

Material Index Number	Material Name
XI-A-2	Reinforced Polyester Skin, Polyester Honeycomb Core
XI-H-5	Reinforced TAC Polyester
XI-H	Reinforced Plastics (and so called Laminates)
XI-D-1	Reinforced Polyester Skin, Aluminum Honeycomb Core
XI-H-6	Reinforced Silicone
XI-H-5	Reinforced TAC Polyester
XI-A-1	Reinforced TAC Polyester Skin, Alkyd Isocyanate Foam Core
XI-H-1	Reinforced Teflon
XI-H-5	Reinforced Vibrin-135
XI-H-5	Reinforced Vibrin-X-1068
II-D	Remalloy, Fe-Mo Alloy
IV-A-5	Rene 41
IX-B	ReSi
IX-B	$ReSi_2$
X-E	Resimene 814 Resin (Monsanto)
X	Resin 501 CIBA
XI-A-3	Resin Impregnated Glass Fabric Cotton Duck Laminate
I-R-3	Rh
VI	Rh_2Ge
VI	Rh_3Ge_4
VI	Rh_5Ge_3
I-R-2	Rhenium
VI	Rhenium Germanide
VI	Rhenium Intermetallics
IX-B	Rhenium Silicide
VI	Rhenium + Tungsten + X
VI	RhGe
I-R-3	Rhodium
I-C-3	Ringsdorff RKS Carbon Electrode
VII-B-9	Ripidolite
XI-B-4	Riveted Aluminum Alloy Joint
XI-B-4	Riveted Aluminum Joint
XI-B-4	Riveted Joint
I-C-3	RKS Type Ringsdorff Carbon Electrode
IV-A-1	R-Monel, Free Cutting
VII-A-1-a	Rokide
VII-A-1-a	Rokide A
V-A-2-a	RR-50C Aluminum Alloy (British)

Material Index Number	Material Name
V-A-2-a	RR-53C Aluminum Alloy (British)
V-A-1	RR-59 Aluminum Alloy (British)
V-A-4	RR-77 Aluminum Alloy (British)
V-A-3	RR-131-D Aluminum Alloy (British)
V-C-2	RS-120 Titanium Alloy
I-R-4	Ru
X-J	Rubberlike Polyester
X-J	Rubber
X-J	Rubber Board No. 2266
VII-B-3-g	Rubidium Aluminosilicate
VII-D-5-a	Rubidium Fluoride
VII-E-3-d	Rubidium Modified Magnesium Aluminosilicate
VII-A-8	Rutile
I-R-4	Ruthenium
VII-A-8	Rutile
II-D-	S-497 Alleghany Fe-Co Steel
II-D-6-a	S-495 Alleghany Steel
II-D-3	S-590 (AMS-5333) Alleghany Steel
II-D-6	S-590 Alleghany Steel
IV-B-1	S-816
IV-B-1	S-816 + B
IV-B-1	S-844
V-A-2-a	SA-1 Aluminum Alloy (British)
V-A-2-a	SA-44 Aluminum Alloy (British)
III-A-2	SAE-73 Naval Brass
II-A-3	SAE 1010
II-A also II-A-1, 2, 3	SAE 1010
II-C-7	SAE 4130
II	SAE Steels... see AISI-....
XI-C	Safety Glass
VII-A-4-n	Samaria
VII-A-4-n	Samaria + Godolinia + X
I-S-1	Samarium
IX-C	Samarium Boride
IX-H-12	Samarium Intermetallic
VII-A-4-n	Samarium Oxide
XI-A-2 also XI-E also XI-H	Sandwich Material

Material Index Number	Material Name
XI-A-2 also XI-E also XI-H	Sandwich Structure
VII-A-1-a	Sapphire
VII-A-1-a	Sapphire, Synthetic
II-D-3	SAS-8 (German)
I-A-4	Sb
IX-F-1 also IX-F-2	Sb_2Te_3
I-S-2	Sc
VII-A-15	Sc_2O_3
VII-A-15	Scandia
I-S-2	Scandium
VII-A-15	Scandium Oxide
VII-E-10	Schamotte Brick, Basic
X-F	Selectron 400 Acrylic Resin
X-A	Selectron 5026
VII-D-6	Selenides
VII-E-3	Self Glazed Fired Steatite
II-C-6	Shock Resisting Tool Steel
I-S-3	Si
VII-D-1-a	SiC
XI-C	Sierracote I on Glass
VII-E-3	Sierralite
VII-B-2-e also VII-E-3	Sierra Talc
VI-G	Si + B
VI-G-1	Si + Fe + X
VI-G	Si + Ge
X-J	Silastic 160
X-J	Silastic 180
VII-A-6	Silica
VII-E-11	Silica Brick
VII-C-6	Silica Glass
VII-A-6	Silica Rock
VII-C-1	Silicate Glass
VII-B-2	Silicates of Ba, Be, Ca, Fe, Mg, Ma, Ni, Sr and Zn
VII-A-6	Silica + Titania
IX-B	Silicide Base Systems with Other Intermetallics
IX-B	Silicide of Chromium
IX-B-1	Silicide of Molybdenum
IX-B	Silicide of Thorium
IX-B	Silicide of Tungsten

Material Index Number	Material Name
IX-B-2	Silicide of Uranium
IX-B	Silicide Systems
I-S-3	Silicon
VI-G	Silicon-Base Alloy
VI-G	Silicon + Boron
III-F	Silicon Bronze
VII-D-1-a	Silicon Carbide
VII-D-1-b	Silicon Carbide + Boron Carbide
VIII-A-5	Silicon Carbide Cermet
VIII-A-5	Silicon Carbide Cermet, Cr-Mo Bonded
VIII-A-5	Silicon Carbide Cermet, NiAl Bonded
VIII-A-5	Silicon Carbide Cermet, Vitallium Bonded
VII-A-6	Silicon Dioxide
X-J	Silicone
XI-D	Silicone Coated Aluminum Alloy 24ST
XI-D	Silicone Coated Aluminum Alloy 75ST
XI-D	Silicone Coated Dow Metal
XI-D	Silicone Coated Mild Steel
XI-D	Silicone Coated Stainless Steel
X	Silicone Foam
VI-G	Silicon and Germanium
XI-H-6	Silicone Glass Laminate
XI-H-6	Silicone Laminate
XI-H-6	Silicone, Reinforced
X-J	Silicone Rubber
VI-G-1	Silicon + Iron + X
IX-J-4	Silicon-Molybdenum Intermetallic.
IX-D	Silicon Nitride
VII-A-6	Silicon Oxide
VIII-B	Silicon Oxide Cermet
VIII-B	Silicon Oxide Cermet, Aluminum Bonded
VIII-B	Silicon Oxide Cermet, Stainless Steel Bonded
VII-A-6	Silicon Oxide + Titanium Oxide
VI-G	Silicon + Phosphorous
IX-J-7	Silicon-Tantalum Intermetallic
IX-F-2	Silicon Telluride
IX-J-8	Silicon-Thorium Intermetallic
VII-E-11	Silicrete Fire Brick

Material Index Number	Material Name
VII-B-1	Sillimanite
VII-B-1	Sillimanite Brick
I-S-4	Silver
VI-B-1	Silver + Aluminum + X
VI-B	Silver-Base Alloy
VI-B-2	Silver + Cadmium + X
IX-H-1	Silver-Cerium Intermetallic
VI-B-3	Silver + Copper + Cadmium + X
VI-B-3	Silver + Copper + Tin + X
VI-B-3	Silver + Copper + X
VI-B-3	Silver + Copper
VI-B	Silver + Gold + X
I-S-4	Silver, Inquartation
IX-H-7	Silver-Lanthanum Intermetallic
VI-B	Silver + Lead + X
VI-B	Silver + Magnesium + X
VI-B	Silver + Manganese + X
VI-B	Silver + Molybdenum + X
VI-B	Silver + Nickel + X
VI-B-4	Silver + Palladium + X
VI-B	Silver + Platinum + X
IX-H-10	Silver-Praseodymium Intermetallic
VI-B	Silver + Tungsten + X
I-S-4	Silver, U.S. Mint Proof
VI-B	Silver + Zinc + Beryllium
VI-B	Silver + Zinc + Gold
VI-B	Silver + Zinc + X
IX-D	SiN
II-C	Sintered Porous Low Alloy Steel
VII-A-6	SiO_2
VII-C-6	SiO_2, Fused
VII-C-1-m	$SiO_2 \cdot PbO$ Glass
VII-A-6	$SiO_2 + TiO_2$
VII-C-6	SiO_2, Vitreous
VI-G	Si + P
IX-F-2	SiTe
I-S-1	Sm
VII-A-4-n	Sm_2O_3

Material Index Number	Material Name
VII-A-4-n	$Sm_2O_3 + Gd_2O_3 + X$
IX-C	SmB_6
IV-A-1	S-Monel, contains Si
VI	Sn_3U
VI	Sn + Mg
VII-A-15	SnO_2
IX-F-2	SnTe
VI	Sn + U
III-B-2	Sn-Zn Bronze
VII-B-2-e	Soapstone
VII-C-1-b	Soda Barium Aluminosilicate
VII-C-5	Soda Borosilicate Glass
VII-C-2	Soda Beryllia Borate Glass
VII-C-1-m	Soda Lead Silicate Glass
VII-C-1-b	Soda Lime Aluminosilicate Glass
VII-C-1-b	Soda Lime Silica Glass
VII-C-1-b	Soda Lime Silicate Glass
VII-C-1-b	Soda Lime Window Glass
VII-C-2	Soda Magnesia-Borate Glass
VII-C-1-b	Soda-Strontia Silicate Glass
VII-B-3-h	Sodium Aluminosilicate
VII-C-2	Sodium Aluminum Borate Glass
VII-C-1-b	Sodium Barium Aluminosilicate Glass
VII-C-1-b	Sodium Barium Silicate Glass
VII-C-2	Sodium Beryllium Borate Glass
VII-C-2	Sodium Borate Glass
VII-C-2	Sodium Boroaluminate Glass
VII-C-5	Sodium Borosilicate Glass
VII-C-1-b	Sodium Calcium (Lime) Silicate Glass
VII-B-2-c	Sodium Calcium Silicate
VII-B-3-h	Sodium Feldspar
VII-C-1-m	Sodium Lead Silicate Glass
VII-C-1-b	Sodium Lead Silicate Glass
VII-C-2	Sodium Magnesium Borate Glass
VII-C-1-b	Sodium Magnesium Copper Silicate Glass
VII-C-1-b	Sodium Magnesium Silicate Glass
VII-E-3-b	Sodium Modified Magnesium Aluminosilicate
VII-C-5	Sodium Potassium Borosilicate Glass
VII-B-3-h	Sodium Potassium Feldspar

Material Index Number	Material Name
VII-C-1-b	Sodium Silicate Glass
VII-C-1-b	Sodium Strontium Aluminosilicate Glass
VII-C	Sodium Uranate
VII-C-5	Sodium Zinc Borosilicate Glass
VII-C-1-b	Solex 2808X Plate Glass
VII-C-1-b	Solex "S" Glass
XI-A-3	Solid Plastic Layers
I-C-3-p	Soot
VII-E-3-g	Sparks North Carolina Kaolin
I-C-3	Spectrochemical Carbon Electrode
III-B-3	Speculum
II-C	Spiegeleisen
VII-B-7-a	Spinel
VII-B-3-e	Spodumene
I-Z-1	Sponge Zirconium
XI-B	Sprayed Aluminum on Stainless Steel
XI-B	Sprayed Stainless Steel on Copper
XI-E	Sprayed Zirconia on Inconel
I-S-5	Sr
VII-B-6-k	Sr_2TiO_4
VII-A-15	SrO
VII-B-7-k	$SrO \cdot 2Al_2O_3$
VII-B-6-k	$SrO + TiO_2$
VII-B-6-k	$SrTiO_3$
VII-C	$SrUO_4$
II-D-2	SS-310
II-D-3	Stabilized Stainless Steel AISI-347
XI-B-5	Stainless Clad Steel Plate
II-D-1	Stainless Iron
II-D-1 also II-D-2 also II-D-3	Stainless Steel
II-D-3	Stainless Steel 17-7 PH
II-D-2	Stainless Steel 18-8
II-D-2	Stainless Steel 18-8 type
II-D-2	Stainless Steel AISI-301
II-D-3	Stainless Steel AISI-302B
II-D-2	Stainless Steel AISI-303, Free Cutting
II-D-2	Stainless Steel AISI-310
II-D-3	Stainless Steel AISI 316

Material Index Number	Material Name
II-D-3	Stainless Steel AISI-321
II-D-3	Stainless Steel AISI-347
II-D-1	Stainless Steel AISI-410
II-D-1	Stainless Steel AISI-430
II-D-1	Stainless Steel AISI-446
XI-D	Stainless Steel Coated with Silicone
XI-B-1	Stainless Steel Skin and Honeycomb Core
XI-B	Stainless Steel Sprayed on Copper
VII-B	Stannates
VII-B-2-e also VII-E-3-c	Steatite
VII-E-3-c	Steatite 10B-2
VII-E-3-c	Steatite 12C-2
VII-E-3-c	Steatite, Fired
II	Steel
XI-E	Steel-Uranium Carbide Joint
XI-E	Steel-Uranium Oxide Joint
IV-B-1	Stellite No. 1
IV-B-1	Stellite No. 6, contains W
IV-B-1	Stellite No. 12
IV-B-1	Stellite No. 21
IV-B-1	Stellite No. 23 (61)
IV-B-1	Stellite No. 25
IV-A-3-a	Stellite No. 27 (6059)
IV-B-1	Stellite No. 30 (422-19)
IV-B-1	Stellite No. 31 (X-40), contains W
IV-B-1	Stellite No. 36
IV-B-1	Stellite "2400"
IV-B-1	Stellite Star J-Metal
I-S-4	Sterling Silver
I-S-5	Strontium
VII-B-6-k	Strontium-Barium Titanate
VII-C-2	Strontium Borate Glass
VII-B-3-j	Strontium Feldspar
VII-C-1-m	Strontium Lead Silicate Glass
VII-B-6-k	Strontium Metatitanate
VII-E-3-h	Strontium Modified Magnesium Aluminosilicate
VII-B-6-k	Strontium Orthotitanate
VII-A-15	Strontium Oxide

Material Index Number	Material Name
VII-A-15	Strontium Peroxide
VII-B-2-h	Strontium Silicate
VII-B-6 also VII-B-6-k	Strontium Titanate
VII-C	Strontium Vanadate Glass
VII-C	Strontium Uranate
X-J	Styrene-Butadiene Copolymer
X	Styrofoam Polystyrene
VII-D-6	Sulfides
VII-A-6	Super Duty Silica
IV-A-4	Supermalloy
III-D	Supernickel No. 701
VII-B-4-b	Superpax Zircon
XI-J	Supramica 557 (Mycalex)
VII-C-5	Supremax Glass (German)
I-J-2	Svea Iron
VII-B-1	Syenite
XI-J	Synthetic Mica, Glass Bonded
VII-A-1-a	Synthetic Sapphire
I-T-1	Ta
VII-A-15	Ta_2O_5
IX-B	Ta_2Si
IX-C also IX-J-7	Ta_3B_4
IX-J-7	Ta_4Ge
IX-B	Ta_5Si_3
IX-B	$Ta_5Si_3 + Mo_2B$
IX-B	$Ta_5Si_3 + Mo_2C$
IX-B	$Ta_5Si_3 + TaC$
IX-C also IX-J-7	TaB
IX-C also IX-J-7	TaB_2
VII-B-2-c	Tabular Spar
IX-A-5 also IX-J-7	TaC
IX-A-5	$TaC + Nb_5Si_3$
IX-A-5	$TaC + Ta_5Si_3$
IX-J-2 also IX-J-7	$TaCo_2$
IX-J-1	$TaCr_2$
X-B	TAC Polyester
XI-H-5	TAC Polyester, Reinforced
IX-J-7	$TaCr_2$

Material Index Number	Material Name
IX-J-7	$TaFe_2$
VII-B-2-e	Talc
IX-D	TaN
I-T-1	Tantalum
IV-H	Tantalum-Base Alloy
IX-C	Tantalum Boride
IX-A-5 and IX-J-7	Tantalum Carbide
VIII-A	Tantalum Carbide Cermet
VIII-A	Tantalum Carbide Cermet, Iron Bonded
IX-J-1	Tantalum-Chromium Intermetallic
IX-J-2	Tantalum-Cobalt Intermetallic
IX-C also IX-J-7	Tantalum Diboride
IX-J-7	Tantalum Germanide
IX-E	Tantalum Hydride
IX-J-7	Tantalum Intermetallics
IX-J-7	Tantalum-Iron Intermetallic
IX-D	Tantalum Nitride
VII-A-15	Tantalum Oxide
VII-A-15	Tantalum Pentoxide
IX-B	Tantalum Silicide
IX-J-7	Tantalum-Silicon Intermetallic
IV-H	Tantalum + Titanium + X
IX-J-7 also IX-B	$TaSi_2$
IX-B	$TaSi_2 + Mo_2B$
IV-H	Ta + Ti + X
I-T-3	Tb
I-T-2	Tc
III-E	Te-Al Bronze
I-T-2	Technetium
I-J-2	Technical Iron
VI	Te + Cr + X
X-G	Teflon
X-G	Teflon-Barium Titanate Filled
X-G	Teflon-Boron Carbide Filled
X-G	Teflon-Calcium Boride Filled
X-G	Teflon-Carbonyl Iron Filled
X-G	Teflon-Ferrite Filled
X-G	Teflon Filled with Quartz No. 900

Material Index Number	Material Name
XI-H-1	Teflon, Glass Fabric Reinforced
X-G	Teflon-Iron Filled
X-G	Teflon-Litharge Filled
X-G	Teflon-Mica Filled
X-G	Teflon-Quartz Filled
XI-H-1	Teflon, Reinforced
X-G	Teflon-Titania Filled
X-G	Teflon Type TF-1
X-G	Teflon-Zero Plast Filled
VII-C-1-m	Television Tube Glass
IX-F-2	Telluride
VII-A-15	Tellurite
IX-F-1 also IX-F-2	Tellurium Antimonide
VI	Tellurium + Chromium + X
III-J	Tellurium Copper
VII-A-15	Tellurium Dioxide
VII-C	Tellurium Oxide Glass
VII-A-13	Tellurium Monoxide
III-A	Tellurium Nickel Brass
VII-A-15	Tellurium Oxide
VII-A-15	Tellurium Trioxide
VII-C	Tellurium Vanadate Glass
III-D	Tempaloy 836
III-E	Tempaloy 841
X-A-1	Tenite I, Formula 0072-MS
X-A-3	Tenite II, Formula 205A-MS
X-A-3	Tenite G 204-H2
X-A-1	Tenite I 204-MS
X-A-3	Tenite Q 264-H-2
X-A-3	Tenite S 264-MS
VII-A-13	Tenorite
VII-A-15	TeO
VII-A-15	TeO_2
VII-C	$TeO_2 + MoO_3$ Glass
VII-C	$TeO_2\text{-}WO_3$ Glass
VII-A-15	TeO_3
VII-A-4-p	Terbia
I-T-3	Terbium

Material Index Number	Material Name
IX-H-13	Terbium Intermetallics
VII-A-4-p	Terbium Oxide
IX-C	Ternary Boride Systems or Larger
VIII-A	Ternary Carbide Cermets
IX-D	Ternary Nitride Systems
IX-B	Ternary Silicide Systems
VII-E-4	Terra Cotta
IX-F-2	TeSn
I-T-4	Th
VII-D-6	Th_2S_3
IX-F-1 also IX-J-8	Th_3Sb_4
VII-D-6	Th_4S_7
IX-J-3	Th_6Mn_{23}
VII-D-6	Th_7S_{12}
IX-H-1	Thallium-Cerium Intermetallic
VII-D-5	Thallium Chloride
IX-H-7	Thallium-Lanthanum Intermetallic
VII	Thallium Phosphide
IX-H-10	Thallium-Praseodymium Intermetallic
IX-C	ThB_4
IX-A	ThC
IX-A	ThC_2
VII-D-5	$ThCl_4$
V-A-1	Thermafond C3-INA (Italian)
I-P-2	Thermocouple Grade Platinum
IV-A-5	Thetalloy
VII-D-5-a	ThF_4
IX-E	ThH_4
IX-J-8	$ThMn_{12}$
IX-D also IX-J-8	ThN
VII-A-7	ThO_2
VII-A-7	$ThO_2 + Al_2O_3$
VII-A-7	$ThO_2 + UO_2$
VII-A-7	Thoria
VII-A-7	Thoria + Alumina
VII-A-7	Thorianite
VII-A-7	Thoria + Uranium Dioxide
I-T-4	Thorium

Material Index Number	Material Name
IX-F-1	Thorium Antimonide
IV-L	Thorium-Base Alloy
IX-C	Thorium Boride
IX-A	Thorium Carbide
VIII-A	Thorium Carbide Cermet
VII-D-5	Thorium Chloride
VII-A-7	Thorium Dioxide
VII-D-5-a	Thorium Fluoride
IX-E	Thorium Hydride
IX-J-8	Thorium Intermetallic
IX-J-3	Thorium-Manganese Intermetallic
IX-D also IX-J-8	Thorium Nitride
VII-A-7	Thorium Oxide
VIII-B-4	Thorium Oxide as Major Refractory Phase of Cermet
VII-A-7	Thorium Oxide
VII-A-7	Thorium Oxide + Aluminum Oxide
VIII-B-4	Thorium Oxide Cermet-Tungsten Bonded
VII-A-7	Thorium Oxide + Uranium Oxide
IV-L	Thorium + Plutonium + X
IX-B also IX-J-8	Thorium Silicide
VII-D-6	Thorium Sulfide
IV-L	Thorium + Titanium
IV-L	Thorium + Uranium
IV-L	Thorium + Uranium + Zirconium
IV-L	Thorium + Zirconium + Uranium
IV-L	Thorium + Zirconium + X
IV-L	Th + Pu + X
VII-D-6	ThS
VII-D-6	ThS_2
IX-F-1 also IX-J-8	ThSb
IX-F-1 also IX-J-8	$ThSb_2$
IX-B also IX-J-8	$ThSi_2$
IV-L	Th + Ti
IV-L	Th + U
VII-A-4-q	Thulia
I-T-5	Thulium
IX-H-14	Thulium Intermetallic
VII-A-4-q	Thulium Oxide

Material Index Number	Material Name
IV-L	Th + U + Zr
IV-L	Th + Zr + U
IV-L	Th + Zr + X
I-T-6	Ti
VII-A-8	Ti_2O_3
IX-G-4	Ti_3Au
VII-A-8	Ti_3O_5
I-T-6	Ti-75A Titanium
V-C-5	Ti-140-A Titanium Alloy
V-C-1 also V-C-2	Ti-150-A Titanium Alloy
V-C-1	Ti-155A Titanium Alloy
IX-G-1 also IX-G-4	TiAl
V-C-1	Ti + Al + Cr + Mo
V-C-1	Ti + Al + Fe + Cr + Mo
V-C-1	Ti + Al + Fe + X
V-C-1	Ti + Al + Mn + X
V-C-1	Ti + Al + Mo + X
V-C-1	Ti + Al + Nb + Ta
V-C-1	Ti + Al + Sn + X
V-C-1	Ti + Al + V + X
V-C-1	Ti + Al + V + Mo
V-C-1	Ti + Al + Mo + X
V-C-1	Ti + Al + V + Mo
V-C-1	Ti + Al + Sn + X
V-C-1	Ti + Al + V + X
V-C-1	Ti + Al + X
IX-G-4	TiAu
IX-C-2	TiB
IX-C-2	TiB_2
IX-C-2	$TiB_2 + (Al + 2B)$
IX-C-2	$TiB_2 + CrB_2$
IX-A-6	$TiB_2 + Mo_2C$
IX-C-3	$TiB_2 + Nb_5Si_3$
IX-C-2	$TiB_2 + TaSi_2$
IX-C-2	$TiB_2 + TiC$
IX-C-2	$TiB_2 + TiN$
IX-C-2	$TiB_2 + VB_2$
IX-G-2 also IX-G-4	TiBe

Material Index Number	Material Name
IX-G-2 also IX-G-4	$TiBe_2$
IX-A-2 also IX-G-4	TiC
IX-A-2	$TiC + Mo_2B$
IX-A-2	$TiC + TiB_2$
V-C-5	Ti + Cr
V-C-5	Ti + Cr + Al + X
V-C-5	Ti + Cr + Fe + X
V-C-5	Ti + Cr + X
V-C	Ti + Cu + X
IX-G-4	TiFe
IX-G-4	$TiFe_2$
V-C-7	Ti + Fe + Cr + X
V-C-6	Ti + Fe + X ($X_1 \neq$ Cr)
V-C	Ti + Ge
IX-E	TiH
V-C	Ti + H_2
VII-E-4	Tile
II-D-6-a	Timken 16-25-6
V-C-2	Ti + Mn
V-C-2	Ti + Mn + Al + X
V-C-2	Ti + Mn + X
V-C-3	Ti + Mo + X
IX-D-1	TiN
V-C	Ti + Nb + X
IX-H-1	Tin-Cerium Intermetallic
VII-A-15	Tin Dioxide
IX-H-7	Tin-Lanthanum Intermetallic
VI	Tin + Magnesium
VII-A-15	Tin Monoxide
VII-A-15	Tin Oxide
VII-A-15	Tin Oxide + Magnesium Oxide + X
IX-H-10	Tin-Praseodymium Intermetallic
IX-F-2	Tin Telluride
IX-D-1	$TiN + TiB_2$
VI	Tin + Uranium
VII-A-8	TiO
VII-A-8	TiO_2
VII-A-8	$TiO_2 + Nb_2O_5$

Material Index Number	Material Name
VII-A-8	$TiO_2 + SiO_2$
VII-A-8	$TiO_2 + SiO_2 + X$
V-C-8	$Ti + O + X$
V-C	$Ti + Sn + X$
VII-A-8	Titania
X-G	Titania Filled Teflon
VII-A-8	Titania + Niobium Pentoxide
VII-A-8	Titania + Silica
VII-A-8	Titania + Silica + X
VII-B-6-g	Titanic Iron Ore
I-T-6	Titanium
V-C	Titanium Alloy
V-C-2	Titanium Alloy RS-120
V-C-1	Titanium, Alpha Phase
IX-G-1 also IX-G-4	Titanium Aluminide
V-C-1	Titanium + Aluminum + Chromium + X
V-C-1	Titanium + Aluminum + Iron + X
V-C-1	Titanium + Aluminum + Manganese + X
V-C-1	Titanium + Aluminum + Molybdenum + X
VIII	Titanium-Aluminum-Nickel Cermet
V-C-1	Titanium+Aluminum + Niobium + X
V-C-1	Titanium + Aluminum + Tin + X
V-C-1	Titanium + Aluminum + Vanadium + X
V-C	Titanium-Base Alloy
IX-G-2 also IX-G-4	Titanium Beryllide
IX-C-2	Titanium Boride
IX-C-2	Titanium Boride + "Aluminum Boride"
IX-C-2	Titanium Boride + Chromium Boride
VIII-C	Titanium Boride Cermet, Aluminum Bonded
VIII-C	Titanium Boride Cermet, Stellite 31 Bonded
IX-C-2	Titanium Boride + Titanium Nitride
IX-C-2	Titanium Boride + Vanadium Boride
IX-A-2 also IX-G-4	Titanium Carbide
VIII-A-2	Titanium Carbide as Major Refractory Phase of Cermet
VIII-A-2	Titanium Carbide Cermet
VIII-A-2	Titanium Carbide Cermet, Cobalt Bonded
VIII-A-2	Titanium Carbide Cermet, Molybdenum Bonded
VIII-A-2	Titanium Carbide Cermet, Nickel Bonded

Material Index Number	Material Name
VIII-A-2	Titanium Carbide Cermet, Tungsten Bonded
V-C-5	Titanium + Chromium + Aluminum + X
V-C-5	Titanium + Chromium + Iron + X
V-C	Titanium + Copper + X
I-T-6	Titanium, Crystal Bar
IX-C-2	Titanium Diboride
VII-A-8	Titanium Dioxide + X
VII-A-8	Titanium Dioxide + Silicon Dioxide
VII-A-8	Titanium Dioxide + Silicon Dioxide + X
V-C	Titanium + Germanium
IX-E	Titanium Hydride
V-C	Titanium + Hydrogen
IX-G-4	Titanium Intermetallic
IX-G-4	Titanium-Iron Intermetallic
I-T-6	Titanium, Iodide Process
V-C-7	Titanium + Iron + Chromium + Molybdenum
V-C-6	Titanium + Iron + Vanadium + X
V-C-2	Titanium + Manganese
V-C-2	Titanium + Manganese + Aluminum + X
VIII-D	Titanium-Molybdenum-Silicon Cermet
VII-A-8	Titanium Monoxide
IX-D-1	Titanium Nitride
V-C	Titanium + Niobium + X
VIII-E	Titanium Nitride Cermet, Chromium + Titanium Bonded
VIII-E	Titanium Nitride Cermet, Cr_3Ti Bonded
VIII-B	Titanium Oxide Cermet, Cr-Ti Bonded
VII-A-8	Titanium Oxide + Niobium Oxide
V-C-8	Titanium + Oxygen + X
VII-A-8	Titanium Sesquioxide
IX-B	Titanium Silicide
V-C	Titanium + Tantalum + X
V-C	Titanium + Tin + X
V-C	Titanium + Tungsten + X
V-C-4	Titanium + Vanadium +X
V-C	Titanium + Zirconium + X
VII-A-8	Titanox
V-C	Ti + Ta + X
IX-G-4	TiU_2

Material Index Number	Material Name
V-C-4	Ti + V + Al + X
V-C-4	Ti + V + X
V-C	Ti + W + X
V-C	Ti + X
V-C	Ti + Zr + X
VII-D-5	TlCl
I-T-5	Tm
IV-A-5	Tophet A
IV-A-4	Tophet C
I-C-7	Tough Pitch Copper
X-B	Tri-Allyl Cyanurate
XI-H-5	Triallyl Cyanurate Modified Polyester Resin with Reinforcement
VII-B-2-c	Tricalcium Disilicate
VII-B-6-f	Tricalcium Dititanate
VII-B-2-c	Tricalcium Silicate
VII-A-6	Tridymite
X-A	Trolitul LUV-M 150 Polyester (German)
I-T-7	Tungsten
IV-C	Tungsten-Base Alloy
IX-C also IX-J-9	Tungsten Boride
IX-A-1 also IX-J-9	Tungsten Carbide
VIII-A-1	Tungsten Carbide Cermet, Cobalt Bonded
IV-C	Tungsten + Copper
VIII-A-1	Tungsten Carbide as Major Refractory Phase of Cermet
VIII-A-1	Tungsten Carbide Cermet
VIII-A-1	Tungsten Carbide Cermet, Cobalt Bonded
II-D-8	Tungsten-Cobalt High Speed Tool Steel
IX-J-2	Tungsten-Cobalt Intermetallic
IX-B	Tungsten Disilicide
II-D-8	Tungsten High Speed Tool Steel
II-C-8 also II-D-8	Tungsten Hot Work Tool Steel
IX-E	Tungsten Hydride
IX-J-9	Tungsten Intermetallic
IV-C	Tungsten + Iron + X
IV-C	Tungsten + Molybdenum + X
IV-C	Tungsten + Nickel + Copper
IV-C	Tungsten + Nickel + Iron
IV-C	Tungsten + Niobium

273

Material Index Number	Material Name
IX-D	Tungsten Nitride
II-C-8	Tungsten, Shock Resisting Tool Steel
IX-B also IX-J-9	Tungsten Silicide
II-C-8	Tungsten-Silicon Shock Resisting Tool Steel
X-C	Type 31 Phenolic Resin
I-C-3-a	Type 3474D Extruded Acheson Graphite
VII-E-4	Type 4811 Commercial Porcelain
I-C-3-a	Type 7087 Extruded Acheson Graphite Multicrystalline
I-C-3-a	Type AG-1 Extruded Acheson Graphite
I-C-3-a	Type AGKT Artificial Pitch Bonded Petroleum Coke
I-C-3-a	Type AGOT-C Extruded Acheson Graphite
I-C-3-a	Type AGOT Extruded Acheson Graphite
I-C-3-a	Type AGOT-KC Extruded Acheson Graphite
I-C-3-a	Type AGOT-W Extruded Acheson Graphite
I-C-3-d	Type AWG(EPB) Molded Acheson Graphite
I-C-3-a	Type GBE Extruded Acheson Graphite
I-C-3-d	Type GBH Molded Acheson Graphite
I-C-3-g	Type SA-25 Lampblack Base Graphite
X-C-1	Type S Phenolic Resin
I-U-1	U
IX-A-7	U_2C_3
VII-A-10	U_2O_5
IX-G-4	U_2Ti
VI	U_3Bi_4
VII-A-10	U_3O_8
IX-B-2	U_3S_i
IX-B-2	U_3Si_2
VI	U_4Bi_5
VI-F also IX-J-2	U_6Co
VI-F	U_6Mn
IX-J-5	U_6Ni
VI-F	U_6Ni
IX-G-1	UAl_2
IX-G-1	UAl_3
IX-G-1	UAl_4
IX-C	UB_2
IX-C	UB_4
VI-F also IX-G-2	UBe_{13}

Material Index Number	Material Name
VI-F	UBi
VI-F	U + Bi
VI-F	UBi_2
VII-D-5	UBr_3
IX-A-7	UC
VII-D-5	UCl_3
VII-D-5	UCl_4
VI-F also IX-J-2	UCo
VI-F	U + Co
VI-F-1	U + Cr + X
III	UCu_5
IX-E	UD_3
IV-A-5	Udimet 500, contains Co
IV-A-5	Udimet 600, contains Co
VI-F	U + Fe
IX-E	UH_3
IX-J-5	UNi_2
VI-F	UPb
VI-F	U + Pb
VI-D	UPd_3
VI-F	Uranium + Iron
VI-F	Uranium + Nickel
VII-B-2-e also VII-E-3	Ultra-Steatite
VI-F	U + Mg
VI-F	UMn
VI-F	U + Mn
VI-F	UMn_2
VI-F-2	U + Mo
VI-F-2	U + Mo + Ru + X
VI-F-2	U + Mo + X
IX-D-2	UN
IX-D-2	UN_2
VI-F	U + Nb
XI-B-2	Unbonded Metal Layers
XI-B-2	Unbonded Sandwich
VI-F	U + Ni
X-A-11	Unsaturated Polyester
VII-A-10	UO_2

Material Index Number	Material Name
VII-A-10	$UO_2 + Al_2O_3$
VII-A-10	$UO_2 + BeO$
VII-A-10	$UO_2 + CaF_2$
VII-A-10	$UO_2 + MgO$
VII-A-10	$UO_2 + MnO_2$
VII-C	$UO_2 \cdot P_2O_5$
VII-A-10	$UO_2 + ThO_2$
VII-A-10	$UO_2 + TiO_2$
VII-A-10	$UO_2 + X$
VII-A-10	$UO_2 + ZrH_2$
VII-A-10	$UO_2 + ZrO_2$
VII-A-10	UO_3
VI	UPb
VI	UPb_3
VI-F	$U + Pu + Mo + Ru + X$
VI-F	$U + Pu + Ru + Mo + X$
VI-F	$U + Pu + X$
VII-C	Uranate
VII-A-10	Urania
VII-A-10	Urania + Magnesia
I-U-1	Uranium
IX-G-1	Uranium Aluminide
XI-B-2	Uranium-Aluminum Joint
VI-F	Uranium-Base Alloy
IX-G-2	Uranium Beryllide
VI-F	Uranium + Bismuth
IX-C	Uranium Boride
VII-D-5	Uranium Bromide
IX-A-7	Uranium Carbide
VIII-A	Uranium Carbide Cermet
VII-D-5	Uranium Chloride
VI-F-1	Uranium + Chromium + X
VI-F	Uranium + Cobalt
IX-J-2	Uranium-Cobalt Intermetallic
IX-E	Uranium Deuteride
IX-G-1	Uranium Dialuminide
X-C	Uranium Diboride
VII-A-10	Uranium Dioxide

Material Index Number	Material Name
VII-A-10	Uranium Dioxide + Alumina
VII-A-10	Uranium Dioxide + Thoria
VII-A-10	Uranium Dioxide + Titania
VII-A-10	Uranium Dioxide + X
VII-A-10	Uranium Dioxide + Zirconia
IX-B-2	Uranium Disilicide
XI-E	Uranium-Graphite Joint
IX-E	Uranium Hydride
IX-K-14 also IX or VI-F	Uranium Intermetallic
VI-F	Uranium + Lead
VI-F	Uranium + Manganese
VI-F-2	Uranium + Molybdenum + Ruthenium + X
VI-F-2	Uranium + Molybdenum
VI-F-2	Uranium + Molybdenum + X
VI-F	Uranium + Magnesium
IX-J-5	Uranium-Nickel Intermetallic
VI-F	Uranium + Niobium
IX-D-2	Uranium Nitride
VII-A-10	Uranium Octoxide
VII-A-10	Uranium Oxide
VII-A-10	Uranium Oxide + Aluminum Oxide
VIII-B-3	Uranium Oxide as Major Refractory Phase of Cermet
VII-A-10	Uranium Oxide + Beryllium Oxide
VII-A-10	Uranium Oxide + Calcium Fluoride
VIII-B-3	Uranium Oxide Cermet, Zirconium Bonded
XI-C	Uranium Oxide- Graphite Joint
VII-A-10	Uranium Oxide + Magnesium Oxide
VII-A-10	Uranium Oxide + Manganese Oxide
VII-A-10	Uranium Oxide Powder
VII-A-10	Uranium Oxide + Thorium Oxide
VII-A-10	Uranium Oxide + X
VII-A-10	Uranium Oxide + Zirconium Hydride
VII-A-10	Uranium Oxide + Zirconium Oxide
VI-F	Uranium + Plutonium + Molybdenum + Ruthenium + X
VI-F	Uranium + Plutonium + Ruthenium + Molybdenum + X
VI-F	Uranium + Plutonium + X
IX-B-2	Uranium Silicide
VI-F	Uranium + Thorium + Zirconium

Material Index Number	Material Name
VII-D-5	Uranium Trichloride
VII-A-10	Uranium Trioxide
IX-B-2	Uranium Trisilicide
VI-F-3	Uranium + Zirconium + Thorium
VI-F-3	Uranium + Zirconium + X
X-C-3	Urea Formaldehyde
X-C-3	Urea Formaldehyde, Alpha Cellulose Filled
VII-D-6	US
VII-D-6	US_2
IX-B-2	USi
IX-B-2	USi_2
IX-B-2	USi_3
VI	USn_3
IX-A-5	$UTa_{10}C_4$
VI-F	U + Th + Zr
VI-F-3	U + Zr + Th
VI-F-3	U + Zr + X
I-V-1	V
VII-A-15	V_2O_3
VII-A-15	V_2O_5
IV-B-1	V-36
II-D-3	V-444D (German)
IV-G	Va + Fe + X
IV-G	V + Al
IX-J-10	VAl_3
I-V-1	Vanadium
IX-J-10	Vanadium-Aluminide
IV-G	Vanadium + Aluminum
IV-G	Vanadium + Antimony
IV-G	Vanadium-Base Alloy
IX-C also IX-J-10	Vanadium Boride
IX-C	Vanadium Boride + Chromium Boride
IX-C	Vanadium Boride + Titanium Boride
IX-A and IX-J-10	Vanadium Carbide
VIII-A	Vanadium Carbide Cermet
IV-G	Vanadium + Chromium
IV-G	Vanadium + Copper
IX-C also IX-J-10	Vanadium Diboride

Material Index Number	Material Name
VII-A-15	Vanadium Dioxide
IX-J-3 also IX-J-10	Vanadium-Hafnium Intermetallic
IX-E	Vanadium Hydride
IX-J-10	Vanadium Intermetallic
IV-G	Vanadium + Iron + X
IV-G	Vanadium + Manganese
VII-A-15	Vanadium Monoxide
IV-G	Vanadium + Nickel
IX-D	Vanadium Nitride
VII-A-15	Vanadium Oxide
IV-G	Vanadium + Palladium
VII-A-15	Vanadium Sesquioxide
IX-B	Vanadium Silicides
IV-G	Vanadium + Tin
IV-G	Vanadium + Titanium + X
XI-D	Varnish Coated Aluminum Alloy 75ST
IV-G	Vanadium + Zirconium
IX-J-11	Vanadium-Zirconium Intermetallic
XI-D	Varnish Base Lacquer Coated Aluminum Alloy 24ST
XI-D	Varnish Base Lacquer Coated Dow Metal
IX-C also IX-J-10	VB_2
IX-C	$VB_2 + CrB_2$
IX-C	$VB_2 + TiB_2$
IX-A and IX-J-10	VC
IV-G	V + Cr
IV-G	V + Cu
IV-G	V + Fe
XI-H-5	Vibrin 135, Reinforced
X	Vibrin 135 TAC Polyester
XI-H-5	Vibrin X-1068, Reinforced
X-F	Vinylidene
X-A-8	Vinylite VMCH
X-A-8	Vinylite VYDR
IV-B-1	Vitallium
VII-E	Vitreous Bonded Aluminum Titanate
VII-E also see VII-A and VII-B	Vitreous Bonded Crystalline Ceramics
VII-C-6	Vitreous Silica
VII-C	Vitreous Structures

Material Index Number	Material Name
VII-C-6	Vitrosil
IV-G	V + Mn
IX-J-10	VMn_2
IX-D	VN
IV-G	V + Ni
VII-A-15	VO
IV-G	V + Pd
IV-G	V + Sb
IV-G	V + Sn
IV-G	V + Ti
IV-G	V + Ti + X
X-A-9	Vulcollan
IV-G	V + X
VII-C-6	Vycor
VII-C-6	Vycor 790
VII-C-6	Vycor 7900
IV-G	V + Zr
I-T-7	W
IX-C also IX-J-9	W_2B_2
IX-C	W_2B_5
I-Z-1	WAPD Grade 1 Crystal Bar Zirconium
IV-A-5	Waspaloy
II-C-6	Water Hardening Tool Steel
VII-C-1-b	Water White Plate Glass
IX-C also IX-J-9	WB_2
IX-A-1 also IX-J-9	WC
IV-C	W + Cu
IX-J-2 also IX-J-9	WCO_2
VII-E-4	Wet Process Porcelain No. 7A2
II-D-3	WF-100D (German)
IV-C	W + Fe
II-B-4	White Cast Iron, Alloyed
II-B-3	White Cast Iron, Low Alloy
II-B-3	White Cast Iron, Unalloyed
VII-B-9	White Mica
VII-C-1-b	White Plate Glass
VII-E-4	Whiteware
IV-B-1	WI-52

Material Index Number	Material Index
VII-B-2-j	Willemite
IV-C	W + Mo + X
IV- C	W + Nb
IV-C	W + Ni + Cu
IV-C	W + Ni + Fe
VII-B-2-c	Wollastonite
XI-H-3	Wood Base Phenol-Formaldehyde
II-D-2 also II-D-3	Wrought Chromium-Nickel Heat Resistant Steel
IX-B also IX-J-9	WSi_2
IV-B-1	X-40, Stellite No. 31, contains W
IV-B-1	X-50
IV-B-1	X-63
I-Y-2	Y
VII-A-15	Y_2O_3
V-A-1	Y-Alloy (British)
I-Y-1	Yb
I-B-3	YB-9052 Beryllium
I-B-3	YB-9053 Beryllium
I-B-3	YB-9054 Beryllium
IX-C	YbB_6
IX-A	YC
III-A-3	Yellow Brass
VII-E-3	Yellowstone Talc, Fired
VII-E-2	Yellowstone Talc, Unfired
IX-D	Yn
VII-A-4-r	Ytterbia
I-T-1	Ytterbium
IX-C	Ytterbium Boride
IX-H-15	Ytterbium Intermetallic
VII-A-4-r	Ytterbium Oxide
VII-A-15	Yttria
I-Y-2	Yttrium
IX-A	Yttrium Carbide
IX-D	Yttrium Nitride
VII-A-15	Yttrium Oxide
VII-B-1	Zeolite
VII-B-7-m	Zinc Aluminate
IX-F-1	Zinc Antimonide

Material Index Number	Material Name
VII	Zinc Arsenide
XI-D	Zinc Chromate Painted on Alclad 2024
VII-B	Zinc Chromite
VI	Zinc + Copper
VII-B-8-p	Zinc Ferrite
VII-A-15	Zincite
VII-C-1-m	Zinc Lead Silicate Glass
VII-C-5	Zinc-Magnesium-Aluminum Borosilicate Glass
VII-C-5	Zinc-Magnesium Borosilicate Glass
VII-B-2-j	Zinc Orthosilicate
VII-B-6-m	Zinc Orthotitanate
VII-A-15	Zinc Oxide
VII-B-2-j	Zinc Silicates
VI	Zinc + Silver
VII-D-6	Zinc Sulfide
VII-B-6-m	Zinc Titanate
VI	Zinc + Zirconium
VII-B-9	Zinn Waldite
IV-J	Zircaloy Series
IV-J-1	Zircaloy 2
IV-J-1	Zircaloy B
VII-B-4-b	Zircon
VII-B-4-b	Zircon 475
VII-E-4	Zircon Procelain
VII-A-9-b	Zirconia
VII-A-9-b	Zirconia + Beryllia + Alumina + X
VII-A-9-b	Zirconia + Beryllia + Magnesia
VII-A-9-b	Zirconia + Calcia
VII-A-9-b	Zirconia + Calcia + X
VII-A-9-b	Zirconia, Calcium Stabilized
VII-A-9-b	Zirconia + Ceria
XI-E	Zirconia Coated Inconel
VII-A-9-b	Zirconia + Magnesia
VII-A-9-b	Zirconia + Magnesia + X
VII-A-9-b	Zirconia, Magnesium Stabilized
VII-A-9-b	Zirconia + Niobium Pentoxide + X
VII-A-9-b	Zirconia + Silica
VII-A-9-b	Zirconia + Titania
VII-A-9-b	Zirconia + Thoria

Material Index Number	Material Name
I-Z-1	Zirconium
IV-J	Zirconium + Aluminum
IV-J	Zirconium-Base Alloy
IX-C-3	Zirconium Boride
VIII-C-1	Zirconium Boride Cermet
IX-C-3 also IX-J-11	Zirconium Boride
IV-J	Zirconium + Boron + X
IX-A-4 also IX-J-11	Zirconium Carbide
IX-J-2	Zirconium-Cobalt Intermetallic
IX-C-3 also IX-J-11	Zirconium Diboride
VIII-C-1	Zirconium Diboride Cermet
VIII-C-1	Zirconium Diboride Cermet (Borolite)
VII-A-9-b	Zirconium Dioxide
VII-A-9-b	Zirconium Dioxide + Cerium Dioxide
VIII-B	Zirconium Dioxide Cermet
VIII-B	Zirconium Dioxide Cermet, Titanium Bonded
VII-A-9-b	Zirconium Dioxide + Silicon Dioxide
VII-A-9-b	Zirconium Dioxide + Thorium Dioxide
VII-A-9-b	Zirconium Dioxide + Titanium Dioxide
VII-A-9-b	Zirconium Dioxide + Uranium Dioxide
IX-C-3 also IX-J-11	Zirconium Dodecarboride
VII-D-5-a	Zirconium Fluoride
VII-D-5-a	Zirconium Fluoride + Lithium Fluoride
VII-D-5-a	Zirconium Fluoride + Rubidium Fluoride
VII-D-5-a	Zirconium Fluoride + Sodium Fluoride
I-Z-1	Zirconium, Grade 1 Iodide Process
IX-E-2	Zirconium Hydride
IV-J	Zirconium + Indium + X
IX-J-11	Zirconium Intermetallic
IX-J-11	Zirconium-Iron Intermetallic
IV-J	Zirconium + Iron + X
IV-J-2	Zirconium + Niobium + X
IX-D-3	Zirconium Nitride
VII-A-9-b	Zirconium Oxide + Beryllium Oxide + Magnesium Oxide
VII-A-9-b	Zirconium Oxide + Calcium Oxide
VII A-9-b	Zirconium Oxide, Calcium Stabilized
VII-A-9-b	Zirconium Oxide + Cerium Oxide
VIII-B	Zirconium Oxide Cermet

Material Index Number	Material Name
VIII-B	Zirconium Oxide Cermet, Titanium Bonded
VIII-B	Zirconium Oxide Cermet, Zirconium Bonded
VII-A-9-b	Zirconium Oxide, Fused, Stabilized
VII-A-9-b	Zirconium Oxide + Magnesium Oxide
VII-A-9-b	Zirconium Oxide, Magnesium Stabilized
VII-A-9-b	Zirconium Oxide + Neptunium Oxide
VII-A-9-b	Zirconium Oxide - Non Stabilized
VII-A-9-b	Zirconium Oxide + Silicon Oxide
VII-A-9-b	Zirconium Oxide + Titanium Oxide
VII-A-9-b	Zirconium Oxide + Thorium Oxide
VII-A-9-b	Zirconium Oxide + Uranium Oxide
IV-J	Zirconium + Oxygen + X
VII-B-5	Zirconium Phosphate
VII-B-4-b	Zirconium Silicate
VII-B-4	Zirconium Silicate + Beryllium Aluminosilicate
IX-B	Zirconium Silicide
IV-J	Zirconium + Silver
I-Z-1	Zirconium, Sponge
IV-J	Zirconium + Tantalum + X
IV-J	Zirconium + Thorium
IV-J-1	Zirconium + Tin + X
VII-B-6-n	Zirconium Titanate
IV-J	Zirconium + Titanium + X
IV-J-3	Zirconium + Uranium
IV-J-3	Zirconium + Uranium + Tin + X
IX-J-10	Zirconium - Vanadium Intermetallic
I-Z-1	Zirconium, WAPD Grade I Crystal Bar
VII-A-9-b	Zirox
V-B-6	ZK-60 Magnesium Alloy
V-B-6	ZK-60-A Magnesium Alloy
VII-B-2-j	Zn_2SiO_4
VII-B-6-m	Zn_2TiO_4
VI	Zn + Ag
VI	Zn + Cu
IV-A	Z-Nickel, contains Al
VII-B-8-p	$Zn Fe_2O_4$
VII-A-15	ZnO
VII-B-8-p	$ZnO \cdot Fe_2O_3$

284

Material Index Number	Material Name
VII-D-6	ZnS
IX-F-1	Zn Sb
VI	Zn + Zr
IV-A-4	Zorite
I-Z-1	Zr
IV-J	Zr + Ag + X
IV-J	Zr + Al
IV-J	Zr + B + X
IX-C-3 also IX-J-11	ZrB_2
IX-A-6 also IX-C-3	$ZrB_2 + Mo_2C$
IX-C-3	$ZrB_2 + MoSi_2$
IX-C-3	$ZrB_2 + NbB_2$
IX-C-3	$ZrB_2 + TaB_2$
IX-C-3	$ZrB_2 + TiC$
IX-C-3	$ZrB_2 + X$
IX-C-3 also IX-J-11	ZrB_{12}
IX-A-4 also IX-J-11	ZrC
IX-J-2 also IX-J-11	$ZrCo_2$
VII-D-5-a	ZrF_4
VII-D-5-a	$ZrF_4 + LiF$
VII-D-5-a	$ZrF_4 + NaF$
VII-D-5-a	$ZrF_4 + RbF$
IX-J-11	$ZrFe_2$
IV-J	Zr + Fe + X
IX-E-2	ZrH
IV-J	Zr + In + X
IX-D-3	ZrN
IV-J-2	Zr + Nb + X
VII-A-9-b	ZrO_2
VII-A-9-b	$ZrO_2 + BeO + Al_2O_3 + X$
VII-A-9-b	$ZrO_2 + BeO + MgO$
VII-A-9-b	$ZrO_2 + CaO$
VII-A-9-b	$ZrO_2 + CaO + X$
VII-A-9-b	$ZrO_2 + CeO_2$
VII-A-9-b	$ZrO_2 + MgO$
VII-A-9-b	$ZrO_2 + MgO + X$
VII-A-9-b	$ZrO_2 + Nb_2O_5$
VII-A-9-b	$ZrO_2 + Nb_2O_5 + X$

Material Index Number	Material Name
VII-A-9-b	$ZrO_2 + SiO_2$
VII-A-9-b	$ZrO_2 + TiO_2$
VII-A-9-b	$ZrO_2 + ThO_2$
VII-A-9-b	$ZrO_2 + UO_2$
IV-J	$Zr + O_2 + X$
IV-J-2	$Zr + Nb + X$
VII-B-4-b	$ZrSiO_4$
IV-J-1	$Zr + Sn + X$
IV-J	$Zr + Ta + X$
IV-J	$Zr + Th$
VII-B-6-n	$ZrTiO_4$
IV-J	$Zr + Ti + X$
IV-J-3	$Zr + U$
IX-J-10 also IX-J-11	ZrV_2
IV-J	$Zr + U + Sn + X$